HOLT

Earth Science
The Physical Setting

NEW YORK

Regents Review Guide
with Practice Exams

HOLT, RINEHART AND WINSTON

A Harcourt Education Company

Orlando • **Austin** • New York • San Diego • Toronto • London

Contributing Writers

Rachel Warren is a science writer based in Brooklyn, New York. She holds a B.A. in biochemistry from Connecticut College, and has more than 5 years of experience writing science assessment items. Ms. Warren, who frequently writes about Earth science topics, has contributed to several study guides for the Earth Science Regents Exam.

Taryn Puleo is an environmental educator based in Gardiner, New York. She holds a B.S. in Biology from Binghamton University, and has more than 6 years of experience tutoring high school students for the Regents Exams. Ms. Puleo has extensive experience in writing material for standardized tests and in preparing students to take standardized tests, having designed and instructed courses for the ACT, SAT, GRE, LSAT, and GMAT.

Deane Rink has been a writer, director, and producer, and researcher for numerous PBS documentary series on Earth science, including *Planet Earth*, *The Infinite Voyage*, and Carl Sagan's *Cosmos*. In addition to his television work, Mr. Rink is a staff writer and science advisor for the Hall of Planet Earth at the American Museum of Natural History in New York City.

David Roemer is a former high school science teacher for the New York City Public Schools. Mr. Roemer holds a Ph.D. in Physics from New York University and has been a science writer for more than 8 years.

Natalie Goldstein has been an educational writer for more than 15 years. Based in Brooktondale, N.Y., Ms. Goldstein holds Master's degrees in Education and Environmental Science from CUNY City College, and has extensive experience in writing material for standardized science tests.

Printed in the United States of America

ISBN 0-03-036374-8

2 3 4 5 6 054 09 08 07 06 05

Contents

UNIT I

Holt Earth Science: The Physical Setting

Earth Structure

Geology is the study of planet Earth, including its composition and structure. Scientists who study Earth and the processes that shape Earth over time are called *geologists*. Though geologists cannot see inside Earth, they can, in a sense, listen to it. The waves from earthquakes travel through Earth in a manner similar to the way that sound waves travel through the air and into our ears. Scientists are able to interpret these waves to learn about the structure and composition of Earth.

Earth Structure

Earth is the third planet from the sun in our solar system. Our planet formed approximately 4.5 billion years ago and is made mostly of rock. Earth is the only planet known to have liquid water on its surface and a large amount of oxygen in its atmosphere. Most importantly, it is the only planet known to support life.

Viewed from space, Earth appears to be a perfect sphere. In reality, Earth is more accurately described as an *oblate spheroid*, because it is slightly flattened at its poles and bulging at its equator. The circumference of Earth measured around the poles is 40,007 km (24,859 mi). The circumference around the equator measures 40,074 km (24,901 mi). The diameter of Earth at its equator is 12,756 km (7,926 mi). But if you measure Earth through the poles, the diameter is a bit shorter—12,715 km (7,901 mi). Earth's oblate spheroid shape is due to the spinning of Earth on its axis, which causes the polar regions to flatten and the equatorial zone to bulge.

Self-Check Describe Earth's shape. Why is it shaped like that?

Earth can be divided into three main layers—the crust, mantle, and core—based on the materials that make up each layer. Physical conditions in Earth's interior vary from layer to layer. Temperature and pressure in Earth's interior change with depth. As the temperature and pressure increase, the properties of the materials inside Earth also change.

What You'll Need to Learn

This topic is part of the Regents Curriculum for the Physical Setting Exam.

Standard 4, Performance Indicator 2.1: *Use the concepts of density and heat energy to explain observations of weather patterns, seasonal changes, and the movements of Earth's plates.* Major Understandings: 2.1j

What Terms You'll Need to Know

asthenosphere
core
crust
geology
lithosphere
mantle
Mohorovicic discontinuity
P-wave
seismic wave
shadow zone
S-wave

Where You Can Learn Even More

Holt Earth Science: The Physical Setting
Chapter 2: Earth as a System
Chapter 12: Earthquakes

Unit I Earth Structure *continued*

**Notes/Study
Ideas/Answers**

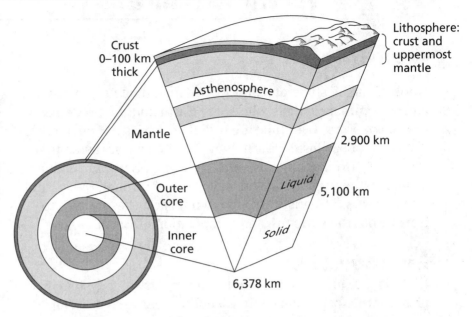

Crust
0–100 km
thick

Asthenosphere

Mantle

Lithosphere:
crust and
uppermost
mantle

2,900 km

Liquid

5,100 km

Outer
core

Inner
core

Solid

6,378 km

The "Inferred Properties of Earth's Interior" diagram on page 237 in the *Earth Science Reference Tables* section shows the variations in density, temperature, and pressure of Earth's three main layers.

The **crust** is the thin, rocky, outermost layer of Earth. There are two types of crust: continental crust and oceanic crust. *Continental crust*, the crust that makes up the continents, consists mainly of less-dense rocks, such as granite. Continental crust averages about 35 km (25 mi) in thickness, although it ranges in thickness from about 15 to 80 kilometers (9 to 50 miles). It is thickest beneath high mountain ranges such as the Himalaya Mountains. The rock that makes up the ocean floor is *oceanic crust*. Oceanic crust is composed mostly of dense rocks such as basalt. Oceanic crust is about 7 km (4 mi) thick on average, and so is much thinner than continental crust.

Self-Check How does continental crust differ from oceanic crust?

Beneath the crust lies Earth's **mantle,** a layer of molten rock that is denser than the crust. As the diagram shows, the mantle extends about 2,900 km, from beneath the crust to the top of the core. Both temperature and pressure increase tremendously the deeper you go into the mantle. The mantle is rich in metals such as iron and magnesium, and so is denser throughout than the crust.

Geologists divide the mantle into different layers based on the physical properties of the rock. The uppermost layer of the mantle is part of the **lithosphere,** a layer of relatively cool, rigid rock that also includes Earth's crust. On average, the lithosphere measures about 100 km (62 mi) thick, although it is

Unit I Earth Structure *continued*

thicker below the continents and thinner beneath the oceans. Beneath the lithosphere in the mantle is the **asthenosphere,** a layer of softer rock that can flow slowly like a fluid. This is why the asthenosphere is sometimes called the "plastic mantle." Beneath the asthenosphere is the stronger, lower part of the mantle called the *mesosphere*, or "stiffer mantle." The stiffer rock of the mesosphere extends all the way down to the upper surface of Earth's core.

Self-Check Describe the structure and properties of Earth's mantle.

Under the mantle lies Earth's **core,** a large sphere of metal that occupies Earth's center. Scientists think that the core is composed mostly of iron, with lesser amounts of nickel and lighter elements. Within the core, pressure increases greatly with depth. The core is divided into two parts—the outer core and the inner core. In the *outer core*, high temperatures keep the metal in the liquid state. In the *inner core*, very high pressure is a more important factor than temperature. As a result, the inner core is solid metal.

REVIEW YOUR UNDERSTANDING

Some questions may require use of the *Earth Science Reference Tables*.

_____ **1.** Compared to Earth's circumference measured at the equator, the circumference of Earth measured through the poles is
(1) exactly the same
(2) slightly larger
(3) slightly smaller

_____ **2.** Compared to Earth's outer core, Earth's inner core
(1) has a greater average density
(2) is mostly liquid
(3) begins 3,000 km below the surface
(4) has a lower pressure

_____ **3.** Earth's outer core is inferred to be
(1) solid, with an average density of approximately 11 g/cm^3
(2) solid, with an average density of approximately 4 g/cm^3
(3) liquid, with an average density of approximately 11 g/cm^3
(4) liquid, with an average density of approximately 4 g/cm^3

_____ **4.** Compared to Earth's crust, its core is inferred to be
(1) less dense, cooler, and composed of more iron
(2) less dense, hotter, and composed of more iron
(3) denser, hotter, and composed of more iron
(4) denser, cooler, and composed of less iron

Studying Earth's Interior

Much of what we know about Earth's interior comes from the science of *seismology*, the study of earthquakes. An earthquake is a movement or trembling of the ground that is caused when energy in elastically strained rocks is suddenly released. This release of energy causes intense ground shaking in the area near the source of the earthquake and sends waves of energy, called **seismic waves,** throughout Earth. Earthquakes can be generated by sudden slippage along faults (fractures in rock), volcanic eruptions, and bomb blasts. Earth is constantly shaking and jiggling, and we can record these seismic vibrations on sensitive instruments called *seismographs.*

The two main types of seismic waves are surface waves and body waves. Surface waves travel only along Earth's surface, like ripples on water. Body waves, on the other hand, travel through Earth's interior in all directions. There are two types of body waves: primary waves **(P-waves)** and secondary waves **(S-waves).** P-waves can travel through liquids, solids, and gases, while S-waves can travel only through solids.

The composition of the material through which P-waves and S-waves travel affects the speed and direction of the waves. For example, both P-waves and S-waves travel faster through rigid materials than through soft materials. From observing how P-waves and S-waves travel through the planet, where they are detected, and the speed at which they travel, scientists can make inferences about Earth's structure. (See Unit VII for more information about seismic waves.)

Self-Check What are the differences between P-waves and S-waves?

In 1909, Croatian scientist Andrija Mohorovicic discovered that the speed of seismic waves increases abruptly 32 to 70 km beneath Earth's surface. The location at which the speed of the waves increases marks the boundary between the crust and the mantle. This increase occurs because the mantle is denser than the crust. Today, the boundary between the crust and the mantle is known as the **Mohorovicic discontinuity,** or *Moho,* for short.

Unit I Earth Structure *continued*

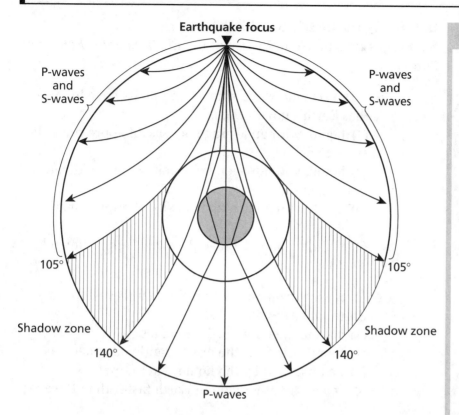

Self-Check What observation about seismic waves led to the discovery of the Moho Discontinuity?

Recordings of seismic waves around the world reveal shadow zones. **Shadow zones** are locations on Earth's surface where no direct seismic waves from a particular earthquake can be detected. Shadow zones exist because the materials that make up Earth's interior are not uniform in rigidity. When seismic waves travel through materials of differing rigidities, their speed changes. The waves will also bend and change direction as they pass through different materials.

As shown in the diagram, a large S-wave shadow zone covers the side of Earth that is opposite an earthquake focus (the place where an earthquake starts). S-waves do not reach the S-wave shadow zone, because they cannot pass through the liquid outer core. Although P-waves can travel through all the layers, the speed and direction of the waves change as the waves pass through each layer. The waves bend in such a way that a P-wave shadow zone forms.

Unit I Earth Structure *continued*

REVIEW YOUR UNDERSTANDING

Some questions may require use of the *Earth Science Reference
Tables*.

_____ **5.** From seismic wave studies, scientists have inferred
that Earth's inner core is
(1) liquid, with an average density of approximately
4 g/cm^3
(2) liquid, with an average density of approximately
13 g/cm^3
(3) solid, with an average density of approximately
4 g/cm^3
(4) solid, with an average density of approximately
13 g/cm^3

_____ **6.** An S-wave from an earthquake that travels toward
Earth's center will
(1) be deflected by Earth's magnetic field
(2) be reflected off the crust-mantle interface
(3) be absorbed by the liquid outer core
(4) reach the other side of Earth faster than P-waves

_____ **7.** After a major earthquake, seismograph stations over
most of Earth recorded P-waves, S-waves, or both.
Some stations around Earth did not receive P-waves
and S-waves at all. This "shadow zone," where seismograph stations did not record any direct P-waves
or S-waves, exists because
(1) seismic waves are bent as they move from one
substance to another
(2) no seismic waves can travel through Earth's liquid outer core
(3) liquids absorb P-waves but can transmit S-waves
(4) liquids absorb P-waves, and solids absorb
S-waves

ANSWERS TO SELF-CHECK QUESTIONS

- Earth is nearly a sphere. It is slightly flattened at the
poles and bulges slightly at the equator. The shape is
due to Earth's rotation on its axis.

- Continental crust is thicker but less dense than oceanic
crust.

Unit I Earth Structure *continued*

- The mantle is the thicker, denser layer underneath the crust. Temperature and pressure increase with depth in the mantle. The mantle is rich in metals such as iron and magnesium. The uppermost layer of the mantle is part of the lithosphere, which also includes the crust. Below the lithosphere is the asthenosphere, a layer of molten rock that can flow like a fluid. Beneath the asthenosphere is the mesosphere, a layer of stiffer rock.

- P-waves can travel through liquids, solids, and gases, while S-waves can travel only through solids.

- Andrija Mohorovicic discovered that the speed of seismic waves increases abruptly at the boundary between the crust and the mantle. This change in speed is due to differences in density. Both P-waves and S-waves travel faster through denser materials than through less-dense materials.

Questions for Regents Practice

Earth Structure

PART A

Some questions may require use of the *Earth Science Reference Tables*.

_____ **1.** Compared to the thickness and density of continental crust, oceanic crust is
   (1) thinner and less dense
   (2) thinner and denser
   (3) thicker and less dense
   (4) thicker and denser

_____ **2.** In which layer of Earth's interior is the pressure inferred to be 2.0 million atmospheres?
   (1) inner core
   (2) stiffer mantle
   (3) outer core
   (4) plastic mantle

_____ **3.** The density of Earth's mantle is
   (1) less than the density of the outer core but greater than the density of the crust
   (2) greater than the density of the outer core but less than the density of the crust
   (3) less than the density of both the inner core and the crust
   (4) greater than the density of both the crust and the outer core

_____ **4.** The boundary between the crust and the mantle, known as the Moho discontinuity, was discovered through the analysis of
   (1) volcanoes
   (2) rocks in the crust
   (3) drill holes in the crust
   (4) seismic waves

_____ **5.** One characteristic of S-waves is that they travel
   (1) only through liquids
   (2) only through solids
   (3) faster than P-waves
   (4) faster through less-rigid materials

_____ **6.** Which choice presents the correct order of Earth's layers, from the center outward?
   (1) inner core, mantle, outer core, crust
   (2) crust, mantle, inner core, outer core
   (3) inner core, crust, mantle, outer core
   (4) inner core, outer core, mantle, crust

_____ **7.** The "Moho" lies between which two layers of Earth?
   (1) inner core and outer core
   (2) outer core and mantle
   (3) crust and mantle
   (4) plastic mantle and stiffer mantle

Unit I Earth Structure *continued*

PART B-1

Base your answer to question 8 on your knowledge of earth science and the *Earth Science Reference Tables*.

_____ **8.** Which graph best represents the relationship between depth below Earth's surface and density?

(1)
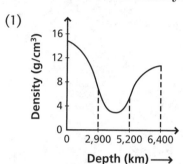

(2)
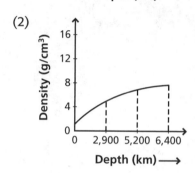

(3)
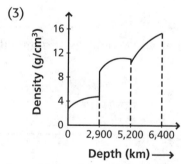

(4)
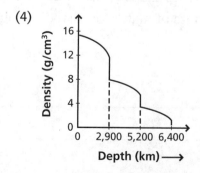

PART B-2

Base your answers to questions 9 to 11 on your knowledge of earth science, the *Earth Science Reference Tables*, and the diagram below, which shows a pattern of seismic waves recorded by seismic stations around the world. Letter A represents a location on Earth's surface.

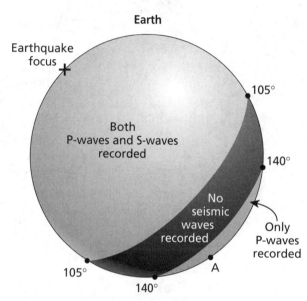

9. What conclusion about the relationship between seismic waves and Earth's structure can be made from this pattern?

_____

_____

_____

_____

_____

10. State the name of the Earth layer that blocked S-waves from traveling to location A.

_____

11. Explain how this Earth layer was able to block S-waves from reaching location A.

_____

_____

Name _____ Class _____ Date _____

Unit I Earth Structure *continued*

PART C

Base your answers to questions 12 through 14 on your knowledge of earth science, the *Earth Science Reference Tables*, and the diagram below, which shows a portion of Earth's interior. Letters A, B, C, and D are separate locations within Earth's interior.

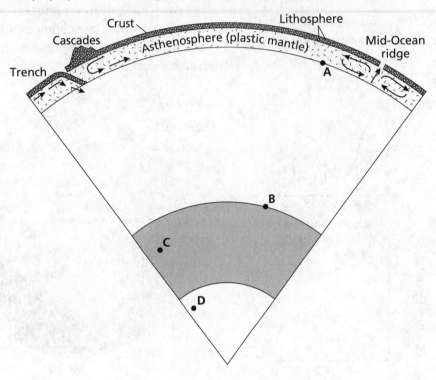

11. State the name of the Earth layer that extends between points A and B.

_____

12. Describe the changes in temperature and pressure that you would experience if it were possible to travel from point A to point B.

_____

_____

_____

14. Compare the temperature, pressure, density, and state of matter observed at points C and D.

_____

_____

_____

Mapping Earth's Surface

Have you ever wondered how the early ocean explorers were able to tell where they were going? Far out in the ocean, how were these explorers able to describe their location without the benefit of detailed maps and familiar landmarks? Long ago, explorers solved this problem by establishing a coordinate system that covers the whole Earth.

Latitude-Longitude Coordinate System

The first coordinate value is **latitude,** which is the angular distance north or south of the equator. Lines of equal latitude are called *parallels*, because they run east and west around the world and parallel to each other. Latitude is measured in degrees, starting with the equator at 0°. Because the distance from the equator to either of the poles is 1/4 of a circle, and a circle has 360°, the latitude of both the North Pole and the South Pole is 1/4 of 360°, or 90°. In actual distance, 1° of latitude is equal to 1/360 of Earth's circumference, or about 111 km.

Latitudes north of the equator are labeled *N*; those south of the equator are labeled *S*. For example, location P on the diagram is at latitude 50°N (50° north latitude).

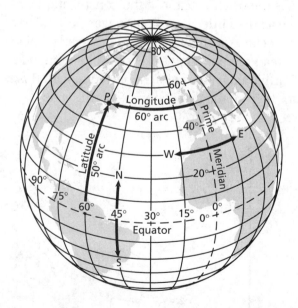

Self-Check Define latitude.

What You'll Need to Learn

This topic is part of the Regents Curriculum for the Physical Setting Exam.

Standard 4, Performance Indicator 1.1: *Explain complex phenomena, such as tides, variations in day length, solar insolation, apparent motion of the planets, and annual traverse of the constellations.* Major Understandings: 1.1c

Standard 4, Performance Indicator 2.1: *Use the concepts of density and heat energy to explain observations of weather patterns, seasonal changes, and the movements of Earth's plates.* Major Understandings: 2.1q

What Terms You'll Need to Know

contour line
elevation
field
latitude
legend
longitude
meridian
Polaris
profile
relief
topographic map

Unit II Mapping Earth's Surface *continued*

The second coordinate value of Earth's imaginary grid system is called **longitude,** which measures angular distance east and west. Lines of longitude are called **meridians.** Each meridian is a semicircle that extends from pole to pole. Meridians are not parallel, because they all meet at the poles. By international agreement, one meridian was selected to be 0°. This meridian, called the *prime meridian*, passes through the city of Greenwich, England. Longitude increases to the east and west of the prime meridian to a maximum of 180°, a line that is opposite the prime meridian, halfway around the world, in the middle of the Pacific Ocean. On the diagram, location P is at longitude 60°W (60° west longitude).

Self-Check Define longitude.

Using the latitude-longitude coordinate system, it is possible to accurately locate any place on Earth's surface. The geographic coordinates of location P on the diagram, for example, are 50°N, 60°W.

Before this system was established, early navigators used celestial navigation to determine location. One method for navigating in the Northern Hemisphere involved making observations of **Polaris,** the North Star, to approximate distance north of the equator.

Polaris is the brightest star in the constellation Ursa Minor, also known as the Little Bear. Polaris was particularly useful for navigation because it appears to stay in the same place as Earth rotates, instead of appearing to revolve like other stars. This is because Earth's axis aligns almost perfectly with this star (Polaris is less than 1° from the projection of Earth's axis).

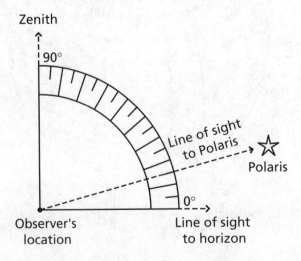

At the North Pole, an observer would see Polaris directly overhead—that is, the angle from the horizon up to Polaris is 90°. That observer is also located 90° north of the equator. At the equator, Polaris appears to lie on the northern horizon. As you move north, away from the equator, Polaris "climbs" in the sky. In the diagram, Polaris is 15° above the horizon, so the observer's latitude must be 15° north. (*Zenith* is the point directly above the observer.)

Longitude is determined by observing the position of the sun. As you know, the sun appears to move across the sky from east to west. Therefore, when it is noon in your location, it is afternoon in locations to your east and it is still morning in locations to your west. Because the sun appears to move in a circle around Earth in 24 hours, each hour of time difference represents 1/24 of 360°, or 15° of longitude. So, using the time difference of 15° per hour, you can determine the numerical value of longitude.

If your local time is earlier than the time in Greenwich, England (Greenwich time), you are located west of the prime meridian (0° longitude). If your local time is later than Greenwich time, you are located east of the prime meridian. For example, suppose it is 3:00 P.M. where you are and 9:00 P.M. in Greenwich, England (near London). Because your local time is earlier than Greenwich time, you must be located west of the prime meridian. How many degrees of longitude west? There is a 6-hour difference between your time and Greenwich time. Therefore, your location must be near 90° west longitude (15° × 6).

REVIEW YOUR UNDERSTANDING

Some questions may require use of the *Earth Science Reference Tables*.

_____ **1.** An airplane takes off from a location at 10°S and flies to a new location 62° north of its starting point. What latitude has the plane reached?
(1) 72°S
(2) 72°N
(3) 52°N
(4) 52°S

_____ **2.** To an observer in Syracuse, New York, Polaris is always located above the horizon at an angle of approximately
(1) 90°
(2) 0°
(3) 23°
(4) 43°

_____ **3.** A car travels 1,000 miles south, from New York to
Florida. As the car travels south, the observed position of Polaris

(1) moves closer to the horizon

(2) moves farther away from the horizon

(3) does not change with respect to the horizon

(4) drops below the horizon

Topographic Maps

Maps are used for a variety of purposes. Some maps are used to
show the locations of cities and towns. Other maps are used to
show temperature differences, pressure variations, or the locations of different types of rocks.

A **topographic map** is a type of map that shows the surface
features, or the *topography*, of Earth's surface. Constructed using
data from aerial photos and land surveys, topographic maps are
used to show natural features, such as hills and rivers, as well as
constructed features, such as roads and buildings. But most
importantly, topographic maps are designed to show the **elevation**—the height above sea level—of the land in great detail.

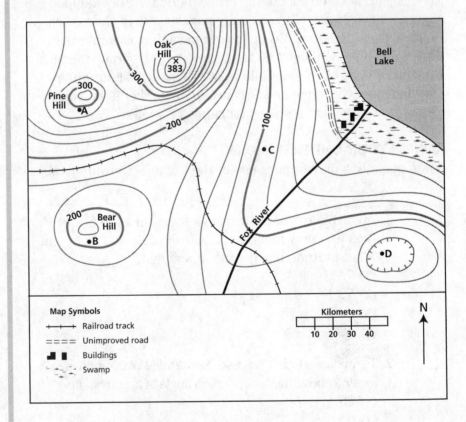

Unit II Mapping Earth's Surface *continued*

	Notes/Study Ideas/Answers

Self-Check How does a topographic map differ from a regular road map?

A topographic map is a type of field map. A **field** is a geographic space in which the same quantity can be measured everywhere. Field maps are used to show how particular field quantities change over the geographic space. Lines on a field map are called *isolines*. Isolines connect places having the same field quantity value.

Contour lines are isolines that connect places that have the same elevation. Each contour line is separated from the lines next to it by a uniform interval, called the *contour interval*. In some maps, the contour interval can be as great as 100 m, whereas on others it can be as small as 1 m. Move your finger across the topographic map above. Each time your finger crosses a contour, the elevation changes an amount equal to the contour interval of the map, which in this case is 20 m. **Relief** is the difference in elevation between the highest and lowest points of the area being mapped.

Self-Check Define contour interval.

On most topographic maps, every fifth contour line is printed more boldly than the others. This is intended to make the maps easier to read. These bold lines are known as *index contours*, and are labeled by elevation. The elevation of the unnumbered lines is easy to find if you know the contour interval. For example, on the map on the previous page, the elevations of the unnumbered contour lines between the 100 m and 200 m index contours would be 120 m, 140 m, 160 m, and 180 m.

If you want to know the elevation of a point between contour lines, you have to make an estimate based on nearby contour lines. For example, point C on the map is located about halfway between the 100 m and 80 m contour lines. Therefore, the elevation of point C is approximately 90 m.

Contour lines that bend to form a V shape indicate a valley. The V points to the higher end of the valley. The width of the valley is shown by the width of the V formed by the contour lines. If a river flows through the valley, the V in the contour lines will point upstream, toward the higher land from which the water flows. A river always flows from a higher elevation to a lower elevation.

Contour lines that form closed loops indicate a hill or a depression. To avoid confusion, depressions are usually indicated by short, straight lines drawn inside the loop and pointing toward its center, indicating the direction of depression.

**Notes/Study
Ideas/Answers**

The spacing and direction of contour lines indicates the shape of the land. Contour lines spaced far apart indicate that the change in elevation is gradual and that the land has only a gentle slope. Contour lines that are close together indicate a rapid change in elevation and a relatively steep slope. Slope is often used to mean gradient. *Gradient* is the change in field value per unit distance. You can find the formula for gradient in the "Equations" table in the *Earth Science Reference Tables* section, on page 221.

Suppose you wanted to calculate the gradient from point C to point B on the map. Point B, about halfway between the 200 m and 220 m contour lines, must be about 210 m. Similarly, point C is about 90 m. Using the scale printed at the bottom of the map, the distance between the two points can be determined. That distance is about 110 km. Therefore, the gradient between points B and C is about 1.9 m/km. In other words, on average, the slope of the land between points B and C increases about 1.9 m for every kilometer of distance.

A **profile** is a picture of what the land would look like from the side. It is a cross-section of the land. A topographic map can be used to draw a profile along any straight-line route. You should be able to identify a correct profile of a topographic map, as well as draw one.

Drawing a Profile from a Topographic Map

Step 1	Obtain a sheet of lined notebook paper and a blank strip of paper that is a little longer than the straight-line profile route you wish to draw.
Step 2	Place the edge of the blank strip along the profile route. Mark a point on the blank strip for each contour line that the strip crosses.
Step 3	Label each mark with the elevation of the corresponding contour line.
Step 4	Along the left side of the notebook paper, label the horizontal lines with the elevations of the contour lines.
Step 5	Place the marked strip of paper along the lowest labeled line on the notebook paper. Directly above each mark, make a dot on the notebook paper at the elevation indicated by that mark.
Step 6	Connect the dots with a smooth line.

Unit II Mapping Earth's Surface *continued*

Most maps have a **legend,** or *key*, printed outside the map area. This explains the meanings of the various symbols on the map. Every topographic map also includes a map *scale*. A *graphic scale*, such as the one used on the topographic map in this section, is a printed line that has markings on it that are similar to those on a ruler. The line represents a unit of measure, such as a mile or a kilometer. Each part of the scale represents a specific distance on Earth. To find the actual distance between the two points on Earth, you first measure the distance between the points as shown on the map. Then, you compare that measurement with the map scale.

REVIEW YOUR UNDERSTANDING

Base your answers on the topographic map shown on page 14. Points A, B, C, D, and X are locations on the map. Elevations are expressed in meters. The maximum elevation of Oak Hill is indicated at point X.

_____ **4.** In what general direction does the Fox River flow?
  (1) southwest to northwest
  (2) southwest to northeast
  (3) northeast to southwest
  (4) northwest to southeast

_____ **5.** Which location, A, B, C, or D, has the highest elevation?
  (1) A
  (2) B
  (3) C
  (4) D

_____ **6.** What is the contour interval on this topographic map?
  (1) 5 m
  (2) 10 m
  (3) 15 m
  (4) 20 m

_____ **7.** On a topographic map, a steep gradient is indicated by contour lines that
  (1) are spaced close together
  (2) are spaced far apart
  (3) are bent to form a V shape
  (4) form closed loops

| Notes/Study Ideas/Answers | **ANSWERS TO SELF-CHECK QUESTIONS** |

- Latitude is the angular distance, measured in degrees, north or south of the equator.

- Longitude is the angular distance, measured in degrees, east or west of the prime meridian.

- Unlike road maps, topographic maps show the elevation of the land. Topographic maps also show natural and constructed surface features.

- A contour interval is the difference in elevation between one contour line and the next.

UNIT II

Holt Earth Science: The Physical Setting

Questions for Regents Practice

Mapping Earth's Surface

PART A

Some questions may require use of the *Earth Science Reference Tables*.

_____ **1.** In New York State, Polaris could be observed above the horizon at an angle of
  (1) 90°
  (2) 0°
  (3) 42°
  (4) 35°

_____ **2.** On a topographic map, point X has an elevation of 1,000 feet and point Y has an elevation of 8,000 feet. The distance between points X and Y is 20 miles. What is the average gradient along a straight line from point X to point Y?
  (1) 50 ft/mi
  (2) 100 ft/mi
  (3) 350 ft/mi
  (4) 400 ft/mi

_____ **3.** What New York State landscape region includes the coordinates 41°N, 73°W?
  (1) Tug Hill Plateau
  (2) Taconic Mountains
  (3) St. Lawrence Lowlands
  (4) Atlantic Coastal Plain

_____ **4.** What are the approximate geographic coordinates of the city of Buffalo, New York?
  (1) 43°N, 79°W
  (2) 40°N, 75°W
  (3) 79°N, 43°W
  (4) 75°N, 40°W

_____ **5.** What is the contour interval of a topographic map if two adjacent index contours are 5,000 feet and 10,000 feet?
  (1) 100 feet
  (2) 500 feet
  (3) 1,000 feet
  (4) 5,000 feet

_____ **6.** Which line of latitude is closest to the North Geographic Pole?
  (1) 0°
  (2) 45°N
  (3) 66°N
  (4) 88°S

_____ **7.** On a topographic map, contour lines that surround a river within a valley point
  (1) parallel to the river
  (2) perpendicular to the river
  (3) in a V shape, pointing upstream
  (4) in a V shape, pointing downstream

Unit II Mapping Earth's Surface *continued*

PART B-1

Base your answers to questions 8 to 10 on your knowledge of earth science, the *Earth Science Reference Tables*, and the diagram below, which shows part of the latitude-longitude coordinate grid of New York State. Letter A represents a location on the grid.

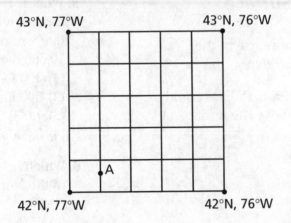

43°N, 77°W   43°N, 76°W

A

42°N, 77°W   42°N, 76°W

_____ **8.** What are the latitude-longitude coordinates of location A to the nearest tenth of a degree?
(1) 42.15°N, 76.8°W
(2) 42.15°N, 77.8°W
(3) 43.15°N, 76.8°W
(4) 43.15°N, 77.8°W

_____ **9.** For a traveler positioned at location A, at what angle above the horizon would Polaris appear in the night sky?
(1) 76.8°
(2) 77.8°
(3) 42.15°
(4) 43.15°

_____ **10.** Which city in New York State is closest to location A?
(1) Buffalo
(2) Jamestown
(3) Riverhead
(4) Elmira

Unit II Mapping Earth's Surface *continued*

PART B-2

Base your answers to questions 11 to 13 on your knowledge of earth science and the topographic map below. Letters A, B, and C represent separate locations on the map. Elevation is expressed in feet.

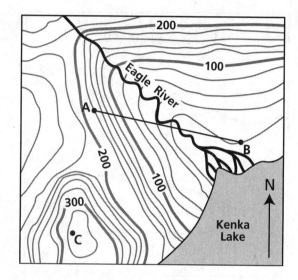

11. State the contour interval used on this topographic map. How are you able to determine the interval?

_____

_____

_____

12. What is the approximate elevation of location C?

_____

13. Draw a topographic profile for the landscape region between locations A and B.

Unit II Mapping Earth's Surface *continued*

PART C

Base your answers to questions 14 to 16 on your knowledge of earth science, the *Earth Science Reference Tables*, and the topographic map below, which shows a region of New York State. Letters X, Y, and Z represent separate locations. Elevation is expressed in feet.

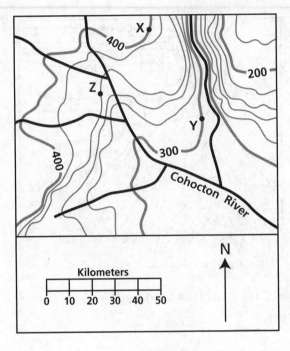

14. Describe how the contour lines on this map can be used to determine the direction of flow of the Cohocton River.

    _____

    _____

    _____

15. The geographic coordinates of location Z are 42°N, 77°W. Identify the New York State landscape region in which this mapped area is located.

    _____

    _____

    _____

16. Determine the average gradient of the Cohocton River between points X and Y. Show all work.

    _____

    _____

    _____

Focus On

The Regents Exam

Earth Chemistry and Mineral Resources

Earth materials, such as rocks, air, and water, are all composed of matter. **Matter** is anything that takes up space and has mass.

Properties of Matter

Every substance can be described by two types of properties: physical properties and chemical properties. *Physical properties* are the characteristics of a substance—such as color, hardness, and density—that can be observed without changing the substance. For example, some physical properties of lead are a light-gray color, softness, and a very high density.

Chemical properties are characteristics that describe how a substance interacts with other substances to form new substances. For example, a chemical property of iron is that it interacts with oxygen to form rust.

Self-Check Describe some physical properties of an apple.

Matter is made up of elements. An **element** is a substance that cannot be broken down into simpler substances by chemical methods. Every element has its own characteristic set of properties. Metals such as gold, silver, and iron are elements. Gases such as oxygen, nitrogen, helium, neon, and chlorine are also elements. More than 90 elements exist naturally on Earth.

Elements are made up of tiny particles called atoms. An **atom** is the smallest unit of an element that has all the basic properties of that element. Atoms are so small they can't be seen with the naked eye. Atoms consist of still smaller particles called *subatomic particles*. There are three types of subatomic particles: *electrons*, which have a negative charge; *protons*, which have a positive charge; and *neutrons*, which have no electrical charge.

What You'll Need to Learn

This topic is part of the Regents Curriculum for the Physical Setting/Earth Science Exam.

Standard 4, Performance Indicator 3.1: *Explain the properties of materials in terms of the arrangement and properties of the atoms that compose them.* Major Understandings: 3.1a, 3.1b, 3.1c

Which Terms You'll Need to Know

atom
cleavage
conservation
density
element
fossil fuel
hardness
luster
matter
mineral
nonrenewable resource
nucleus
ore
renewable resource
streak

Where You Can Learn Even More:

Holt Earth Science: The Physical Setting
Chapter 4: Earth Chemistry
Chapter 5: Minerals of Earth's Crust
Chapter 7: Resources and Energy

Unit III Earth Chemistry and Mineral Resources *continued*

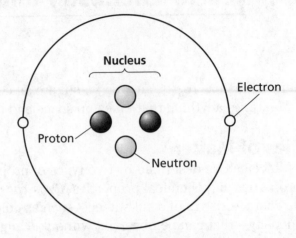

Subatomic particles are arranged similarly in all atoms, as shown in the diagram. Protons and neutrons are packed close together in the central region of the atom known as the **nucleus.** Electrons move rapidly around the nucleus.

The number of protons in the nucleus of an atom is called the **atomic number.** The sum of the number of protons and neutrons in an atom is the *mass number*. All atoms of the same element have the same atomic number. However, because atoms of the same element may contain different numbers of neutrons, atoms of the same element may have different mass numbers. Atoms with different numbers of neutrons but the same number of protons are called *isotopes*.

The number of electrons in an atom is equal to the number of protons. It is the arrangement of these electrons that determines the chemical behavior of the element. The periodic table lists elements according to their atomic numbers. Elements in the same column on the periodic table have similar arrangements of electrons and have similar chemical behavior.

REVIEW YOUR UNDERSTANDING

Some questions may require use of the *Earth Science Reference Tables*.

_____ **1.** Which describes a chemical property of the substance iron?
(1) It has a silvery color.
(2) It reacts with oxygen to form rust.
(3) It has a density of 7.86 g/cm^3.
(4) It is relatively hard.

Unit III Earth Chemistry and Mineral Resources *continued*

_____ **2.** The smallest unit of an element that has all the basic
properties of that element is called
(1) an electron
(2) a proton
(3) a nucleus
(4) an atom

_____ **3.** Which kinds of subatomic particles are located in the
nucleus?
(1) electrons and protons
(2) neutrons and electrons
(3) protons and neutrons
(4) protons, neutrons, and electrons

_____ **4.** If an atom has 12 protons, then it must
(1) have a mass number of 12
(2) also contain 12 neutrons
(3) have an atomic number of 12
(4) be an isotope

Minerals

A **mineral** is a naturally occurring, inorganic solid with a definite chemical formula and definite physical and chemical properties. Minerals are the basic components of rocks. All rocks
are made up of one or more minerals.

All minerals have a crystalline structure. A crystal is a solid
with a specific geometric shape. Salt crystals, for example, are
shaped like cubes because their atoms line up and bond to one
another in a regular geometric arrangement.

More than 3,000 different minerals have been identified
on Earth. Each mineral has specific properties that are the
result of its chemical composition and crystal structure.
Fewer than 20 of these minerals are common. These are
called *rock-forming minerals* because they form the vast
majority of the rocks that make up Earth's crust. (Please see
the "Properties of Common Minerals" table in the *Earth
Science Reference Tables* section, page 251, for a list of common minerals and their properties.)

Self-Check Define *mineral*.

A mineral's identity can be determined by observing its physical properties (such as crystal shape, hardness, color, streak,
luster, cleavage, and density) and its chemical properties.
Hardness is the resistance of a mineral to being scratched.
The hardness of a mineral is largely determined by the strength

Unit III Earth Chemistry and Mineral Resources *continued*

Notes/Study
Ideas/Answers

of the bonds between its atoms. The *Mohs Hardness Scale* is a list of 10 common minerals arranged in order from softest (talc) to hardest (diamond). A mineral's hardness may be determined by comparing it with minerals from the Mohs scale or with other minerals or common objects of known hardness, such as a fingernail (hardness 2.5), a copper penny (hardness 3.0), or a glass plate (hardness 5.5).

Mohs Hardness Scale		
Mineral	**Hardness**	**Common Test**
Talc	1	Easily scratched by a fingernail
Gypsum	2	Can be scratched by a fingernail
Calcite	3	Barely can be scratched by a copper penny
Fluorite	4	Easily scratched with a steel file or glass
Apatite	5	Can be scratched by a steel file or glass
Feldspar	6	Scratches glass with difficulty
Quartz	7	Easily scratches both glass and steel
Topaz	8	Scratches quartz
Corundum	9	No simple tests
Diamond	10	Scratches everything

To determine the hardness of a mineral not on the scale, you find the softest mineral on the scale that can scratch it. Galena, for example, can be scratched by calcite (3) but not by gypsum (2). Thus, the hardness of galena is between 2 and 3.

Self-Check What is the approximate hardness of a mineral that can be scratched by quartz but not by feldspar?

Color is an easily observable property, but is not very useful for identification purposes. Many minerals have the same color, and many come in a variety of colors. Color may also be affected by weathering. For example, pyrite is the color of gold, but its color ranges from dark yellow to black when it is weathered. When examining a mineral for color, it is often necessary to inspect a freshly exposed surface.

A more reliable way of determining a mineral's identity is the color of the mineral in powder form. This is called its **streak.** A mineral's streak is determined by rubbing it on a piece of unglazed ceramic tile called a *streak plate*. Galena, for example, has a silver color, but its streak is gray-black.

Unit III Earth Chemistry and Mineral Resources *continued*

Luster is the appearance or quality of light reflected from the surface of a mineral. Some minerals reflect light like polished metals—they have *metallic luster*. All other minerals have *nonmetallic luster*. Nonmetallic luster can be further described with adjectives such as *dull, glassy, waxy,* or *pearly*.

Cleavage is the tendency of a mineral to split along certain planes at certain angles. Mica, for example, tends to split into thin, parallel sheets. Halite (rock salt) shows cleavage in three directions, all at right angles to one another. The surface along which cleavage occurs generally runs parallel to a plane in the crystal in which bonding is relatively weak. A mineral that does not exhibit cleavage when broken is said to *fracture*. For example, if quartz were to break, it would shatter into pieces of different shapes.

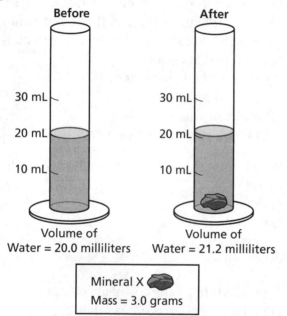

Before

30 mL

20 mL

10 mL

Volume of
Water = 20.0 milliliters

After

30 mL

20 mL

10 mL

Volume of
Water = 21.2 milliliters

Mineral X
Mass = 3.0 grams

Density is the mass of a mineral sample per its volume. The volume of an irregular solid can be determined through the method of water displacement. In the diagram, a 3.0-g sample of Mineral X is placed into a graduated cylinder holding 20 mL (20 cm^3) of water. After the sample is placed underwater, the water level rises to 21.2 mL (an increase of 1.2 cm^3). Therefore, the volume of the mineral sample is 1.2 cm^3. Using the formula for density, d = mass/volume, we can now calculate the density of Mineral X:

$$\text{Density} = \frac{3.0 \text{ g}}{1.2 \text{ cm}^3} \quad \frac{\text{(mass)}}{\text{(volume)}}$$

$$\text{Density} = 2.5 \text{ g/cm}^3$$

Unit III Earth Chemistry and Mineral Resources *continued*

**Notes/Study
Ideas/Answers**

Minerals can also be tested for their chemical properties. A simple chemical test is applying a drop of hydrochloric acid to a mineral sample. If the mineral is a carbonate, such as calcite, there will be a fizzing sound, and bubbles of carbon dioxide will form.

Self-Check Name and describe seven physical properties used to identify minerals.

REVIEW YOUR UNDERSTANDING

Some questions may require use of the *Earth Science Reference Tables*.

_____ **5.** Coal is a natural substance in Earth's crust formed from the remains of plants that lived millions of years ago. One reason why coal is not considered a mineral is that coal
(1) is an organic substance
(2) is used as a fuel
(3) sinks in water
(4) can be ground into powder

_____ **6.** Which mineral could be scratched by halite but not by talc?
(1) diamond
(2) biotite mica
(3) gypsum
(4) calcite

_____ **7.** A mineral that exhibits cleavage must
(1) have a hardness of less than 2.5
(2) contain silicon and oxygen
(3) have a density of less than 1.5 g/cm^3
(4) have weak bonding across a plane in the crystal

_____ **8.** What is the density of a rock that has a mass of 25.0 g and a volume of 12.0 cm^3?
(1) 0.48 g/cm^3
(2) 2.08 g/cm^3
(3) 13.00 g/cm^3
(4) 20.80 g/cm^3

Unit III Earth Chemistry and Mineral Resources *continued*

Natural Resources

Earth's crust contains a wealth of useful mineral resources. The chemical composition and physical properties of minerals determine how they can be used. Diamond, for example, is the hardest known substance and can cut through any material. These properties make diamond particularly useful as an abrasive and in cutting and grinding applications, such as drilling holes in rock to find water, oil, and natural gas. Diamonds are also prized for their beauty and color, which is why they are used extensively in jewelry.

Self-Check Name two uses for each of the following minerals: quartz, olivine, and halite.

A mineral is an **ore** if it contains a useful substance that can be mined at a profit. For example, aluminum can be refined from bauxite and made into a variety of useful products, including foil and electrical transmission lines. These products are worth more money than the cost of the mining, so bauxite is an ore.

All mineral ores form inorganically by the process of crystallization as a result of specific environmental conditions. Some ores, such as those containing lead, chromium, and nickel, form within cooling magma (molten rock in Earth's interior). As magma cools, the dense metals and metal-containing compounds within the magma begin to sink. Layers of these minerals accumulate below and form ore deposits within the hardened magma.

Other ores, including those containing copper and zinc, form when hot magma comes into contact with existing rock. Heat and chemical fluids from the magma release the minerals from the surrounding rock.

A third method of ore formation happens when water containing dissolved minerals accumulates at the top of a magma chamber. As the magma in the chamber cools and hardens, the water sinks through cracks, and new minerals precipitate, or settle out, forming ore deposits called *veins*. Ores of heavy minerals, such as gold, tin, lead, copper, and platinum, often form in this way.

Natural resources are also used to generate energy. Much of the energy people use comes from the burning of materials buried deep within Earth's crust. These natural resources are called **fossil fuels** because they are formed from the buried remains of plants and microorganisms that lived millions of years ago. The primary fossil fuels are coal, petroleum, and

Notes/Study Ideas/Answers

Unit III Earth Chemistry and Mineral Resources *continued*

**Notes/Study
Ideas/Answers**

natural gas. Today, fossil fuels provide more than 90% of the energy used in the United States to generate electricity, manufacture goods, and provide transportation.

Self-Check What are the three primary fossil fuels?

Coal is a dark-colored, organic rock and is the most abundant fossil fuel in the world. The process of coal formation occurs in a number of stages and requires millions of years. The partial decomposition of plant remains produces a brownish-black material called *peat*. Over time, peat deposits are covered by layers of sediment. Heat inside Earth's crust and pressure produced by the weight of overlying sediment layers slowly change the peat into coal.

Petroleum is another name for oil and consists of a mixture of liquid hydrocarbons, which are compounds of carbon and hydrogen. Petroleum is refined into gasoline and other types of fuel.

Natural gas is mostly the hydrocarbon methane (CH_4) and is used for heating and cooking. Petroleum and natural gas are found in similar environments and occur together.

Mineral resources and fossil fuels are considered to be **nonrenewable resources,** because they exist in limited amounts and cannot be replaced once they are used. **Renewable resources** are resources that can be replaced within a human life span or as they are used. An example of a renewable resource is sunlight. We use sunlight to grow plants, provide heat, and generate solar energy. Yet, sunlight is never used up. Other renewable energy sources include moving water, wind, and heat inside Earth, which are all used to generate electricity.

Although natural resources provide many benefits for society, there are negative effects of natural resource use. For example, at the present rate of use, scientists estimate that worldwide coal reserves will last about 200 years. In addition to the depletion of important resources, resource use also affects Earth's ecosystems. The burning of fossil fuels, for example, can pollute the air and damage fragile ecosystems.

Conservation is the preservation and wise use of natural resources. By conserving natural resources, humans can ensure that natural resources last longer. *Recycling* is one way to conserve mineral resources. Many metals, including iron, aluminum, and copper, can be recycled. Fossil fuels can be conserved by reducing the amount of energy used every day or by using alternative energy sources, such as solar energy, nuclear energy, or hydroelectric energy.

Unit III Earth Chemistry and Mineral Resources *continued*

REVIEW YOUR UNDERSTANDING

_____ **9.** Which process could lead to the formation of an ore?
(1) the cooling and solidification of magma
(2) the application of heat and pressure on peat
(3) the refining of petroleum into gasoline
(4) the extraction of aluminum from bauxite

_____ **10.** Which is a nonrenewable resource?
(1) natural gas
(2) sunlight
(3) moving water
(4) wind

_____ **11.** Coal is considered to be a "fossil" fuel because coal
(1) comes from dinosaur fossils
(2) has been on Earth since the planet first formed
(3) forms from the buried remains of ancient plants
(4) consists of a mixture of fossils

_____ **12.** Which is a renewable resource?
(1) water
(2) coal
(3) gold
(4) petroleum

ANSWERS TO SELF CHECK QUESTIONS

- round shape; red, yellow, or green color; softness; smooth texture; palm-sized; and so on

- A mineral is an inorganic solid with a crystal shape and definite chemical and physical properties.

- hardness between 6 and 7

- crystal shape, density, color, hardness, cleavage, luster, streak

- uses for quartz: glass, jewelry, electronics; uses for olivine: furnace bricks, jewelry; uses for halite: food additive, melting ice

- petroleum, coal, and natural gas

Questions for Regents Practice

Earth Chemistry and Mineral Resources

PART A

Some questions may require use of the *Earth Science Reference Tables*.

_____ **1.** A mineral sample sits on a table. Which mineral property could you observe without actually touching the mineral sample?
  (1) density
  (2) atomic structure
  (3) luster
  (4) streak

_____ **2.** The Mohs scale is most useful for
  (1) calculating the density of a mineral sample
  (2) identifying a mineral sample
  (3) finding the mass of a mineral sample
  (4) determining how a mineral sample cleaves

_____ **3.** Which mineral produces a black streak when rubbed on a piece of unglazed porcelain?
  (1) gypsum
  (2) calcite
  (3) fluorite
  (4) magnetite

_____ **4.** A mineral that is softer than dolomite exhibits a nonmetallic luster and bubbles in acid. This mineral most likely is
  (1) galena
  (2) calcite
  (3) fluorite
  (4) halite

_____ **5.** What is the best way to determine whether a mineral sample is calcite or quartz?
  (1) Measure the mass of the material.
  (2) Touch the sample with a magnet.
  (3) Place a drop of acid on it.
  (4) Do a streak test.

_____ **6.** Which group contains only minerals?
  (1) pyroxene and limestone
  (2) hematite and quartzite
  (3) fluorite and coal
  (4) halite and olivine

_____ **7.** Which mineral cleaves in two directions and can be scratched by olivine?
  (1) fluorite
  (2) potassium feldspar
  (3) quartz
  (4) pyrite

_____ **8.** Which two minerals would be most difficult to distinguish from each other based on their color, luster, and hardness?
  (1) pyroxene and pyrite
  (2) magnetite and amphiboles
  (3) halite and sulfur
  (4) pyroxene and amphiboles

Unit III Earth Chemistry and Mineral Resources *continued*

PART B-1

Base your answers to questions 9, 10, and 11 on your knowledge of earth science, the *Earth Science Reference Tables*, and the diagram below, which shows a mineral sample undergoing three different physical tests: A, B, and C.

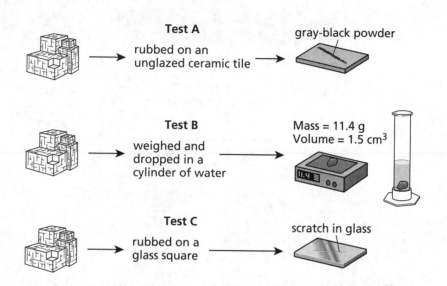

Test A
rubbed on an unglazed ceramic tile → gray-black powder

Test B
weighed and dropped in a cylinder of water → Mass = 11.4 g Volume = 1.5 cm³

Test C
rubbed on a glass square → scratch in glass

_____ **9.** Which choice correctly matches each test (A, B, and C) with the mineral property tested?
  (1) A–hardness; B–density; C–streak
  (2) A–streak; B–density; C–hardness
  (3) A–density; B–streak; C–hardness
  (4) A–streak; B–hardness; C–density

_____ **10.** The results of these physical tests would be useful for determining the
  (1) time when the mineral formed
  (2) environment where the mineral was found
  (3) chemical properties of the mineral
  (4) identity of the mineral

_____ **11.** The mineral being tested is very soft and has a metallic luster. Based on the results of the physical tests, the mineral could be identified as
  (1) quartz
  (2) pyrite
  (3) galena
  (4) gypsum

Unit III Earth Chemistry and Mineral Resources *continued*

PART B-2

Base your answers to questions 12 through 14 on your knowledge of earth science, the *Earth Science Reference Tables*, and the table below, which shows some properties of selected minerals.

Mineral Breaking	Color	Luster	Streak
Magnetite	black to silver	metallic	black
Halite	colorless	nonmetallic	colorless
Quartz	colorless	nonmetallic	colorless
Biotite Mica	black to dark brown	nonmetallic	white

12. Using one of the minerals from the table as an example, explain why streak is a more useful property for identifying a given mineral sample than color is.

_____

_____

_____

13. Explain why magnetite could be scratched by quartz but not by halite.

_____

_____

14. Describe a physical test that you could do to distinguish a sample of quartz from a sample of halite.

_____

_____

_____

Unit III Earth Chemistry and Mineral Resources *continued*

PART C

Base your answers to questions 15 through 19 on your knowledge of earth science, the *Earth Science Reference Tables*, and the diagram below, which shows some physical proper ties of four unknown mineral samples, A through D.

A student was given the task of identifying the mineral samples, A through D. Some phys ical properties are indicated for each sample.

A	B	C	D
Mass: ?	Mass: 3.0 g	Mass: 10.0 g	Mass: 16.0 g
Volume: 2.0 cm³	Volume: 1.8 cm³	Volume: 3.7 cm³	Volume: 2.1 cm³
Density: 2.7 g/cm³	Density: ?	Density: ?	Density: ?
Color: white	Color: white	Color: pink	Color: gray
Streak: white	Streak: white	Streak: white	Streak: gray-black

15. Suppose a student broke mineral sample A into many fragments. What is the density of one of the fragments. Explain how you know.

_____

_____

_____

16. What is the mass of mineral sample A? Show all work.

_____

17. Calculate the density of mineral sample B. Show all work.

_____

Unit III Earth Chemistry and Mineral Resources *continued*

18. Which two samples might be the same mineral? Explain the evidence that supports this conclusion.

_____

_____

_____

_____

19. In addition to the physical characteristics given, sample D exhibits a metallic luster and cleavage. Based on its physical properties, what is the likely identity of mineral sample D?

_____

_____

_____

UNIT IV
Rocks

As you have learned, Earth's crust is composed of rock. A **rock** is a substance that is or was a natural part of the solid Earth. Rock can be a collection of one or more minerals, or rock can be made of solid organic matter. In some cases, rock is made of mineral matter that is not crystalline, such as glass. Geologists study the forces and processes that form and change the rocks of Earth's crust. Based on these studies, geologists have classified rocks into three major types by the way the rocks form.

Rocks and the Rock Cycle

Scientists recognize three major classifications of rocks: igneous rock, sedimentary rock, and metamorphic rock. Each group has its own unique set of chemical and physical properties that are the result of how and where it formed. The physical characteristics of a rock reflect the chemical composition of the rock as a whole and the individual minerals that make up the rock.

Studies of volcanic activity provide information about the formation of one rock type, called igneous rock. The word *igneous* is derived from a Latin term meaning "from fire." **Igneous rock** forms when molten rock, or *magma*, cools and hardens. Magma is called *lava* when it is exposed at Earth's surface.

Natural forces, such as wind and waves, break down all types of rock into small fragments. Rocks, mineral crystals, and organic matter that have been broken into fragments are known as *sediment*. Sediment is carried away and deposited by water, glaciers, and wind. When sediment deposits are compressed or cemented together, **sedimentary rock** forms.

Certain forces and processes, including tremendous pressure, extreme heat, and chemical processes, also can change the form of existing rock. The rock that forms when existing rock is altered is called **metamorphic rock.** The word metamorphic means "changed form."

Self-Check What is the main difference between a sedimentary rock and an igneous rock?

Any of the three major types of rock can be changed into another of the three types. Natural processes such as weathering, erosion, compaction, melting, and cooling cause rock to change from one type to another and back again. This series of changes is called the **rock cycle.** For example, as shown in the diagram, a

What You'll Need to Learn

This topic is part of the Regents Curriculum for the Physical Setting Exam.

Standard 4, Performance Indicator 3.1: *Explain the properties of materials in terms of the arrangement and properties of the atoms that compose them.* Major Understandings: 3.1c

What Terms You'll Need to Know

chemical sedimentary rock
clastic sedimentary rock
contact metamorphism
extrusive igneous rock
igneous rock
intrusive igneous rock
metamorphic rock
organic sedimentary rock
regional metamorphism
rock
rock cycle
sedimentary rock

Where You Can Learn Even More

Holt Earth Science: The Physical Setting
Chapter 6 Rocks

sedimentary rock can be changed by heat and pressure to form a metamorphic rock. The metamorphic rock can then melt and later cool to form an igneous rock. The igneous rock may then weather and erode, and the rock particles from it might form another sedimentary rock. (See the "Rock Cycle in Earth's Crust" diagram in the *Earth Science Reference Tables* section, page 231.)

Much of the rock in Earth's continental crust has probably passed through the rock cycle many times during Earth's history. However, a particular body of rock does not always pass through each stage of the rock cycle. For example, igneous rock may never be exposed at Earth's surface where the rock could change into sediment. Instead, the igneous rock may change directly into metamorphic rock while still beneath Earth's surface. Sedimentary rock may be broken down at Earth's surface, and the sediment may become another sedimentary rock. Metamorphic rock can be altered by heat and pressure to form a different type of metamorphic rock.

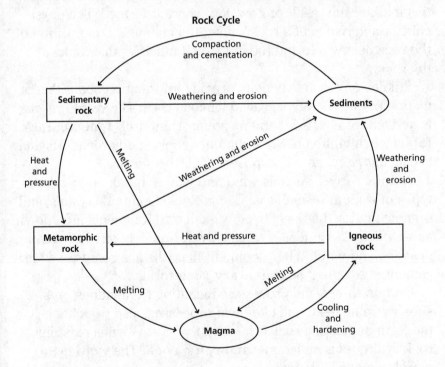

Rock Cycle

REVIEW YOUR UNDERSTANDING

Some questions may require use of the *Earth Science Reference Tables*.

_____ **1.** Which statement describes the process of metamorphism?
   (1) It is the compaction and cementation of rock particles.
   (2) It is the changing of existing rock by heat and pressure.
   (3) It is the solidification of magma by cooling.
   (4) It is the breaking down of rock into sediments.

_____ **2.** When a sedimentary rock melts as a result of heat and pressure, the material formed is
   (1) metamorphic rock
   (2) lava
   (3) magma
   (4) sediment

_____ **3.** Which describes the process by which igneous rock becomes metamorphic rock?
   (1) erosion
   (2) weathering
   (3) application of heat and pressure
   (4) cooling and solidifying

Igneous Rock

Igneous rocks are classified according to where magma cools and hardens. Magma that cools deep inside the crust forms **intrusive igneous rock.** The magma that forms these rocks enters, or *intrudes*, into other rock masses beneath Earth's surface. The magma then slowly cools and hardens. Lava that cools at Earth's surface forms **extrusive igneous rock.**

Intrusive and extrusive igneous rocks differ from each other not only in where they form but also in the size of their crystals or grains. The texture of igneous rock is determined by the size of the crystals in the rock. The size of the crystals is determined mainly by the cooling rate of the magma.

Intrusive igneous rocks commonly have large mineral crystals. The slow loss of heat allows the minerals in the cooling magma to form large, well-developed crystals. Igneous rocks that are composed of large mineral grains are described as having a *coarse-grained texture*. An example of a coarse-grained igneous rock is granite.

Many extrusive igneous rocks are composed of small mineral grains that cannot be seen by the unaided eye. Because

Unit IV Rocks *continued*

Notes/Study
Ideas/Answers

these rocks form when magma cools rapidly, large crystals are unable to form. Igneous rocks that are composed of small crystals are described as having a *fine-grained texture*. An example of a fine-grained igneous rock is basalt.

Self-Check Differentiate between intrusive and extrusive igneous rocks.

The mineral composition of an igneous rock is determined by the chemical composition of the magma from which the rock formed. Rocks in the *felsic* family form from magma that contains a large proportion of silica. Felsic rock generally has the light coloring of its main mineral components, potassium feldspar and quartz.

Rocks in the *mafic* family form from magma that contains lower proportions of silica than felsic rock does and that is rich in iron and magnesium. Mafic rocks are generally dark in color due to the presence of olivine and iron-bearing minerals such as hornblende.

Self-Check What is the difference between a mafic rock and a felsic rock?

The "Scheme for Igneous Rock Identification" in the *Earth Science Reference Tables* section, page 231, is a chart that can help you understand and classify igneous rocks primarily by color and texture. Rocks with the smallest crystals (fine-grained, extrusive rocks) are at the top of the chart. In these rocks, the grains of the different minerals are too small to be seen without magnification. Below them are the coarse-grained igneous rocks in which it is easy to see the different minerals.

Variations in mineral composition occur between the light-colored (felsic) rocks, such as granite and rhyolite on the left side of the chart, and the mafic rocks, such as basalt and gabbro, on the right side. However, it should be made clear that color is not always a good indicator of whether an igneous rock is mafic or felsic. For example, obsidian is an extrusive igneous rock in the felsic family that is black in color. Along with this variation in composition (felsic to mafic) comes a change not only in color (light to dark) but also a change in density.

Unit IV Rocks *continued*

Among the terms that you will find on the chart is *vesicular*. A vesicular texture refers to the gas pockets, called *vesicles*, that are common in extrusive igneous rocks. When magma rises, dissolved gases in the magma form bubbles. For example, the extrusive igneous rock called pumice is filled with many small vesicles, which makes it light enough to float on water. When a highly viscous magma cools quickly, few crystals are able to grow. If such magma contains a very small percentage of dissolved gases, a rock that has a *glassy* texture called obsidian forms.

Notes/Study Ideas/Answers

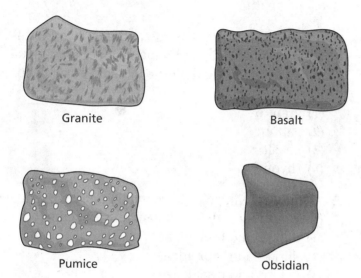

Granite Basalt

Pumice Obsidian

The properties of the other igneous rocks listed in the chart can be determined from their position on the chart. For example, pegmatite appears at the bottom left of the chart. Like other igneous rocks on the left, pegmatite is relatively light in color. Its position at the bottom means that pegmatite is composed of very large crystals.

Below the chart portion is a section that shows the minerals that are common in igneous rocks. For example, granite usually contains potassium feldspar, quartz, plagioclase feldspar, biotite, and amphibole. If you imagine a vertical line running directly below the word *granite* and into this section, you will see that quartz and potassium feldspar make up about 66% of the volume of granite.

Name _____ Class _____ Date _____

REVIEW YOUR UNDERSTANDING

Some questions require use of the *Earth Science Reference Tables.*

_____ **4.** Which coarse-grained igneous rock is composed of 50% plagioclase feldspar, 25% biotite, and 25% amphibole?
(1) granite
(2) diorite
(3) gabbro
(4) pegmatite

_____ **5.** A light-colored igneous rock with large mineral grains contains several minerals, including potassium feldspar, quartz, and biotite mica. The rock should be identified as
(1) granite
(2) gabbro
(3) basalt
(4) rhyolite

_____ **6.** As the percentage of felsic materials in an igneous rock increases, the rock generally becomes
(1) darker and less dense
(2) darker and more dense
(3) lighter and less dense
(4) lighter and more dense

_____ **7.** Which statement best explains why a given igneous rock has large mineral grains?
(1) The rock formed as a result of cooling magma.
(2) The magma from which the rock formed was high in quartz.
(3) The pressure exerted on the cooling magma was low.
(4) The magma from which the rock formed cooled slowly.

| Unit IV Rocks *continued*

Sedimentary Rock

Most of the rocks below Earth's surface are igneous rocks. By contrast, the vast majority of rocks at Earth's surface are sedimentary rocks. Most sedimentary rocks are made of the weathered remains of other rocks (sediments) that have been eroded and later deposited in layers. Over time, the sediments are compressed by the weight of the layers above them or cemented by mineral material left by water circulating through the sediments. Scientists group sedimentary rocks by the way they form. There are three main classes—clastic, chemical, and organic.

Clastic sedimentary rocks are composed of the weathered remains of other rocks. Clastic rocks are formed by the processes of deposition, compression, and cementing of sediments.

Clastic rocks are classified by the size of the sedimentary particles from which they are formed. Information about the range of sizes of the various particles in sedimentary rocks is found in the "Scheme for Sedimentary Rock Identification" chart in the *Earth Science Reference Tables* section, page 233. Clastic rock composed of rounded pebbles is called *conglomerate*. If the rock fragments have sharp corners, it is called *breccia*. Another group of clastic sedimentary rock is made up of sand-sized grains that have been cemented together. These rocks are called *sandstone*. A third group of clastic rock is *shale*, which consists of clay-sized particles that have been cemented and compacted under pressure.

Breccia

Conglomerate

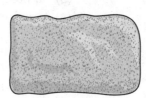
Sandstone

Notes/Study
Ideas/Answers

Self-Check What is clastic sedimentary rock? Describe the different groups of clastic rock.

Chemical sedimentary rock forms from minerals that were once dissolved in water. Some chemical sedimentary rocks form when dissolved minerals crystallize out of water as a result of changing temperature. Chemical limestone is an example. Another type of sedimentary rock forms when water evaporates, leaving the minerals behind. Gypsum and halite are examples of chemical sedimentary rock formed by evaporation.

The third class of sedimentary rock is **organic sedimentary rock,** which forms from the remains of living things. Coal and some limestones are examples. Coal forms over millions of years from the buried remains of plants. Organic limestone forms from the shells of once-living marine organisms, such as clams and oysters. Like chemical limestone, organic limestone is made of the mineral calcite.

REVIEW YOUR UNDERSTANDING

Some questions may require use of the *Earth Science Reference Tables*.

_____ **8.** A sedimentary rock is composed of rounded rock fragments about 3 cm in diameter embedded in sand. The rock should be identified as
   (1) breccia
   (2) sandstone
   (3) siltstone
   (4) conglomerate

_____ **9.** A sedimentary rock is formed from inorganic sediment particles about 0.0005 cm in diameter. The rock should be identified as
   (1) conglomerate
   (2) shale
   (3) siltstone
   (4) sandstone

_____ **10.** Which sedimentary rock may be formed both chemically and organically?
   (1) halite
   (2) conglomerate
   (3) gypsum
   (4) limestone

Unit IV Rocks *continued*

Metamorphic Rock

Notes/Study
Ideas/Answers

Metamorphic rocks form deep within Earth's crust from existing sedimentary, igneous, or metamorphic rocks. During metamorphism, heat, pressure, and hot fluids can cause some minerals to change into other minerals. Minerals may also change size or shape, or separate into parallel bands that give the rock a layered appearance. The types of minerals that form during metamorphism act as indicators of the conditions that were in place when the rock changed.

The metamorphic process causes visible changes. Consider, for example, what happens to the sedimentary rock shale when it undergoes continued heat and pressure. Shale is composed of clay-sized particles. Under metamorphic pressure, the mineral crystals are flattened and pushed into parallel bands. The resulting metamorphic rock is called *slate* and has the well-known property of separating into flat sheets of rock. When the minerals in a metamorphic rock are arranged in bands or planes, the rock is described as being *foliated*. Foliation is a feature common to many metamorphic rocks.

When additional heat and pressure are exerted on slate, the crystals become larger and the slate transforms into *phyllite*. Under more pressure and heat, phyllite becomes the coarser-grained metamorphic rock called *schist*. The layering in schist is sometimes wavy. Deep underground, intense heat and pressure cause schist to change into a greatly metamorphosed rock with bands of light and dark minerals. This rock is called *gneiss*.

Slate   Gneiss   Schist

The *Earth Science Reference Tables* section contains a "Scheme for Metamorphic Rock Identification" chart on page 233. Notice in the chart that the four rock types in the top half are the four foliated metamorphic rocks. They are listed in order of increasing metamorphic changes and increasing grain size. These four rocks show the progressive metamorphism of shale that was explained above. Note also the shaded bars in

**Notes/Study
Ideas/Answers**

the "composition" column that indicate the mineral makeup of these rocks. These bars show that minerals in the mica family are found in all four foliated metamorphic rock types. Quartz, feldspar, amphibole, and garnet are not common in slate, but are common in the three foliated rock types below slate. Of the six minerals shown here, pyroxene is the best indicator of extreme conditions of heat and pressure.

In some metamorphic rocks, the mineral grains in the parent rock change, grow, and rearrange, but no banding occurs. Rocks without foliations are said to be *nonfoliated*. Unlike the rocks in the top half of this chart, the four nonfoliated rocks at the bottom right of the chart do not show a progressive change. Each has a different mineral and chemical composition. These are the four most common metamorphic rocks that do not show foliation.

Self-Check What is the difference between a foliated rock and a nonfoliated rock?

Metamorphic rocks can be separated into two groups by origin. Sometimes large-scale movements of Earth's crust cause a vast region of rock to sink into the ground. When this occurs, a large mass of rock experiences increased heat and pressure. This process is called **regional metamorphism.** As the rock is drawn deeper into Earth, chemical changes in the minerals, crystal growth, and compaction cause the original parent rock to be metamorphosed.

The next group of metamorphic rocks occurs over a smaller area. An intrusion of hot magma will change the rock with which it comes in contact. This process is called **contact metamorphism.** In this environment, rocks are not always exposed to the intense pressure that is found deeper within Earth.

REVIEW YOUR UNDERSTANDING

Some questions may require use of the *Earth Science Reference Tables*.

_____ **11.** Which sedimentary rock is most likely to change to slate during regional metamorphism?
(1) breccia
(2) dolostone
(3) conglomerate
(4) shale

_____ **12.** A coarse-grained metamorphic rock composed mainly of calcite has a nonfoliated structure. The rock should be identified as
(1) gneiss
(2) marble
(3) hornfels
(4) slate

_____ **13.** Between which two adjoining bedrock layers could one find a zone of contact metamorphism?
(1) shale and conglomerate
(2) limestone and granite
(3) limestone and gneiss
(4) dolostone and sandstone

_____ **14.** What kind of rock results from the contact metamorphism of quartz sandstone?
(1) schist
(3) granite
(2) quartzite
(4) marble

ANSWERS TO SELF-CHECK QUESTIONS

- These rocks differ in the manner in which they form. Igneous rocks form when magma cools and hardens. Sedimentary rocks form by the compaction and cementation of sediments.

- Intrusive igneous rocks form by slow cooling of magma beneath Earth's surface. Extrusive igneous rocks are volcanic in origin and form by rapid cooling of lava at Earth's surface.

- Mafic rocks are generally dark-colored igneous rocks rich in magnesium and iron. Felsic rocks are generally light-colored igneous rocks rich in feldspar and silicon.

- Clastic sedimentary rocks are made up of rock fragments. One group is made up of pebble-sized rock fragments that become cemented together. Another group is made up of sand-sized fragments that become cemented together. The third group consists of clay-sized particles that become cemented and compacted.

- Foliated metamorphic rocks have layers or patterns of banding. Nonfoliated metamorphic rocks do not have these features.

UNIT IV

Holt Earth Science: The Physical Setting

Questions for Regents Practice

Rocks

PART A

Some questions may require use of the *Earth Science Reference Tables*.

_____ 1. The classification of rocks as sedimentary, igneous, or metamorphic is based on
(1) mineral composition
(2) method of formation
(3) texture and color
(4) absolute age

_____ 2. Which statement best explains why there are no coarse-grained extrusive igneous rocks?
(1) Extrusive rock forms beneath Earth's surface.
(2) Extrusive rock forms by rapid cooling of magma.
(3) Extrusive rock is volcanic in origin.
(4) Extrusive rock is subject to weathering.

_____ 3. Which kind of rock is formed from the solidification of molten material?
(1) breccia
(2) sandstone
(3) gneiss
(4) granite

_____ 4. Which type of rock is categorized by whether it is organic or inorganic?
(1) felsic rock
(2) sedimentary rock
(3) metamorphic rock
(4) mafic rock

_____ 5. Compared to mafic igneous rocks, felsic igneous rocks contain a greater amount of
(1) aluminum
(2) iron
(3) olivine
(4) pyroxene

_____ 6. An igneous rock can transform into sediments by
(1) the processes of compaction and cementation
(2) application of heat and pressure
(3) melting below Earth's surface
(4) the processes of weathering and erosion

_____ 7. Which statement best describes the difference between granite and basalt?
(1) Granite is metamorphic and basalt is igneous.
(2) Granite has larger mineral grains than basalt.
(3) Granite contains less amphibole and biotite than basalt.
(4) Granite is denser than basalt.

_____ 8. A sedimentary rock is composed of rock particles that are all close to 2 cm in diameter. This rock can be described as having a
(1) clastic texture consisting of sand-sized particles
(2) clastic texture consisting of pebble-sized particles
(3) nonclastic texture consisting of mixed particle sizes
(4) nonclastic texture with coarse-grained particles

PART B-1

Base your answers to questions 9 through 12 on the *Earth Science Reference Tables* and your knowledge of earth science.

_____ **9.** A coarse-grained igneous rock with mineral grains larger than 10 mm in diameter contains 25% potassium feldspar, 25% quartz, 20% plagioclase feldspar, 15% biotite, and 15% amphibole. The rock should be identified as
(1) gabbro
(2) granite
(3) pegmatite
(4) basalt

_____ **10.** Which sequence of change in rock type occurs as shale is subjected to increasing heat and pressure?
(1) schist $\longrightarrow$ phyllite $\longrightarrow$ slate $\longrightarrow$ gneiss
(2) slate $\longrightarrow$ phyllite $\longrightarrow$ schist $\longrightarrow$ gneiss
(3) gneiss $\longrightarrow$ phyllite $\longrightarrow$ slate $\longrightarrow$ schist
(4) gneiss $\longrightarrow$ phyllite $\longrightarrow$ schist $\longrightarrow$ slate

_____ **11.** Which relative concentration of elements is found in felsic rock?
(1) a high concentration of aluminum and a low concentration of iron
(2) a high concentration of iron and a low concentration of aluminum
(3) a high concentration of magnesium and a low concentration of aluminum
(4) a high concentration of iron and a low concentration of magnesium

_____ **12.** Which mineral is common in gneiss and schist, but not common in slate and phyllite?
(1) feldspar
(2) mica
(3) quartz
(4) pyroxene

Unit IV Rocks *continued*

PART B-2

Base your answers to questions 13 through 16 on your knowledge of earth science, the *Earth Science Reference Tables*, and the diagram below, which shows a cross-section of Earth's crust. Letters A through C represent different types of rock.

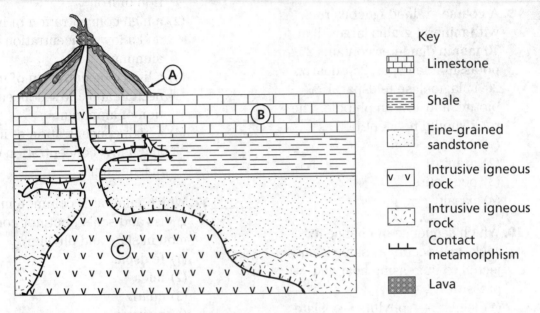

Key
- Limestone
- Shale
- Fine-grained sandstone
- Intrusive igneous rock
- Intrusive igneous rock
- Contact metamorphism
- Lava

13. Rock A is a dark-colored crystalline rock that formed when a lava flow cooled and solidified quickly. Is Rock A an intrusive igneous rock or an extrusive rock?

_____

14. Describe the chemical composition and texture of Rock A.

_____

_____

_____

15. Compare the mineral grain sizes for Rocks A and C.

_____

_____

_____

16. Describe how Rock B likely formed.

_____

_____

_____

_____

Unit IV Rocks *continued*

PART C

Base your answers to questions 17 through 19 on your knowledge of earth science, the *Earth Science Reference Tables*, and the rock cycle diagram below.

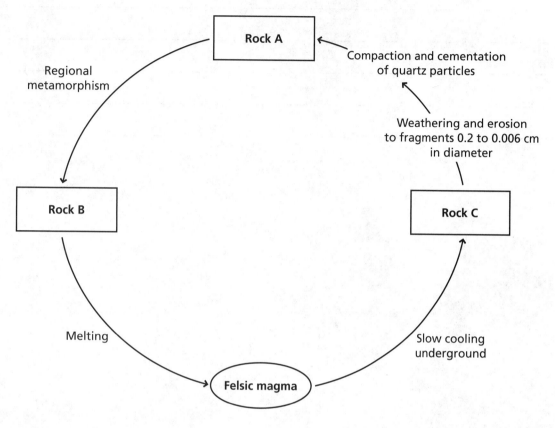

17. State the specific names of rocks A, B, and C. (Note: The answers are not "igneous," "sedimentary," and "metamorphic.")

_____

_____

_____

18. State one condition or process that would cause the metamorphism of Rock A.

_____

_____

_____

Unit IV Rocks *continued*

19. Describe one natural process that would result in the deposition of sediment particles that formed Rock A.

_____

_____

_____

_____

_____

Weathering and Soils

As you look around the natural environment, you probably notice many changes taking place. For example, you probably notice the apparent motion of the sun through the sky from east to west and the weather conditions that change from day to day. The solid Earth is also changing. Weathering is a good example of a slow process that, through thousands of years, can radically change the shape of the land. **Weathering** is the natural process by which environmental agents on Earth's surface decompose and disintegrate rocks.

Weathering Processes

There are two types of weathering processes: mechanical weathering and chemical weathering. Each process affects rock differently; however, both processes often occur at the same time.

Mechanical weathering is the process by which rock breaks down into smaller pieces. It is strictly a physical process, like breaking a stick of chalk into pieces. The chemical composition of rock does not change as a result of mechanical weathering. Natural agents of mechanical weathering include wind, ice, gravity, running water, and certain plant and animal activities.

Ice wedging, or *frost wedging*, is one kind of mechanical weathering process. Water that seeps into small cracks in rock freezes at high altitudes and in temperate climates, such as that of New York State. Because water expands as it freezes, ice makes these cracks grow wider. Alternating cycles of freezing and thawing deepen and widen the cracks. Over time, this process eventually will break the rock into pieces.

Ice Wedging

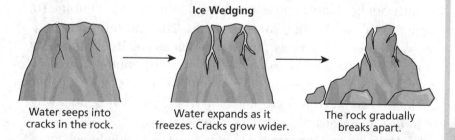

Water seeps into cracks in the rock.

Water expands as it freezes. Cracks grow wider.

The rock gradually breaks apart.

Abrasion is the process by which rocks slowly wear down as a result of collisions with other rocks. These collisions are commonly caused by gravity, running water, and wind. Gravity pulls loose rocks down the slopes of hills and mountains. Tiny particles of rock break off as these rocks tumble and collide with other rocks. Running water, such as ocean waves and

What You'll Need to Learn

This topic is part of the Regents Curriculum for the Physical Setting Exam.

Standard 4, Performance Indicator 2.1: *Use the concepts of density and heat energy to explain observations of weather patterns, seasonal changes and the movements of the Earth's plates.* Major Understandings: 2.1s, 2.1t, 2.1u

What Terms You'll Need to Know

abrasion
chemical weathering
erosion
groundwater
horizon
humus
ice wedging
infiltration
mass movement
mechanical weathering
permeability
porosity
runoff
soil
soil profile
weathering

Where You Can Learn Even More

Holt Earth Science: The Physical Setting
Chapter 14: Weathering and Erosion
Chapter 16: Groundwater

Unit V Weathering and Soils *continued*

streams, can carry small particles of rock and sand. As they move, the small particles scrape against other rocks, wearing them down bit by bit and giving them a rounded shape. Wind is another powerful agent of abrasion. Like moving water, wind can lift and carry small rock particles, such as sand, and spray them at exposed rock surfaces. This process gradually wears away rock and makes it smooth.

Plant roots are also capable of physically breaking rock. Have you ever seen plants growing inside cracks in rock? As the plant grows, the roots get longer and expand, widening the cracks. Like ice wedging, root wedging can gradually break a rock into pieces.

Self-Check Name the common agents of mechanical weathering.

Chemical weathering is the process in which rock is broken down by chemical reactions. Chemical weathering involves chemical reactions that dissolve the minerals making up rock or change them into new minerals. Over time, the effects of chemical weathering can be dramatic. Pits or holes may form in the rock surface. Eventually, the rock crumbles and disintegrates.

Water is the main agent of chemical weathering. Water is an effective solvent. All minerals dissolve in water, though most do very slowly. Oxygen in the air is another major agent of chemical weathering. You've seen cars and bicycles rust. Oxygen can also make rocks "rust" by combining with iron-bearing minerals in the rock to form iron oxide. This is called *oxidation*. The rust eventually flakes off the rock and into the soil. The red-brown soil common in the southeastern United States is due mainly to the presence of iron oxide.

Chemical weathering also can be caused by rain, which is slightly acidic. Water and carbon dioxide naturally combine to form a weak acid called *carbonic acid.* The carbonic acid in rainwater dissolves many minerals, such as calcite. Calcite is a major component of limestone. Huge underground caverns, such as Howe Caverns and Secret Caverns near Cobleskill, New York, are produced as carbonic acid in groundwater eats away at limestone deposits in Earth's crust.

Certain living organisms, such as mosses and lichens, can also contribute to the chemical weathering of rock. Lichens and mosses grow on rocks and produce weak acids that can dissolve the surface of the rock. The acids can also seep into the rock and produce cracks that eventually cause it to break apart.

Self-Check Name three agents of chemical weathering.

The rate at which mechanical and chemical weathering take place depends on three main factors: temperature, availability of water, and the type of rock. Chemical weathering occurs more rapidly in places with high temperatures and abundant rainfall. These conditions generally speed up chemical reactions. Mechanical weathering occurs faster in places where temperature conditions frequently alternate between freezing and thawing.

The chemical composition of rocks is another important factor that affects the rate of weathering. For example, among sedimentary rocks, limestone and other rocks containing calcite weather more rapidly than other rocks because they are easily weathered by carbonic acid in groundwater. On the other hand, quartz, because of its chemical composition and rigid internal structure, strongly resists both chemical and physical weathering. Sedimentary rock, in general, weathers much more rapidly than does metamorphic and igneous rock.

The amount of surface area that is exposed to oxygen, water, and other weathering agents is an important factor in determining how quickly a rock will break down. A rock exposed at the surface will weather more quickly than a similar rock underground. In addition, as a rock breaks down into smaller pieces, the surface area that is exposed increases, so the rock weathers more and more rapidly.

REVIEW YOUR UNDERSTANDING

_____ **1.** How does weathering affect rocks?
(1) Weathering causes the mineral grains to increase in size.
(2) Weathering makes rock harder.
(3) Weathering compacts sediments to form sedimentary rock.
(4) Weathering weakens rock.

_____ **2.** Which is an example of chemical weathering?
(1) A rock breaks into pieces as it tumbles down a hill.
(2) Wave action makes beach rocks smooth and round.
(3) Expanding plant roots crack and split a rock.
(4) A bicycle left in the rain develops rust spots.

**Notes/Study
Ideas/Answers**

_____ **3.** Which statement best describes mechanical weathering that occurs when ice forms within cracks in rock?

(1) Lichens secrete chemicals that weaken rock surfaces.

(2) Cracks in rock widen because water expands as it freezes.

(3) Cracks become wider due to chemical reactions between water and rock.

(4) Ice wedging is most common in regions with warm, wet climates.

_____ **4.** Which factor has the greatest influence on the weathering rate of bedrock at Earth's surface?

(1) burrowing animals

(2) local weather and climate

(3) moss plants and lichens

(4) age of the bedrock

Soil

One result of weathering is the formation of *regolith*, the layer of weathered rock fragments that cover much of Earth's surface. *Bedrock* is the solid, unweathered rock that lies beneath the regolith. The uppermost layer of the regolith is called soil. **Soil** consists of small rock particles produced by weathering, as well as water, gases, and the decaying remains of plants and animals.

There are many different kinds of soil. A soil's characteristics largely depend on the *parent rock* from which the soil was weathered. Sometimes, the parent rock is the underlying bedrock, but soil may be transported from elsewhere via wind and water. For example, soils derived from granite or quartz have a sandy texture, whereas soils derived from iron-rich rock have the consistency of clay. The color of soil is related to its composition. Soil that is rich in organic material is black in color, while red soils may form from iron-rich parent rocks.

Self-Check What is soil? How does soil form?

The rock material in soil consists of three main types—clay, sand, and silt—which are classified by the size of their particles. (See the "Relationship of Transported Particle Size to Water Velocity" graph in the *Earth Science Reference Tables* section, page 231.) Clay particles are less than 0.0004 cm in diameter. Silt particles range from 0.0004 cm to 0.006 cm in diameter. Sand particles range from 0.006 cm to 0.2 cm in diameter. Different proportions of these three particles give soils different textures.

For example, a soil that contains a large proportion of sand would have a gritty, sandy texture.

Notes/Study
Ideas/Answers

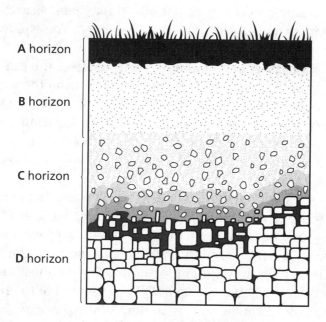

A horizon

B horizon

C horizon

D horizon

    A **soil profile** describes the different soil layers, or soil **horizons.** The uppermost layer is called the A-horizon, or *topsoil*. It contains **humus,** derived from the remains of plants and animals, and supports the activities of living organisms. The A-horizon is susceptible to weathering because it is exposed to wind, rain, and oxygen. The B-horizon, or *subsoil*, is located beneath the A-horizon. This layer contains larger soil particles and little organic matter, and is less susceptible to weathering since it is unexposed. The C-horizon consists of slightly broken-up bedrock and very little organic material. Plant roots do not penetrate into this layer. The D-horizon contains the bedrock, which will contribute material to the soil above it as it breaks apart.

Self-Check Describe a soil profile. Identify and describe the different horizons.

    Various forces may move weathered rock particles away from the parent rock. **Erosion** is the process by which the products of weathering are transported away from their original location. Moving water, wind, gravity, and glaciers carry rock particles from one location and deposit them elsewhere.

    Soil erosion occurs worldwide and is normally a slow process. As with weathering, the rate at which soil erosion occurs depends on the physical properties of the soil and environmental factors. The downward pull of gravity on slopes pulls rock fragments down inclines. This movement of rock fragments

Unit V Weathering and Soils *continued*

down a slope is called **mass movement.** Mass movement may occur suddenly and dramatically as in a landslide, or it may happen so slowly that it goes unnoticed for years, as is the case with the mass movement process called *creep.* You will learn more about erosion in Unit VI.

Vegetation cover and land-use practices affect the rate of soil erosion. Plant cover protects the soil surface from the weathering effects of wind, water, and air. Additionally, plant roots anchor soil particles, making it more difficult for wind and moving water to carry them from one location to another. As plant cover is removed from land, the top layer of soil is exposed to agents of erosion.

Some soils don't soak up water as rapidly as other soils, forcing water to spill onto the surface. Water that doesn't soak into the ground or evaporate flows across the surface and is called **runoff.** Surface runoff contributes to soil erosion by carrying soil particles to different locations. The composition of soil determines whether the soil will be susceptible to erosion by runoff. For instance, soils with thin A-horizons can't hold much water. This allows water to collect on the surface as runoff, carrying soil particles with it.

As one might expect, the slope of the land also affects whether soil erosion due to runoff occurs slowly or quickly. Generally speaking, water running down a steep slope can transport more and larger soil particles in a shorter amount of time than water running down a gradual slope.

> **Self-Check** Describe what could happen to soil located on a hillside if vegetation cover were removed. Why?

REVIEW YOUR UNDERSTANDING

Some questions may require use of the *Earth Science Reference Tables.*

_____ **5.** Which change does *not* directly contribute to the formation of soil?
  (1) melting of rock to make molten magma
  (2) plant roots growing into cracks in the ground
  (3) acidic rainfall reacting with the mineral calcite
  (4) rocks splitting apart by water freezing in cracks

_____ **6.** Which soil particle is smallest in size?
  (1) clay
  (2) silt
  (3) sand
  (4) pebble

Unit V Weathering and Soils *continued*

_____ **7.** The deepest soil horizon is composed primarily of
  (1) organic remains
  (2) solid bedrock
  (3) broken bedrock
  (4) products of intense chemical weathering

_____ **8.** After sudden and complete removal of vegetation from a hillside, which is likely to occur next?
  (1) growth of grasses and shrubs
  (2) erosion of the A-horizon
  (3) weathering of underlying bedrock
  (4) abrasion of subsoil particles

Groundwater

Gravity pulls water below the soil surface and into the small spaces, or *pores*, between soil particles. The process by which water seeps into the soil is called **infiltration.** Water that is absorbed into the soil is called **groundwater.** Groundwater seeps into the soil layers until it reaches an impermeable layer, such as bedrock. The underground pool of water that forms above bedrock is called an *aquifer*. Residential wells draw water from aquifers. If water is used more quickly than it is replaced, the top of the aquifer, or *water table*, drops much like the water level of a pond falls during summer droughts.

Self-Check How does an aquifer form?

The speed with which water can move through the soil (the infiltration rate) is controlled by porosity and permeability. Soil **porosity** is the percentage of soil volume that is open space. Soils consisting of particles of similar size (*well-sorted soils*) have high porosity; that is, they have lots of open spaces between particles that can hold water. Loosely packed soils— such as sand, which consist of irregularly shaped particles— also have high porosity, because the irregular shapes of the sand grains create many open spaces. In contrast, soils containing particles of different sizes (*poorly sorted soils*) have low porosity. Small particles fill the spaces between large particles, leaving smaller spaces.

Self-Check Describe two conditions that could make a soil more porous.

Unit V Weathering and Soils *continued*

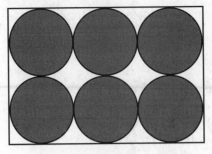

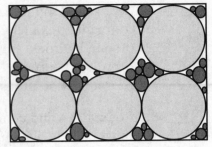

Well-sorted soil

- high porosity
- same-size particles
- many large gaps between particles

Poorly sorted soil

- low porosity
- mixed particle sizes
- small particles fill spaces between large particles

Permeability is the ability of water to pass through a rock or soil. In order for soil to be permeable, the open spaces must be large enough for water to pass through. Soils consisting primarily of large, well-sorted particles are highly permeable—water is able to flow from one space to another with relative ease. Soils consisting of small, tightly packed particles, such as clay-rich soils, may be very porous but are relatively impermeable, because the pores are too small for water to pass through easily.

Self-Check How do porosity and permeability affect water flow into and through the soil?

REVIEW YOUR UNDERSTANDING

Some questions may require use of the *Earth Science Reference Tables*.

_____ **9.** Which soil is likely to be most porous?
   (1) soil consisting of clay only
   (2) soil consisting of cobbles, sand, and clay
   (3) soil consisting of cobbles and sand
   (4) soil consisting of sand only

_____ **10.** Rainfall is most likely to infiltrate a soil that is
   (1) saturated and permeable
   (2) saturated and impermeable
   (3) unsaturated and permeable
   (4) unsaturated and impermeable

Unit V Weathering and Soils *continued*

_____ **11.** Which best expresses the relationship among porosity, permeability, and infiltration?

    (1) As porosity and permeability decrease, infiltration rate increases.

    (2) As porosity and permeability increase, infiltration rate increases.

    (3) As porosity increases, permeability and infiltration rate decrease.

    (4) As porosity decreases, permeability and infiltration rate increase.

Notes/Study Ideas/Answers

Unit V Weathering and Soils *continued*

ANSWERS TO SELF-CHECK QUESTIONS

- ice, plant roots, wind, gravity, running water

- water, oxygen, carbon dioxide

- Soil is a mixture of rock particles, gases, and the remains of plants and animals. Soil forms when weathering processes break down rocks into smaller and smaller pieces.

- A soil profile is a cross-section of soil showing the different layers. The A-horizon contains organic material (humus) and small rock materials. The B-horizon contains clays, larger rock particles, and sometimes humus. The C-horizon consists of slightly broken-up bedrock and very little organic material. The D-horizon contains the bedrock from which the soil layers above it may have formed.

- The soil could be carried away by surface runoff. Lack of vegetation increases the likelihood of runoff. Plants hold soil in place, making it more difficult for water to carry it to another location.

- An aquifer is a body of rock or sediment in which large amounts of water can flow and be stored. Aquifers form when gravity causes water to seep into the ground and permeate down through the soil until an impermeable layer stops it.

- Soil porosity describes the percentage of open spaces in soil. In general, soils with similar-sized particles (well-sorted soils) or particles of irregular shape (such as sand) have high porosity.

- Soils with low porosity and low permeability reduce infiltration rate because there are fewer open spaces and pathways for water flow. Soils with high porosity and high permeability allow rapid infiltration.

Questions for Regents Practice

Weathering and Soils
PART A
Some questions may require use of the *Earth Science Reference Tables.*

_____ **1.** Round, smooth pebbles found along the beaches of Long Island are most likely shaped by which process?
(1) alternating freezing and thawing
(2) secretion of acids by plant roots
(3) wave action
(4) oxidation

_____ **2.** As a rock is broken apart by mechanical weathering processes,
(1) its total surface area decreases
(2) its total surface area increases
(3) new minerals form in the rock
(4) the mass of the rock increases

_____ **3.** A soil is most porous if it is composed of
(1) well-sorted, tightly packed particles
(2) well-sorted, loosely packed particles
(3) poorly sorted, tightly packed particles
(4) poorly sorted, loosely packed particles

_____ **4.** A sediment with a diameter of 0.05 cm is called
(1) silt
(2) clay
(3) sand
(4) pebble

_____ **5.** A tree root grows into a crack in a rock and splits the rock. This natural process is an example of
(1) chemical weathering
(3) erosion
(2) infiltration
(4) mechanical weathering

_____ **6.** In general, the probability of surface runoff decreases when there is an increase in the amount of
(1) rainfall
(2) snowmelt
(3) infiltration
(4) groundwater

_____ **7.** In hot, wet climates bedrock rapidly weathers into soil because water
(1) reacts with many minerals
(2) expands when it freezes
(3) cools rock as it evaporates
(4) infiltrates porous sediment

Name _____ Class _____ Date _____

Unit V Weathering and Soils *continued*

PART B-1

Base your answers to questions 8 and 9 on your knowledge of earth science and the *Earth Science Reference Tables*.

_____ **8.** Which graph below most accurately expresses the relationship between soil particle size and rate of infiltration?

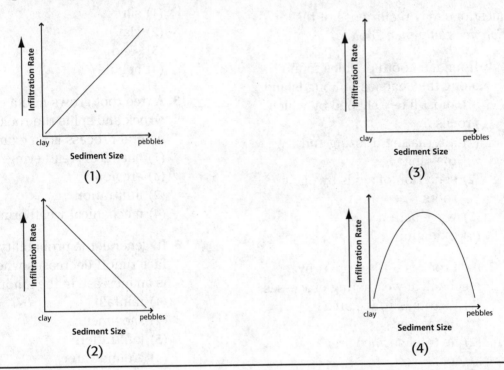

(1)   (3)

(2)   (4)

_____ **9.** Which graph below most accurately expresses the relationship between particle sorting and soil porosity?

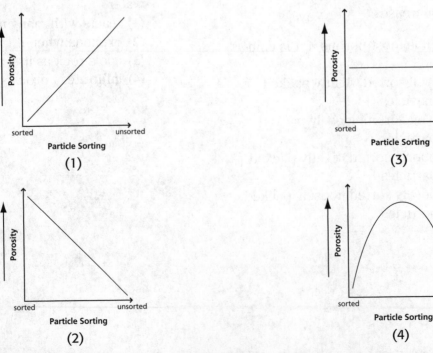

(1)   (3)

(2)   (4)

Unit V Weathering and Soils *continued*

PART B-2

Base your answers to questions 10 and 11 on your knowledge of earth science, the *Earth Science Reference Tables*, and the diagram below, which shows a boulder somewhere in New York State.

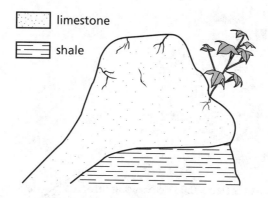

10. List and describe two causes of weathering that might be operating on this boulder.

_____

_____

_____

_____

_____

_____

_____

11. The boulder is moved to a new location that has a hot, wet climate. What changes in weathering could result?

_____

_____

_____

_____

_____

_____

_____

Unit V Weathering and Soils *continued*

PART C

Base your answers to questions 12 and 13 on your knowledge of earth science, the *Earth Science Reference Tables*, and the diagram below, which shows a house sitting atop a steep, soil-covered hill. Characteristics of the soil on the hill are indicated.

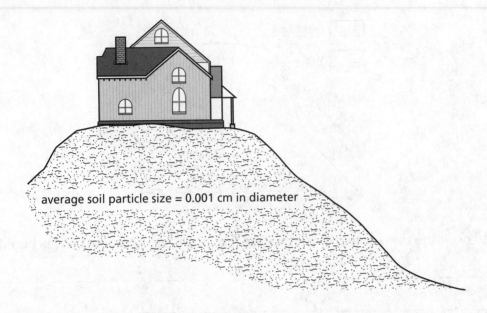

average soil particle size = 0.001 cm in diameter

12. State two natural agents that could cause erosion of the soil on the hill.

_____

_____

_____

_____

_____

13. Identify three things that could be done to reduce erosion of the hill. Explain how each could reduce erosion.

_____

_____

_____

_____

_____

_____

Focus On

The Regents Exam

Name _____ Class _____ Date _____

Erosion and Deposition

Various natural agents—including moving water, wind, glaciers, and gravity—can carry weathered rock particles away from where the weathering occurred. **Erosion** is the transportation of rock particles from one location to another.

Erosion and Deposition by Running Water

As you recall from Unit V, water that doesn't soak into the ground or evaporate into the air flows across the ground and is called *runoff*. Erosion begins when runoff carries small particles of soil downhill. Runoff gradually forms small channels in the soil, which eventually join together to form larger channels, called *gullies*. Gullies, in turn, flow together to form streams.

Streams continue the process of erosion by transporting sediment. Much of the sediment is carried in *suspension*, in which sediments move along with the water. Running water is the most important agent of erosion, because it carries more sediment than any other agent of erosion. Each year streams and rivers carry millions of tons of sediment into lakes and oceans.

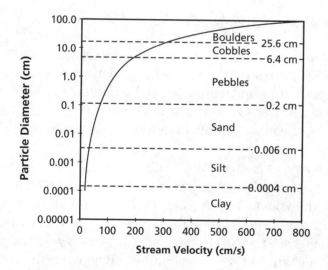

A stream's ability to erode depends mainly on its speed. The graph shown here, from the *Earth Science Reference Tables*, shows this relationship. As the graph shows, the faster a stream flows, the larger the size of rock particles it can transport. For example, the graph shows that the smallest pebbles, which are about 0.2 cm in diameter, require a stream velocity of about 50 cm/sec to keep them moving.

What You'll Need to Learn

This topic is part of the Regents Curriculum for the Physical Setting Exam.

Standard 4, Performance Indicator 2.1: *Use the concepts of density and heat energy to explain observations of weather patterns, seasonal changes, and the movements of Earth's plates.* Major Understandings: 2.1t, 2.1u, 2.1v

What Terms You'll Need to Know

barrier island
beach
delta
deposition
drumlin
dune
erosion
finger lake
glacial drift
glacier
gradient
horizontal sorting
kettle lake
longshore transport
meanders
moraine
outwash plain
river system
sandbar
spit
watershed

Unit VI Erosion and Deposition *continued*

Self-Check What is the minimum water velocity required to transport the smallest cobbles?

Agents of erosion are also agents of deposition. **Deposition** is the settling, or release, of sediments carried by an agent of erosion. The size of sediment particles carried by running water determines the rate at which they are deposited. For example, consider a stream flowing into the ocean. Before it meets the ocean, the stream is moving at a velocity of about 300 cm/sec. At this velocity, the stream can carry a wide range of sediment particle sizes: clay, silt, sand, pebbles, and cobbles.

When the stream enters the ocean, the water velocity will decrease, causing some of the sediment particles to fall out of suspension and settle to the bottom. Which particles will settle first? According to the graph, the first sediments to settle will be the largest particles: cobbles. By the time the stream slows to about 200 cm/sec, all the cobble-sized particles will be deposited. As the stream continues to slow, the other particles will be deposited as well, in order of decreasing size. The process by which sediments are separated in order of decreasing size with increasing distance from the shore is called **horizontal sorting.**

Self-Check What causes horizontal sorting of sediments?

The density and shapes of particles also affect sorting. Because they are streamlined, rounded particles tend to settle more rapidly than angular particles. Flat and irregularly shaped sediments settle slowly due to friction with the water. Denser particles settle more rapidly than less-dense particles of the same size.

All streams exist in a state of *dynamic equilibrium*—that is, there is a balance between erosion and deposition. In most streams, the volume of the water in the stream and the velocity of the water change through time. Streams respond naturally to these changes. Any increase in a stream's energy—perhaps as a result of a change in water velocity—will increase the amount of erosion taking place, resulting in an increase in load (the sediments carried by the stream). The increase in load must then be followed by a corresponding increase in deposition when the stream's energy returns to its normal level.

A **river system** consists of all the streams that drain a particular geographic area. This area is called the river's **watershed,** or drainage basin. All the rain, snow, and other

Unit VI Erosion and Deposition *continued*

precipitation that falls into the watershed and that does not infiltrate the soil or evaporate must exit the watershed through its principal river, stream, or other body of water.

The erosive power of a river depends in part on the velocity of water flow. Velocity, in turn, is partly related to the slope, or **gradient,** of the land. A river's gradient changes over the river's length, with some parts being steeper than others. An average gradient can be calculated by dividing the change in elevation by the distance over which this change occurs. You can find this equation in the *Earth Science Reference Tables* section, on page 221. For example, if the elevation of a river changes 50 m over a distance of 100 km, the average gradient of the river is 20 m/km.

Development of a Meandering River

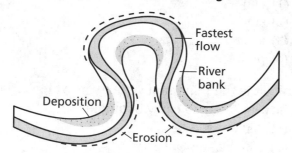

As a low-gradient river flows over relatively flat land, it can develop a sinuous pattern of curves, called **meanders.** Meanders are the result of erosion and deposition. As the diagram shows, meanders form when the fast-moving water on the outside of a river bend erodes the bank of that bend. As this process continues, it enlarges the curve while further sediment deposition takes place on the inside of the river bend, where the water is moving more slowly.

Self-Check Describe how a river forms a meander.

As most rivers continue downstream, they empty into the calm water of a lake or ocean. With loss of velocity, the river's ability to transport sediment decreases. Deposition of sediment occurs as a result. Often, a triangular-shaped deposit, called a delta, forms. A **delta** is a region at the end (mouth) of a river that consists of sediments deposited as the velocity of the river decreases.

Unit VI Erosion and Deposition *continued*

Notes/Study
Ideas/Answers

REVIEW YOUR UNDERSTANDING

Some questions may require use of the *Earth Science Reference Tables*.

_____ 1. A river slopes gradually from an elevation of 100 m to an elevation of 40 m, over a distance of 100 km. What is the average gradient of the river?
(1) 0.6 m/km
(2) 1.7 m/km
(3) 1.4 m/km
(4) 0.4 m/km

_____ 2. A river's velocity decreases from 120 cm/sec to 80 cm/sec as the river reaches the ocean. Which sediment particle will be deposited first?
(1) clay
(2) silt
(3) sand
(4) pebbles

_____ 3. What is the minimum velocity at which a river must flow in order to carry boulders?
(1) 150 cm/sec
(2) 200 cm/sec
(3) 250 cm/sec
(4) 300 cm/sec

_____ 4. When small particles settle through water faster than large particles, the small particles are probably
(1) lighter in color
(2) less dense
(3) less rounded
(4) denser

Erosion and Deposition by Wind and Waves

The areas on Earth at which land meets ocean are among the most rapidly changing regions of Earth's surface. One major factor in causing this change is the effect of the wind. As wind passes over the land, it carries sand grains, soil, and dust particles with it.

Deserts and coastlines are the two landscapes that are most dramatically affected by wind erosion. However, wind erosion can happen anywhere. In some areas, plant roots hold soil in place and reduce the extent of erosion. Moisture can also make soil heavier and cause soil particles to stick together, making them more difficult to move. However, in the desert and on coastlines, where there is little moisture or protective plant cover, soil layers are thin and are likely to be swept away by the wind.

Unit VI Erosion and Deposition *continued*

Like running water, wind deposits sediments when it slows and can no longer carry them. The best-known wind deposits are dunes. **Dunes** are mounds of wind-blown sand that form in places where soil is dry and unprotected and where the wind is strong. This is why dunes are usually seen in the desert and along the shores of oceans and larger lakes. A dune begins to form when a barrier slows the speed of the wind. When wind speed slows, the wind drops its sand particles, and sand begins to accumulate on both sides of the barrier. As more sand is deposited, the dune itself acts as a barrier and continues to increase in size.

The force and direction of the wind shapes sand dunes. Commonly, the gentlest slope of a dune is on the side that faces the wind, the *windward side*. The *leeward side* of a dune—the side away from the wind—tends to have a steeper slope. Thus, a dune's profile (its shape as viewed from the side) can be used to infer the prevailing wind direction in an area.

The movement of dunes is called *dune migration*. If the wind usually blows from the same direction, dunes will move downwind. Dune migration occurs when sand blows over the top of the dune and accumulates on the other side. In mostly level areas, dunes migrate until they reach a barrier. People often build fences or plant trees or bushes to prevent dunes from drifting over roads and farmland.

Self-Check Describe how a sand dune forms.

Not only does wind create sand dunes, but when it's carrying sand, it can actually wear away the face of other rocks and carve intricate patterns as it blows. A rock that has been sculpted by the wind is known as a *ventifact*. The word *ventifact* comes from the Latin word *ventus*, which means "wind." Rock surfaces facing the wind tend to be flatter and more polished. So, the direction of the prevailing wind in an area can be determined by the appearance of ventifacts.

As wind moves over the ocean, the wind produces waves and currents that erode the shoreline. Waves create various shoreline features by eroding the land. For example, in places where waves strike directly against rock, the waves slowly erode the base of the rock. The waves cut under the overhanging rock, until the rock eventually falls and forms a steep *sea cliff*. Waves can also cut deep into fractured and weak rock along the base of a cliff to form a large hole called a *sea cave*.

Unit VI Erosion and Deposition *continued*

**Notes/Study
Ideas/Answers**

Waves can also change a coastline by depositing sediment. A deposit of sand or larger sediment along an ocean or lakeshore is called a **beach.** A beach forms and grows where deposition exceeds erosion. It stops growing when deposition and erosion are in equilibrium.

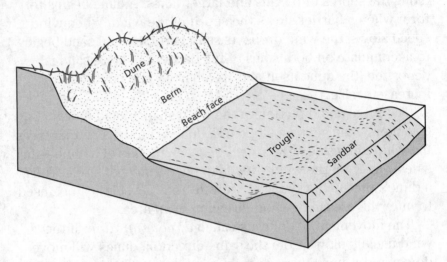

Waves usually do not approach a shore with their crests completely parallel to the beach. Instead, breaking waves strike the shore at a slight angle. As a result, sand grains are carried in a zig-zag pattern, with each in-and-out cycle carrying the sand a little farther along the shore. The resulting motion of the water along the shore is called a *longshore current*, and the motion of the sediment is known as **longshore transport.**

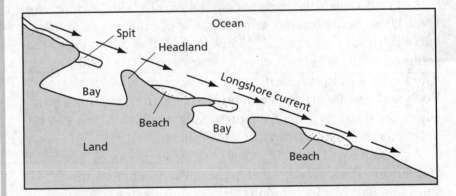

Wave erosion and longshore transport produce a variety of coastal features. Sometimes the advance and retreat of the waves deposits sand that forms low ridges along the shore. They are called **sandbars.** Along some coasts, sandbars form parallel to the shore in shallow water where sediments are abundant. When these sandbars accumulate sufficient material to break the ocean surface, they are called **barrier islands.**

Unit VI Erosion and Deposition *continued*

Once a barrier island is formed, plants help to stabilize the sand and increase the island's elevation by trapping sediments and accumulating organic matter. Long barrier islands along the east coast of the United States (for example, off the southern coast of Long Island) protect the low-lying coastline from direct wave damage.

Self-Check How do barrier islands form?

Along a relatively straight shoreline, the longshore current keeps moving sand until it reaches a place where the shoreline changes direction, at a bay opening or a headland (a resistant rock formation that projects from the shore). When the long-shore current changes direction, it slows, causing sand to be deposited in a long, narrow strip connected at one end to the shore. Such a deposit of sand is called a **spit.**

REVIEW YOUR UNDERSTANDING

_____ **5.** Wind erosion is probably least significant in which of the following geographic areas?
(1) the shores of Lake Superior
(2) the Painted Desert in Arizona
(3) the grasslands of Oklahoma
(4) the shores of the Gulf of Mexico

_____ **6.** Deposits of wind-blown sand are known as
(1) ventifacts
(2) dunes
(3) berms
(4) beaches

_____ **7.** Sand that is carried by waves from the beach and deposited offshore sometimes forms a
(1) dune
(2) spit
(3) sandbar
(4) berm

_____ **8.** Sand that is carried by a longshore current and deposited when the current slows sometimes forms a
(1) dune
(2) berm
(3) sandbar
(4) spit

Erosion and Deposition by Glaciers

At high elevations and in polar regions, snow may remain on the ground all year and form a mass of permanent ice and snow called a *snowfield*. Average temperatures at high elevations and in polar regions are always near or below the freezing point of water. So, snow that falls there accumulates year after year. Cycles of partial melting and refreezing change the snow into grainy ice called *firn*.

In deep layers of snow and firn, the pressure of the overlying layers flattens the ice grains and squeezes the air from between the grains. The continued buildup of snow and firn forms a **glacier**—a large mass of ice that moves downslope or outward under the influence of gravity. Glaciers can be classified into two main categories—valley glaciers (also known as *alpine glaciers*) and continental glaciers. A *valley glacier* is a narrow, wedge-shaped mass of ice that forms in the mountains and that is confined to a small area. Valley glaciers exist in Alaska, the Himalayas, the Andes, the Alps, and New Zealand. *Continental glaciers* are massive sheets of ice that may cover millions of square kilometers. Today, continental glaciers exist only in Greenland and Antarctica.

Glaciers are often called "rivers of ice." Just as rivers move downward in response to gravity, so too can glaciers. Valley glaciers flow from high in the mountains, through valleys, to lower elevations. Some valley glaciers will flow into a lake or ocean and break apart, forming icebergs. Other valley glaciers will flow down to an elevation where temperatures are warm enough to melt the glacier as quickly as it moves downslope. When this occurs, a *dynamic equilibrium* is reached, as the rate of movement of the glacier and the rate of melting are equal. When equilibrium is reached, it will appear as though the glacier is not moving at all. Thus, the end of the glacier will stay in the same place from year to year, even though the glacier is, in fact, advancing downhill at a constant rate.

Glaciers move very slowly. Some may travel only a few centimeters per year, while others may move a kilometer or more per year. Glaciers move by two basic processes: basal slip and internal plastic flow. In *basal slip*, the glacier moves by sliding over a thin layer of water created by its own weight. The weight of the glacier exerts pressure that lowers the melting point of ice. As a result, the glacier melts where it touches the ground. The water forming underneath the glacier acts as a lubricant, which allows the glacier to slide.

In *internal plastic flow*, the glacier flows slowly as its ice grains deform under pressure and slide over each other. The rate of internal plastic flow varies for different parts of a glacier. For

Unit VI Erosion and Deposition *continued*

example, the ice at the edges of a glacier moves more slowly than the ice at the center, because of friction with underlying rock.

Like rivers, glaciers are also agents of erosion. Rivers can pick up, carry, and deposit sediments, and so can glaciers. However, because of the size and density of a glacier, landforms created by glaciers are very different from those formed by rivers. For example, one telltale sign of glacial action is long, parallel scratches, or *striations*, carved in bedrock. Striations are formed when a moving glacier loosens and dislodges large chunks of rock from the bedrock and traps them beneath the ice. As the glacier moves, the rocks scrape against the bedrock. These scratches indicate the direction in which the glacier moved. *Grooves* are deeper and wider cuts formed by glaciers.

Valley glaciers have shaped many mountain ranges through the processes of erosion and deposition. The glacial processes that shape mountain ranges begin in the upper end of the valley where a valley glacier forms. As the glacier slowly moves through a valley, it carves rock from the valley walls and floor. Embedded rock particles in the glacier grind against the valley walls, smoothing and polishing them. At the same time, the valley becomes more U-shaped (in cross-section). Because glacial erosion is the only way by which a U-shaped valley can form, scientists use this feature to determine whether an area has been glaciated in the past.

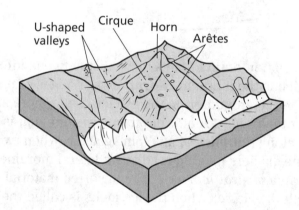

The moving glacier also pulls blocks of rock from the valley floor. These actions create a bowl-shaped depression called a *cirque*. A sharp, jagged ridge, called an *arête*, forms between cirques. Where several arêtes join, they form a sharp, pyramid-like peak called a *horn*, as shown in the diagram.

Self-Check Describe how a valley glacier creates a U-shaped valley.

Unit VI Erosion and Deposition *continued*

Notes/Study Ideas/Answers

Landforms created by continental glaciers are different from the more rugged features produced by valley glaciers. Continental glaciers glide across the land, flattening it and smoothing it out. They also produce scratches and grooves in the rock surfaces over which they travel, parallel to the direction of movement.

Like streams, waves, and winds, glaciers produce characteristic patterns of deposition. As a glacier melts, it deposits the rock material it has accumulated. The general term for all sediments that are deposited by glaciers is **glacial drift.** Unsorted glacial drift (sediments of different sizes) that is deposited by a melting glacier is called *till*. Till is composed of sediments from the base of the glacier and is simply left behind when glacial ice melts. Large rocks transported by a glacier from one location to another are called *erratics*. If the glacial drift is carried away by streams flowing from the melting glacier, the stream deposits the drift in layers sorted by particle size. Such sorted glacial drift is called *stratified till*.

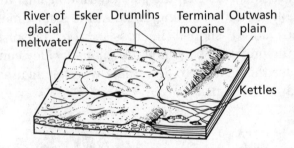

The deposition of till creates many distinctive landforms, one of which is the moraine. **Moraines** are ridges of unsorted sediment on the ground or on the glacier itself. There are several types of moraines. A *lateral moraine* is one that is deposited along the sides of an alpine glacier. When two or more alpine glaciers join, their adjacent lateral moraines combine to form a *medial moraine*. The unsorted material that is left beneath the glacier when the ice melts is called the *ground moraine*.

A glacier may run over and mold a moraine made by a previous glacier, forming long, low, tear-shaped mounds called **drumlins.** Drumlins point in the direction of glacial movement.

How drumlins form is debated among scientists. Some scientists think that drumlins are formed when a glacier rides up and over the till it is pushing forward. *Terminal moraines* are small ridges of till that are deposited at the leading edge of a melting glacier. Terminal moraines contain depressions that may contain lakes or ponds.

| Unit VI Erosion and Deposition *continued*

Self-Check Distinguish between the four types of moraines.	**Notes/Study Ideas/Answers**

As a glacier melts, the resulting sediment-laden water flows from the sides of the glacier to produce an **outwash plain.** An outwash plain is a deposit of stratified, or layered, drift that lies in front of a terminal moraine. Most outwash plains are pitted with depressions called *kettles*. Kettles form when a buried piece of glacial ice melts, forming a cavity, or depression, in the ground. Kettles often fill with water to form **kettle lakes.**

When continental ice sheets melt and recede, long, winding ridges of sediment, called *eskers*, may be left behind. Eskers consist of stratified till deposited by streams of melted ice flowing through the glacier. Eskers may extend for tens of kilometers like raised, winding roadways.

Another important landform that results from glacial erosion and deposition is the *glacial lake*. Lake basins often form where glaciers erode Earth's surface and leave depressions in the bedrock. They can also form in the uneven land surface created by the deposition of ground moraines. Long, narrow **finger lakes,** such as those in western New York, form when moraines block existing streams.

REVIEW YOUR UNDERSTANDING

_____ **9.** The parallel striations in bedrock caused by glaciers are the result of
   (1) moving ice wearing away the rock surface
   (2) rocks trapped beneath the glacier scraping the rock surface
   (3) alternating freezing and thawing of the rock surface
   (4) the weight of the ice, which carves the rock surface

_____ **10.** Which characteristic would best support an inference that a valley had been carved by the passage of a valley glacier?
   (1) distinctive V-shape
   (2) distinctive U-shape
   (3) presence of streams
   (4) presence of boulders

_____ **11.** Scientists use drumlins to determine the
   (1) age of a glacier
   (2) thickness of a glacier
   (3) direction of glacial movement
   (4) rate of glacial movement

**Notes/Study
Ideas/Answers**

_____ **12.** A terminal moraine is formed primarily from till deposited

(1) beneath the glacier

(2) at the glacier's leading edge

(3) along the sides of the glacier

(4) at the glacier's back edge

ANSWERS TO SELF-CHECK QUESTIONS

- Approximately 180 cm/sec

- Horizontal sorting occurs when a stream or river slows, such as when it enters an ocean. As a stream gradually slows, sediment particles are deposited in order of decreasing size.

- Fast-moving water on the outside of a river bend erodes the bank of that bend, enlarging the curve. As this happens, deposition takes place in the slow-moving water on the inside of the bend.

- A sand dune forms when a barrier slows the wind, causing it to drop its sand particles on the impact side of the barrier. As sand builds up, the dune itself acts as a barrier and continues to increase in size.

- A barrier island forms when a sandbar has accumulated sufficient material to break the ocean surface.

- The glacier picks up rock particles of varying sizes as it moves down a valley. Rocks embedded in the glacier scrape against the walls and floor of the valley, carving it into a U-shape.

- *Lateral moraine*: moraine deposited along the sides of an alpine glacier; *medial moraine*: moraine formed by two adjacent lateral moraines; *ground moraine*: moraine made by unsorted sediments left beneath a melting glacier; *terminal moraine*: moraine formed at the leading edge of a glacier.

Questions for Regents Practice

Erosion and Deposition

PART A

Some questions may require use of the *Earth Science Reference Tables.*

_____ **1.** If a stream has a velocity of 200 cm/sec, what is the diameter of the largest particle this stream can carry?
  (1) 0.0004 cm
  (2) 0.006 cm
  (3) 0.2 cm
  (4) 6.4 cm

_____ **2.** A rock found in central New York State contains parallel sets of grooves. The grooves were most likely caused by
  (1) wind erosion
  (2) stream erosion
  (3) glacial erosion
  (4) wave erosion

_____ **3.** Which factor contributes least to the rate at which a stream deposits sediments?
  (1) the stream's elevation above sea level
  (2) the density of sediment particles
  (3) the velocity of the stream
  (4) the size and shape of sediment particles

_____ **4.** A stream with a velocity of 700 cm/sec slows to a speed of 300 cm/sec. Which sediments will be deposited first?
  (1) boulders
  (2) cobbles
  (3) pebbles
  (4) sand

_____ **5.** When erosion and deposition are in dynamic equilibrium
  (1) no erosion or deposition takes place
  (2) the same amounts of erosion and deposition take place
  (3) more deposition than erosion takes place
  (4) more erosion than deposition takes place

_____ **6.** The motion of a glacier is primarily caused by
  (1) deposition
  (2) climate
  (3) wind action
  (4) gravity

_____ **7.** Which feature is formed by wave erosion?
  (1) barrier island
  (2) spit
  (3) sea cave
  (4) beach

Unit VI Erosion and Deposition *continued*

PART B-1

Base your answers to questions 8 and 9 on your knowledge of earth science, the *Earth Science Reference Tables*, and the diagram below, which shows a horizontal sorting of sediments deposited as a river empties into the ocean.

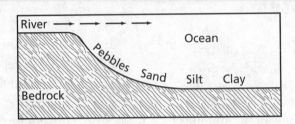

_____ **8.** Which factor most likely caused the sediment to be sorted in the pattern shown?
   (1) temperature of the river water
   (2) hardness of the surface bedrock
   (3) shapes of the sediment particles
   (4) velocity of the river water

_____ **9.** Which statement best describes how this pattern of deposition is produced?
   (1) Bigger sediment particles generally settle first.
   (2) Bigger sediment particles generally settle last.
   (3) High-density materials generally settle more slowly.
   (4) Rounded sediment particles settle more slowly.

| Unit VI Erosion and Deposition *continued*

PART B-2

Base your answers to questions 10 through 12 on your knowledge of earth science, the *Earth Science Reference Tables,* and the diagram below, which shows a river flowing into the ocean. Points A and B represent separate locations along the river. Letter C indicates a major bend in the river.

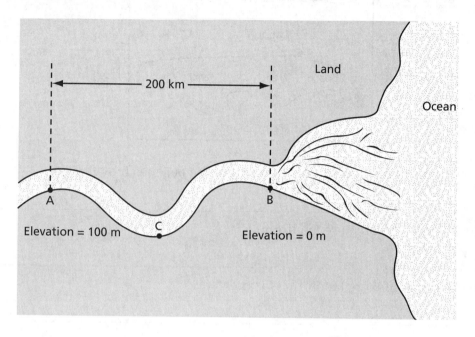

10. At which location, A or B, is the river moving with greatest velocity?

_____

11. Calculate the average gradient of this river between points A and B. Show all work.

12. Describe how erosion and deposition of sediments produced the river feature indicated by the letter C.

_____

_____

_____

| Unit VI Erosion and Deposition *continued*

PART C

Base your answers to questions 13 through 15 on your knowledge of earth science and the diagram below, which shows a landform off the southern shore of Long Island.

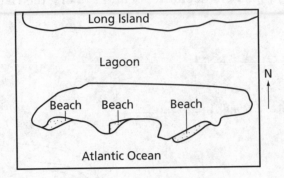

13. In which direction were the waves that created the beaches moving?

_____

14. State the name of the offshore landform.

_____

15. Describe how the offshore landform was created.

_____

_____

_____

Focus On
The Regents Exam

UNIT VII
Plate Tectonics

Plate tectonics, the theory of how and why the continents move, is a major unifying theory of earth science. The discovery of plate tectonics has revolutionized the field of geology and has shed new light on the forces that cause changes to our planet.

Plate Tectonics and Continental Drift

In 1912, scientist Alfred Wegener proposed a hypothesis that is now called **continental drift.** According to this hypothesis, today's continents were once united into a single landmass—a *supercontinent*—that began breaking up into smaller continents about 250 million years ago. Over millions of years, the continents have drifted slowly to their present-day locations.

In supporting his hypothesis, Wegener pointed to the shapes of the continents, which looked like they would fit together like the pieces of a jigsaw puzzle. He also knew that fossils of *Mesosaurus*, a group of small, extinct land reptiles, had been discovered in both South America and Africa. Although Wegener saw no direct evidence that these continents were once connected, he still concluded that South America and Africa had been joined at one time in the past. Geologic and climatic evidence also supported continental drift. For example, layers of debris from ancient glaciers were found in southern Africa and South America. Today, these regions are too warm for glaciers to form. It seemed obvious to Wegener that at one time these regions had been at colder, higher latitudes where glaciers could exist. At the time, Wegener's hypothesis was largely rejected because he provided no evidence to explain how or why the continents moved. However, several decades later, new evidence led geologists to reconsider his ideas.

Self-Check The ages and types of rocks along the coasts of western Africa and eastern South America match closely. How does this evidence support continental drift?

In the 1940s, scientists mapping the ocean floor discovered a chain of mountains along the bottom of the Atlantic Ocean, which they called the *Mid-Atlantic Ridge.* The Mid-Atlantic Ridge is part of a system of **mid-ocean ridges** that snake around the planet along the floor of the world's oceans. As scientists studied the Atlantic mid-ocean ridge, they discovered that it had an unusual feature: a deep valley running the length

What You'll Need to Learn

This topic is part of the Regents Curriculum for the Physical Setting Exam.

Standard 4: Performance Indicator 2.1: *Use the concepts of density and heat energy to explain observations of weather patterns, seasonal changes, and the movements of Earth's plates.* Major Understandings: 2.1a, 2.1b, 2.1k, 2.1l, 2.1n, 2.1o, 2.1p

What Terms You'll Need to Know

body wave
continental drift
convergent boundary
divergent boundary
earthquake
epicenter
fault
fault-block mountain
focus
folded mountain
hot spot
island arc
lava
mid-ocean ridge
modified Mercalli scale
plate tectonics
P-wave
Richter scale
sea-floor spreading
seismic wave
seismogram
seismograph
subduction zone

Unit VII Plate Tectonics *continued*

surface wave
S-wave
transform boundary
volcano
volcanic mountain

**Where You Can
Learn Even More**

of its crest. Scientists also found that ocean rocks and sediment closer to the ridge were younger than rocks and sediment farther away from the ridge.

In the 1950s, scientist Henry Hess proposed a hypothesis known as sea-floor spreading to explain these discoveries. **Sea-floor spreading** is the process by which new oceanic crust (sea floor) forms at mid-ocean ridges as older crust is pushed away. Hess hypothesized that the center of a mid-ocean ridge was a crack, or *rift*, in Earth's crust. At this rift, molten rock, or *magma*, oozes from deep inside Earth to fill the crack. As the ocean floor moves away from the ridge, the rising magma cools and hardens on the ocean bottom to form new crust. Hess believed that sea-floor spreading was the driving force behind continental drift.

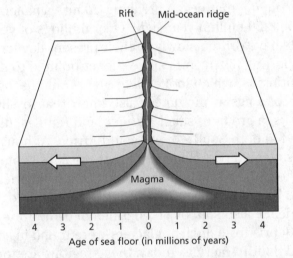

Age of sea floor (in millions of years)

Self-Check Where on the ocean floor are the youngest rocks found?

By the 1960s, evidence supporting continental drift and sea-floor spreading led to the development of the theory of plate tectonics. **Plate tectonics** is the theory that explains why and how continents move. According to plate tectonics, Earth's lithosphere is broken into sections, called *plates*. The plates move around on the plastic-like layer of the upper mantle known as the asthenosphere. Scientists have identified about 15 major tectonic plates. (See the "Tectonic Plates" map in the *Earth Science Reference Tables*, page 229, for the names and locations of the major tectonic plates.)

Self-Check What is the theory of plate tectonics?

Some of Earth's most extreme geologic events, such as earthquakes and volcanic eruptions, happen along *plate boundaries*— the areas where plates touch one another. There are three types

Unit VII Plate Tectonics *continued*

of plate boundaries: divergent boundaries, convergent boundaries, and transform boundaries. Each type is associated with a characteristic set of geologic activities. (See the "Tectonic Plates" map in the *Earth Science Reference Tables*, page 229, to see where the different types of plate boundaries exist.)

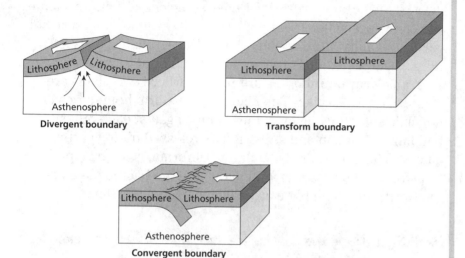

Divergent boundary

Transform boundary

Convergent boundary

At a **divergent boundary,** two plates move away from each other. Here, magma from the asthenosphere rises to the surface as the plates move apart. The magma then cools to form new crust at the edge of each plate. In the Atlantic Ocean, the North American plate is moving away from the Eurasian and African plates. That divergent boundary is called the Mid-Atlantic Ridge. The Great Rift Valley in eastern Africa is another example of a divergent boundary.

Plates come together, or collide, at a **convergent boundary.** Three types of collisions can happen at convergent boundaries, depending on the plates involved. When an oceanic plate collides with a continental plate, the denser oceanic plate *subducts,* or sinks, under the continental plate and into the mantle. This area is called a **subduction zone.** As the subducted plate is driven into the mantle, it heats up and melts to form magma. The newly formed magma is forced upward through the crust, forming volcanic mountains. The Andes Mountains of South America, which contain many volcanoes, were formed at the convergent boundary between the South American and Nazca plates. Deep-ocean trenches also form at the intersection of the two plates.

A second type of convergent boundary occurs when two continental plates collide. Because they are of equal density, neither plate is subducted. As the two plates push against each other, their leading edges crumple and thicken, forming large mountain ranges. Earthquakes are common at these plate

Unit VII Plate Tectonics *continued*

Notes/Study
Ideas/Answers

boundaries. The Himalaya Mountains were formed when the Indian-Australian plate collided with the Eurasian plate.

A third type of convergent boundary happens when two oceanic plates collide. One plate is driven beneath the other, forming a subduction zone. A deep-ocean trench is formed, and the subducted plate begins to melt. The magma rises and breaks through the oceanic crust. Over time, sufficient lava may accumulate on the ocean floor to rise above sea level and form a string of volcanic islands called an **island arc.** The Aleutian Islands, off Alaska, and the islands of Japan are examples of island arcs.

Transform boundaries are regions where two plates are sliding past each other. The plates at transform boundaries do not slide smoothly. Instead, they scrape against each other, building up friction and stress that is released during earthquakes. The San Andreas Fault, in California, is an example of a transform boundary. It is a region where the Pacific plate and the North American plate are grinding past each other.

Self-Check Name and describe the three types of tectonic plate boundaries.

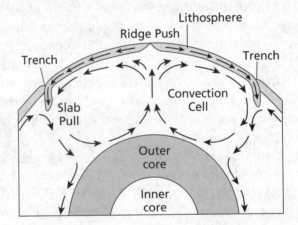

Many scientists think that *convection*, the movement of heated material due to differences in density that are caused by differences in temperature, drives most plate motion, as shown in the diagram. As magma in Earth's mantle is heated, it expands and becomes less dense. As this hot material rises, the cooler, denser material flows away from the hot material and sinks into the mantle to replace the rising material. As the mantle material moves, it drags the overlying plates along with it. *Ridge push*, which happens at divergent boundaries where plates move apart, and *slab pull*, which happens at subduction zones where one plate is pulled down into the mantle, are other important processes that cause plates to move. All three mechanisms of Earth's convecting system work together to drive plate motions.

Unit VII Plate Tectonics *continued*

REVIEW YOUR UNDERSTANDING

Some questions may require use of the *Earth Science Reference Tables*.

_____ 1. Coal deposits found today in Antarctica were formed from tropical vegetation. What conclusion is best supported by this evidence?
  (1) Antarctica has remained stationary over geologic time.
  (2) Antarctica once collided with a tropical continent.
  (3) Antarctica was once near the equator.
  (4) Antarctica collected wind-borne seeds from South America.

_____ 2. The fact that oceanic rock nearest a mid-ocean ridge is younger than rock farther from the ridge is strong evidence that
  (1) tectonic plates are converging at mid-ocean ridges
  (2) rocks age at different rates at mid-ocean ridges
  (3) tectonic forces must be changing the rocks
  (4) new oceanic rock is created at mid-ocean ridges

_____ 3. In California, tectonic plates floating on the asthenosphere are sliding past each other. What type of plate boundary is this?
  (1) transform boundary
  (2) convergent boundary
  (3) mid-ocean boundary
  (4) divergent boundary

_____ 4. At which plate boundary is volcanic activity due to subduction expected?
  (1) Nazca/Pacific plate boundary
  (2) Antarctic/African plate boundary
  (3) Pacific/Eurasian plate boundary
  (4) Antarctic/Pacific plate boundary

Volcanoes

A **volcano** is an opening, or *vent*, in Earth's surface through which magma, as well as volcanic gases, are expelled. When magma emerges onto Earth's surface, it is called **lava.**

Many active volcanoes occur along subduction zones. Here, magma comes to the surface when an oceanic plate is forced down into the mantle and then melts. When the magma erupts onto Earth's surface, lines of volcanic mountains form along the

Unit VII Plate Tectonics *continued*

Notes/Study
Ideas/Answers

edge of the continental plate. For example, a major zone of active volcanoes, called the *Pacific Ring of Fire*, encircles the Pacific Ocean. This zone is formed by the subduction of plates along the Pacific coasts of North America, South America, Asia, and the islands of the western Pacific Ocean.

> **Self-Check** Why do volcanoes occur along subduction zones?

The interconnected mid-ocean ridges that circle Earth are another major zone of volcanic activity. Here, magma comes to the surface as tectonic plates move apart. Most volcanic eruptions along mid-ocean ridges go unnoticed because the eruptions occur beneath the ocean's surface. An exception is found in Iceland, which is a part of the Mid-Atlantic Ridge that rises above sea level. Part of Iceland is on the North American plate. The rest is on the Eurasian plate. As these two plates diverge, magma erupts through large cracks in the ground.

Some volcanoes develop far from plate boundaries. In some places beneath Earth's surface, large columns of magma, called *mantle plumes*, accumulate and rise toward the crust, where they melt surrounding rock. So much rock may be melted that the magma breaks through the crust. A **hot spot** is a site within a tectonic plate where magma emerges through the crust. Volcanoes may form at the site of a hot spot. The Hawaiian Islands are volcanic mountains that formed over a hot spot near the middle of the Pacific plate.

REVIEW YOUR UNDERSTANDING

Some questions may require use of the *Earth Science Reference Tables*.

_____ **5.** What happens to tectonic plates at a subduction zone?
  (1) A continental plate sinks beneath an oceanic plate.
  (2) An oceanic plate sinks beneath a continental plate.
  (3) Plates slide past one another.
  (4) Plates diverge, forming mid-ocean ridges.

_____ **6.** In the Pacific Ring of Fire, tectonic plates are generally
  (1) diverging
  (2) moving along a transform boundary
  (3) converging
  (4) moving over a mantle hot spot

_____ **7.** Which geologic feature commonly forms at the plate boundaries where oceanic crust converges with continental crust?
  (1) a continental volcanic mountain range
  (2) a mid-ocean ridge
  (3) an underwater volcanic mountain range
  (4) a chain of volcanic islands

_____ **8.** A volcano that forms over a hot spot is different from most other volcanoes because
  (1) it forms from a deep-ocean trench
  (2) it forms within a tectonic plate
  (3) it occurs only at subduction zones
  (4) it occurs only on island arcs

Mountains: Deformation of the Crust

Mountains are complicated structures whose rock formations are evidence of the forces that created them. Scientists believe that most mountains form as a result of tectonic plate movements.

In general, mountains are the direct result of plate movement at convergent boundaries. For example, when two continental plates ram into each other, they crumple and fold under the tremendous pressure, forming great mountain ranges. The mountains that result are called **folded mountains.** The Appalachian Mountains and the Rocky Mountains are examples of mountain ranges that were formed by folding.

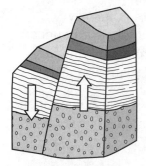

Fault-block mountain

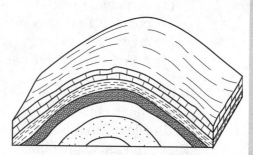

Folded mountain

Mountains are also created when rock layers are forced vertically upward at fault lines (cracks between slabs of rock) by the pressures of plates colliding. Faults allow massive blocks of rock—called *fault blocks*—to shift and move. The rocks on one side of the fault are forced upward as the rocks along the other side sink. This process creates **fault-block mountains,** which typically have steep clifflike faces on one side and gentler inclines on the other side. The Sierra Nevada, in California and Nevada, and the Grand Teton Mountains, in Wyoming, are examples of fault-block mountains.

Unit VII Plate Tectonics *continued*

**Notes/Study
Ideas/Answers**

> **Self-Check** Compare and contrast the formation of folded mountains and fault-block mountains.

Other mountains form when an oceanic plate collides with a continental plate. When these plates collide, the oceanic plate subducts beneath the continental plate. This type of collision produces such large-scale deformation of rock that high mountains are uplifted. For example, scientists believe that the Andes Mountains are growing taller as the Nazca plate subducts beneath the South American plate and uplifts it. In addition, the subduction of the oceanic plate causes it to melt. **Volcanic mountains** form when magma erupts onto Earth's surface. The magma solidifies into lava, and the materials pile up, one layer on top of another, until a cone-shaped structure forms. For example, the Cascade Mountains, in the Pacific Northwest, were formed by an oceanic-continental plate collision. There are many volcanic mountains in this range, including Mount Saint Helens, which erupted violently in 1980.

> **Self-Check** Describe one way that a collision between an oceanic plate and a continental plate could lead to the formation of a mountain range.

REVIEW YOUR UNDERSTANDING

_____ **9.** Along which type of tectonic plate boundary do volcanic mountain ranges form?
   (1) divergent oceanic-oceanic plate boundary
   (2) convergent continental-continental plate boundary
   (3) convergent oceanic-continental plate boundary
   (4) transform oceanic-continental plate boundary

_____ **10.** The Himalaya Mountains formed when two continental plates collided. The rock formations in the Himalaya Mountains probably
   (1) contain many faults
   (2) contain many folds
   (3) are composed of layers of lava
   (4) contain active volcanoes

_____ **11.** In which area is mountain building due to tectonic plate collision unlikely?
   (1) the western coast of South America
   (2) the western coast of the United States
   (3) the Pacific Ring of Fire
   (4) the eastern coast of the United States

| Unit VII Plate Tectonics *continued*

Earthquakes

An **earthquake** is defined as a movement of the crust that is caused by a sudden release of energy when rocks along a fault move. A **fault** is a break in a body of rock along which one block slides relative to another.

What causes an earthquake to happen? Rocks along a fault are commonly pressed together tightly. Friction between rock surfaces prevents them from moving. In this immobile state, the fault is said to be *locked*. Yet the powerful forces in Earth that cause plate motions eventually overcome the rocks' resistance. Huge amounts of energy are released when the rocks are finally forced to move and grind past each other. The resulting slippage causes the trembling and vibration of an earthquake.

Earthquakes occur mainly along or near the edges of tectonic plates, where plate movement causes a tremendous buildup of stress in surrounding rocks. Fault zones are major regions of seismic activity. *Fault zones* are zones of interconnected cracks that form from the stress along plate boundaries. The San Andreas Fault, a transform fault in California, is frequently shaken by earthquakes. The San Andreas Fault zone occurs where the Pacific plate is moving northwest past the North American plate. This movement causes a buildup of stress along the fault. The stress is then released during an earthquake.

The area along a fault in Earth's crust where rock slippage first occurs is called the earthquake's **focus.** An earthquake's **epicenter** is the site on Earth's surface directly above the focus.

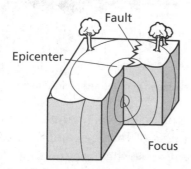

Notes/Study Ideas/Answers

Self-Check What names are given to the underground site of an earthquake and the surface location directly above it?

As rocks along a fault break and slip during an earthquake, they give off energy in the form of vibrations called **seismic waves.** Seismic waves radiate outward in all directions from the focus of the earthquake. There are two primary types of seismic waves: body waves and surface waves.

Body waves travel through an object, such as rock in Earth's crust. There are two main types of body waves. Primary waves,

Unit VII Plate Tectonics *continued*

**Notes/Study
Ideas/Answers**

or **P-waves,** are fast-moving waves that cause rock particles to alternately pack closer together and spread farther apart in the direction of wave movement. Secondary waves, or **S-waves,** cause rock particles to vibrate at right angles to the direction of wave movement. S-waves travel more slowly than P-waves.

Self-Check Compare and contrast P-waves and S-waves.

When P-waves and S-waves reach Earth's surface, their energy can be converted into **surface waves.** There are two types of surface waves. One type (*Love waves*) causes the ground to move from side to side, perpendicular to the direction of wave travel. The other type (*Rayleigh waves*) causes the ground to move in a rolling motion. Surface waves are the slowest-moving seismic waves, yet they cause the greatest damage during an earthquake.

Seismic waves can be detected and recorded by using an instrument called a **seismograph.** A seismograph records earthquake motion by tracing wave-shaped lines on paper. The tracing of earthquake motion that is recorded by a seismograph is called a **seismogram.** Scientists use seismograms to locate the earthquake epicenter.

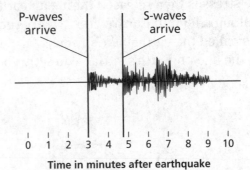

To find the epicenter, scientists analyze the difference between the arrival times of P-waves and S-waves. P-waves are the fastest seismic waves, so they are the first to be recorded by a seismograph. S-waves are slower than P-waves, so they are the second waves to be recorded. Surface waves are the slowest-moving seismic waves. Thus, surface waves are the last waves to be recorded by a seismograph.

The greater the difference between the arrival of the P-waves and the arrival of S-waves, the farther away the earthquake must have occurred. To determine how far an earthquake is from a seismograph station, scientists consult a standard travel-time graph. The start time of the earthquake can also be determined. Recordings from at least three separate seismograph stations must be used to pinpoint the epicenter. (See the

Unit VII Plate Tectonics *continued*

"Earthquake P-wave and S-wave Travel Time" graph in the *Earth Science Reference Tables*, page 241.)

The **Richter scale** is used to report the magnitude (total energy) of an earthquake. Richter scale magnitudes are calculated from the height of the S-waves and the distance between the epicenter and the seismograph. Each one-point increase on the Richter scale (such as the difference between a 4.0 and a 5.0 earthquake) indicates that the S-waves are 10 times as tall, and the total energy released is 30 times as great. The **modified Mercalli scale** classifies earthquake intensity.

The movement of the ground during an earthquake rarely causes injury. Rather, most injuries are caused by the collapse of buildings and other structures or from falling objects and flying glass. Other dangers include landslides, explosions caused by broken gas and electric lines, and floodwaters released from collapsing dams. As one might expect, injury and damage due to earthquakes is much more common in urban, as opposed to rural, areas.

Notes/Study Ideas/Answers

Self-Check What does the Richter scale measure?

REVIEW YOUR UNDERSTANDING

Some questions may require use of the *Earth Science Reference Tables*.

_____ **12.** The place inside a fault where slippage of rock first occurs is called an earthquake's
   (1) epicenter
   (2) magnitude
   (3) intensity
   (4) focus

_____ **13.** A seismic station recorded the arrival of a P-wave at 10:00:00 A.M. The S-wave arrival was recorded at 10:04:20 A.M. What is the approximate distance between the earthquake epicenter and the seismograph?
   (1) 1.1×10^3 km
   (2) 2.2×10^3 km
   (3) 2.9×10^3 km
   (4) 7.2×10^3 km

_____ **14.** In which major earthquake zone are earthquakes produced mainly by converging tectonic plates?
   (1) the Mid-Atlantic Ridge
   (2) the Pacific Ring of Fire
   (3) the San Andreas Fault area
   (4) the East Pacific Ridge

Unit VII Plate Tectonics *continued*

_____ **15.** Which seismic waves are the first to be recorded by a seismograph?
(1) P-waves
(2) Rayleigh waves
(3) Love waves
(4) S-waves

ANSWERS TO SELF-CHECK QUESTIONS

- Africa and South America were once connected. The continents separated and drifted to their present-day locations.

- The youngest rock is found nearest a mid-ocean ridge.

- Plate tectonics is the theory that explains why and how continents move.

- transform boundary: tectonic plates slide past one another; convergent boundary: tectonic plates collide with one another; divergent boundary: tectonic plates pull away from one another

- At a subduction zone, one plate sinks beneath another into the mantle. The subducted plate begins to melt into magma. The magma rises through the lithosphere to form volcanoes.

- Folded mountains form by compression, when two continental plates collide; fault-block mountains form along fault lines from blocks of rock that shift relative to one another.

- The collision drives the oceanic plate beneath the continental plate, causing crumpling and uplifting of rock along the edge of the continental plate.

- The underground site is the focus. The above-ground site is the epicenter.

- P-waves are fast-moving seismic waves that cause rock particles to alternately pack closer together and spread farther apart in the direction of wave movement. S-waves move more slowly than P-waves and cause rock particles to vibrate at right angles to the direction of wave movement.

- The Richter scale measures earthquake magnitude, or the amount of energy released by the earthquake.

Questions for Regents Practice

Plate Tectonics

PART A

Some questions may require use of the *Earth Science Reference Tables*.

_____ **1.** Which represents a divergent plate boundary?
   (1) Indian-Australian/Antarctic plate boundary
   (2) South American/Nazca plate boundary
   (3) Indian-Australian/Pacific plate boundary
   (4) Pacific/North American plate boundary

_____ **2.** Subduction of an oceanic plate beneath a continental plate generally occurs because
   (1) oceanic crust is less dense than continental crust
   (2) oceanic crust is denser than continental crust
   (3) oceanic crust is hotter than continental crust
   (4) oceanic crust is flatter than continental crust

_____ **3.** Collisions between oceanic plates and continental plates are thought to result primarily from
   (1) hot liquid magma in Earth's inner core
   (2) convection currents in the mantle
   (3) volcanic eruptions along coastlines
   (4) earthquakes within fault zones

_____ **4.** Folding of rock layers is most likely to happen when rocks undergo
   (1) compression, due to converging tectonic plates
   (2) cooling, due to changes in climate
   (3) tension, due to diverging tectonic plates
   (4) shearing, due to movement at a fault

_____ **5.** Which statement describes the main difference between P-waves and S-waves?
   (1) P-waves travel through objects and S-waves do not.
   (2) P-waves are faster than S-waves.
   (3) P-waves are slower than S-waves.
   (4) S-waves travel through objects and P-waves do not.

_____ **6.** A seismograph recorded S-waves shortly after it detected P-waves. This information suggests that the earthquake was
   (1) very strong
   (2) very weak
   (3) far away
   (4) nearby

| Unit VII Plate Tectonics *continued*

PART B-1

Base your answers to questions 7 to 9 on your knowledge of earth science, the *Earth Science Reference Tables*, and the map below, which shows the probability that a magnitude 6.7 or greater earthquake will occur between now and the year 2032 in northern California.

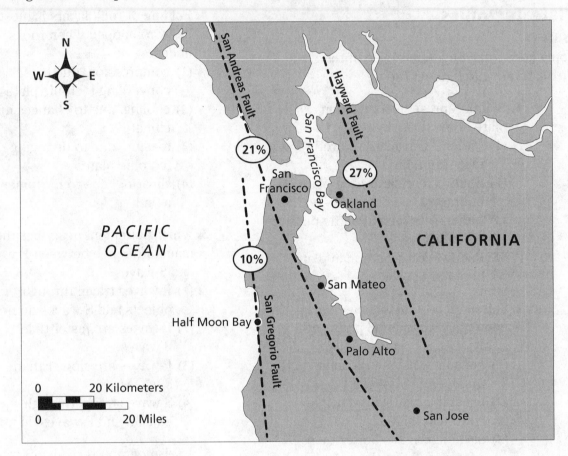

7. Which city has the greatest danger of damage from an earthquake?
(1) San Francisco
(2) Oakland
(3) San Jose
(4) Half Moon Bay

8. The San Andreas Fault zone is located along the boundary between which two tectonic plates?
(1) Pacific plate and Cocos plate
(2) Nazca plate and Cocos plate
(3) Pacific plate and North American plate
(4) Pacific plate and South American plate

9. If a large earthquake were to occur in San Jose, the earliest indication at another California location of the occurrence of that earthquake would be the arrival of
(1) S-waves at Palo Alto
(2) S-waves at San Mateo
(3) P-waves at San Mateo
(4) P-waves at Palo Alto

Unit VII Plate Tectonics *continued*

PART B-2

Base your answers to questions 10 to 13 on your knowledge of earth science, the *Earth Science Reference Tables*, and the earthquake seismogram below.

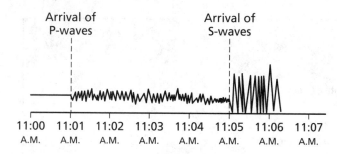

10. At what time did the first P-waves arrive at this seismograph station?

_____

11. What is the approximate distance of this seismograph station to the earthquake epicenter?

_____

12. Assume that P-waves travel at a speed of 8 km/s. At approximately what time did the earthquake occur? Show all work.

_____

13. How many additional seismograph stations are needed in order to locate the epicenter of the earthquake?

_____

| Unit VII Plate Tectonics *continued*

PART C
Base your answers to questions 14 to 16 on your knowledge of earth science, the *Earth Science Reference Tables*, and on the reading passage and map below.

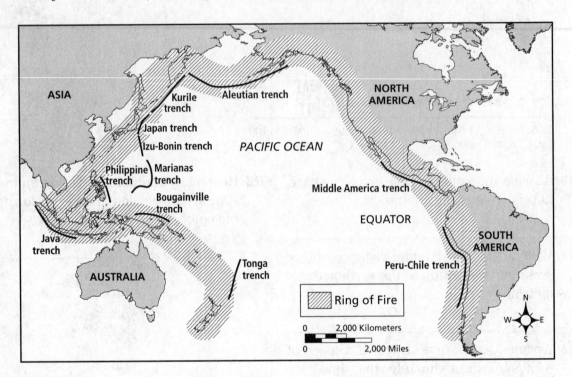

RING OF FIRE
The zone of volcanic arcs and deep-ocean trenches that encircle the Pacific Ocean has earned the nickname "Ring of Fire." The Ring of Fire stretches from New Zealand, along the eastern edge of Asia, north across the Aleutian Islands of Alaska, and south along the coast of North and South America. This zone, notorious for its frequent earthquakes and volcanic eruptions, coincides with the edges of several major tectonic plates. More than half of the world's active volcanoes above sea level are part of this ring.

14. Name the six major (largest) tectonic plates associated with the Ring of Fire.

_____

_____

15. Identify the type of tectonic plate boundary associated with the formation of the volcanic Cascade Mountains in the Pacific Northwest of the United States.

_____

16. Explain in terms of plate motions why the Ring of Fire is such a volcanically active area.

_____

_____

_____

Name _____ Class _____ Date _____

UNIT VIII
Earth History

Geologists estimate that Earth is about 4.6 billion years old. Scientists from many disciplines are curious about what Earth has been like since its birth billions of years ago. They use different methods to learn about the geological and biological history of our planet.

Dating Methods

One thing we can learn about Earth's past is the order in which rock layers and other rock structures formed. In the same way that pages in a book can show an order of events, layers of rock can show the sequence of events that took place in the past. By applying basic geological principles, scientists can determine the order in which rock layers formed. **Relative age** indicates that one rock layer is older or younger than other rock layers. Knowing the order of layer formation helps scientists understand the order of events, because a given type of rock forms only under certain conditions.

A basic principle called the law of superposition is used when determining the relative age of a layer of sedimentary rock. The **law of superposition** states that a sedimentary rock layer is always older than the layers above it and younger than the layers below it, unless the rock layers have been disturbed in some way. Therefore, when scientists assign relative ages to rocks, the oldest rocks are on the bottom and the layers become progressively younger toward the top.

Self-Check What is the law of superposition?

Sedimentary rock is usually the result of deposition of sediments in horizontal layers. In some places, the layers are tilted rather than horizontal. The **principle of original horizontality** states that no matter the present angle or orientation of sedimentary layers, it is almost certain that the layers were originally horizontal and were tilted after deposition. The cause of the tilting could be folding or an uneven uplift of rock layers.

Movements of Earth's crust can lift buried rock layers to the surface and expose them to erosion. Entire layers may be eroded away. If new sediments are deposited on top of the eroded area and form new rock layers, there will be a break in the geologic record, just as tearing some pages from a book creates a break in a story. A break in the geologic record is called an **unconformity.**

What You'll Need to Learn
This topic is part of the Regents Curriculum for the Physical Setting Exam.

Standard 4, Performance Indicator 1.2: *Describe current theories about the origin of the universe and solar system.* Major Understandings: 1.2i, 1.2j

What Terms You'll Need to Know
absolute age
carbon-14 dating
fossil
geologic time scale
half-life
index fossil
law of cross-cutting relationships
law of superposition
principle of original horizontality
radioisotope
radiometric dating
relative age
unconformity

Where You Can Learn Even More
Holt Earth Science: The Physical Setting
Chapter 8: The Rock Record
Chapter 9: A View of Earth's Past

Unit VIII Earth History *continued*

Determining relative age may be difficult when rock layers have been disturbed by faults or igneous intrusions. In these cases, scientists determine relative age using the law of cross-cutting relationships. The **law of crosscutting relationships** states that a fault or igneous intrusion is always younger than the rock layers it cuts through. After all, the rocks must have been there before they were faulted and before magma could cut through them.

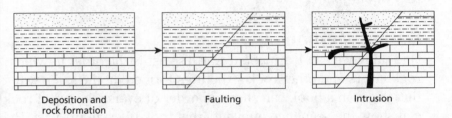

Deposition and rock formation   Faulting   Intrusion

The cross-cutting relationships in this series of diagrams show that faults and intrusions must be younger than the rocks in which they are found. The layers in diagram 1 must exist before they can be faulted as shown in diagram 2. The layers and the fault are crossed by the intrusion in 3, so both must be older than the intrusion.

Relative age may also be determined by the existence or nonexistence of contact metamorphism near an igneous intrusion. Recall from Unit IV that contact metamorphism is the change in the texture, structure, or chemical composition of a rock due to contact with magma. Magma can be confined underground or it may erupt onto the surface. When magma comes to the surface, the rock below it may be altered by contact metamorphism. But because the magma is at the surface, there is no rock on top of the magma to be altered. Sometimes geologists find a layer of igneous rock that has not altered the rock layer immediately above it. This is evidence that the layer above was deposited after the magma cooled.

Self-Check How is the law of cross-cutting relationships applied in dating rocks?

Relative age estimations are useful, but they can only tell the order of rock layer formation, not the age. To learn more about Earth's history, scientists often need to find the numeric age, or **absolute age,** of a rock formation.

Unit VIII Earth History *continued*

Self-Check Differentiate between relative age and absolute age.	**Notes/Study Ideas/Answers**

The absolute ages of rocks can be determined by measuring the small amounts of radioactive material they contain. Recall from Unit III that atoms of the same element that have different numbers of neutrons are called *isotopes*. When a radioactive isotope, or **radioisotope,** breaks down it often changes to a stable isotope of a different element. The stable end material of radioactive decay is known as the *decay product.*

Radioactivity can be used to find absolute ages because radioactive decay occurs at a predictable rate. Scientists have learned that the time required for half of any amount of a given radioisotope to decay is always the same. This time is called the isotope's **half-life.** Some radioisotopes have a half-life period of a fraction of a second. For others, the half-life period is billions of years.

The "Radioactive Decay Data" table in the *Earth Science Reference Tables* section, page 221, lists the disintegration (decay) patterns and half-lives of commonly used radioisotopes. For example, carbon-14 (C^{14}) changes into nitrogen-14 (N^{14}) as it decays. The half-life of carbon-14 is about 5,700 years. This means that no matter how much carbon-14 you start with, after 5,700 years just half of it will remain. The other half of the material is the stable decay product, nitrogen-14. In another 5,700 years, half of the remaining carbon-14 will decay, leaving only one quarter of the original amount. This continues until all of the carbon-14 sample has decayed into the more stable element, nitrogen-14.

Self-Check Define half-life.

Unit VIII Earth History *continued*

**Notes/Study
Ideas/Answers**

The way scientists determine the age of some radioactive samples is to compare the amount of the original radioisotope with the amount of its decay product. For example, consider a rock containing a supply of radioactive uranium-235 atoms, as shown in the sequence of diagrams. As time passes, the radioactive uranium atoms decay and eventually become stable atoms, in this case, lead (Pb) atoms. The rate of decay is constant and the more time that has passed, the greater the number of uranium atoms that have decayed into lead atoms. At any point, a scientist can take a sample of the rock and count the total number of uranium and lead atoms. The proportion of lead atoms to uranium atoms reveals the number of half-lives that have elapsed since the rock formed. If the length of uranium-235's half-life is multiplied by the number of elapsed half-lives, the age of the rock sample is obtained. The method of using radioactive decay to determine absolute age is called **radiometric dating.**

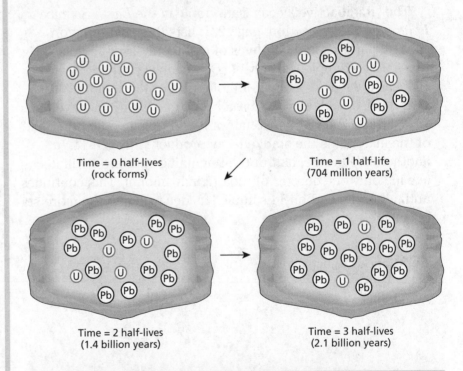

Time = 0 half-lives
(rock forms)

Time = 1 half-life
(704 million years)

Time = 2 half-lives
(1.4 billion years)

Time = 3 half-lives
(2.1 billion years)

Self-Check A newly formed rock contains 40 grams of a radioactive isotope that has a half-life of 10,000 years. How much of the parent isotope will remain after 20,000 years?

Different radioisotopes are best suited to different purposes. The two critical issues are the presence of any particular radioisotope in the rocks being dated and the estimated age of the rocks. For example, except for carbon-14, all the isotopes in the "Radioactive Decay Data" table have relatively long half-life periods. This means that they are more useful for dating older rocks, from 100,000 years old back to the origin of Earth. In

Unit VIII Earth History *continued*

some places, these isotopes are used to determine the age of volcanic ash layers. Thus, volcanic ash layers are often useful markers of absolute time that can be found over a wide geographic area.

Carbon-14 dating is a way of determining the age of wood, bone, shells, and other artifacts of biological origin up to about 50,000 years. Carbon-14 decays so quickly that there is little left in samples older than 50,000 years. This makes measurements difficult and precision poor beyond that age.

Carbon is found in the air in the form of carbon dioxide. Most of the carbon in the air is nonradioactive carbon-12 (C^{12}). The air also contains a smaller amount of radioactive carbon-14 (C^{14}). Plants absorb carbon dioxide, whether it contains C^{12} or C^{14}, for photosynthesis. Then, when animals eat the plants or other plant-eating animals, the C^{12} and C^{14} become part of their body tissues. Thus, all living organisms contain both C^{12} and C^{14}.

To find the age of organic material, scientists first calculate the ratio of C^{14} to C^{12} in the material. Then, they compare that ratio with the ratio of C^{14} to C^{12} known to exist in a living organism. While organisms are alive, the ratio of C^{14} to C^{12} remains relatively constant, because carbon is always entering and leaving the body. When the organism dies, however, the ratio beings to change. Because the organism is dead, it no longer absorbs C^{12} and C^{14}, and the amount of C^{14} begins to decrease, because it decays into the stable, nonradioactive isotope N^{14}. By comparing the ratio of C^{14} to C^{12} in the sample to the ratio known to exist in living organisms, scientists can determine the absolute age of the material.

REVIEW YOUR UNDERSTANDING

Some questions may require use of the *Earth Science Reference Tables*.

_____ **1.** Which observation would provide the best evidence that sedimentary rock layers are undisturbed?
   (1) The rock layers contain many fossils.
   (2) The rock layers are horizontal.
   (3) The rock layers are tilted.
   (4) The rock layers contain many faults.

_____ **2.** The skull of an ancient bear has been discovered. Scientists say it is 25,000 years old. Which radioisotope did they use to determine the age?
   (1) uranium-238
   (2) rubidium-87
   (3) carbon-14
   (4) potassium-40

_____ **3.** One characteristic that makes a radioisotope useful for determining the absolute age of a rock is the isotope's
(1) resistance to weathering
(2) common occurrence in sedimentary rocks
(3) constant half-life
(4) organic origin

_____ **4.** A rock contains a 25% to 75% ratio of original radioisotope potassium-40 to decay product argon-40. What is the absolute age of the rock?
(1) 1.0 million years old
(2) 1.0 billion years old
(3) 2.6 billion years old
(4) 4.6 billion years old

The Fossil Record

Fossils are the remains or traces of plants or animals that lived in a previous geologic time period. Fossils are an important source of information for finding the relative and absolute ages of rocks. Fossils help scientists understand the evolution of living things over time past and provide information about past geologic events and climates. For example, fossils of marine animals have been found in areas far from the ocean. These fossils tell scientists that such areas have been covered by an ocean in the past.

Self-Check How can fossils give scientists clues about ancient environments?

The process by which organic remains are preserved as fossils is called *fossilization*. Generally, it is the hard parts of organisms, such as bones, teeth, or shells, that are fossilized. Softer tissues usually decompose quickly, though in rare cases they may be fossilized. In some cases, no part of the original organism survives in fossil form. Instead, just a trace of the organism's existence is preserved. A *trace fossil* is a fossilized mark in sedimentary rock that formed by the movement of an animal on or within soft sediment. A dinosaur footprint is an example of a trace fossil. Imprints of leaves, stems, flowers, and fish made in mud are other examples.

Index fossils are fossils that scientists can use to help determine the ages of the rock layers in which they are found. To be useful, an index fossil must come from an organism that is distinct, abundant, widespread, and that existed for only a short span of geologic time. Common index fossils of New York State are listed in the "Geologic History of New York State" chart in the *Earth Science Reference Tables* section, page 235.

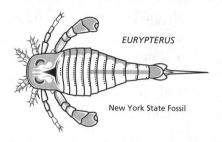

EURYPTERUS

New York State Fossil

Self-Check List four criteria used to classify a fossil as an index fossil.

Scientists can use index fossils to find the absolute age of specific rock layers. Because organisms that formed index fossils lived during short geologic time spans, the rock in which an index fossil is discovered can be dated accurately. For example, scientists know that *Eurypterus* (shown above), an ancient marine animal and the state fossil of New York, lived for a relatively short time span, from about 450 million years ago to about 360 million years ago. Therefore, the presence of *Eurypterus* fossils in any rock layer indicates that the rock must be of similar age.

Self-Check Describe how index fossils can be used to determine the age of rocks.

REVIEW YOUR UNDERSTANDING

Some questions may require use of the *Earth Science Reference Tables*.

_____ **5.** In eastern Africa, fossils of ancient jungle animals are often found in dry, desert-like environments. The presence of these fossils suggests that
(1) these organisms must have died from lack of water
(2) these organisms must have migrated to the desert
(3) the area must have been a jungle environment in the past
(4) people must have deposited the fossils in this area

Unit VIII Earth History *continued*

Notes/Study
Ideas/Answers

_____ **6.** Which is an example of a trace fossil?
  (1) an intact alligator tooth
  (2) a frozen woolly mammoth
  (3) an imprint of a flower
  (4) a petrified log

_____ **7.** Nautiloids are a group of marine animals that have been alive for almost 500 million years. The form of nautiloid called *Centroceras* is known to have been abundant about
  (1) 100 million years ago
  (2) 225 million years ago
  (3) 400 million years ago
  (4) 550 million years ago

_____ **8.** The presence of *Phacops* fossils in a rock layer indicates that the rock layer is probably
  (1) 110–150 million years old
  (2) 175–225 million years old
  (3) 362–418 million years old
  (4) 490–544 million years old

Geologic History

Throughout its 4.6-billion-year history, Earth's surface has changed dramatically, with continents moving and changing shape and oceans rising and receding. As Earth changed, so did the organisms that lived on it, with new species evolving and later becoming extinct. Scientists use the dramatic events in Earth's history to divide geologic time into units, just as a calendar year is divided into months, weeks, and days. The **geologic time scale** outlines the development of Earth and of life on Earth.

The "Geologic History of New York State" chart in the *Earth Science Reference Tables* includes a complete geologic time scale. The chart also provides other information about Earth's history, including a time distribution of important index fossils, a summary of major tectonic and geologic events in North America and in New York State, and maps showing the inferred positions of Earth's landmasses in different time periods. You should be familiar with the information in this chart and how to use it. A more detailed description of this chart and instructions on how to use it can be found on page 234.

The left-most five columns of the chart deal with divisions of geologic time and the evolution of life on Earth. The largest unit of geologic time is the *eon*. The *Phanerozoic Eon* is the current eon.

Unit VIII Earth History *continued*

The next largest unit of geologic time is the *era*. Eras are further divided into *periods* and *epochs*. There are four geologic eras. The earliest era is the *Precambrian Era*, which lasted from the beginning of the planet, about 4.6 billion years ago, until some 544 million years ago. The Precambrian therefore makes up about 88% of Earth's history. The Precambrian Era is divided into two periods, the *Archean Period* and the *Proterozoic Period*.

Few fossils exist in Precambrian rocks because these rocks are very old and because Precambrian organisms lacked bones, shells, and other hard parts that commonly form fossils. Earth's atmosphere and oceans developed early in the Precambrian. At first, the atmosphere consisted mainly of gases such as nitrogen and carbon dioxide—there was very little oxygen. Later, simple bacteria and algae evolved in the oceans and began to influence the physical world. Photosynthetic activity by algae produced oxygen, which built up in the atmosphere. By the end of the period, the surface of the world was much like it is today—but for the lack of life.

Self-Check Why are so few fossils found in Precambrian rocks?

Following the Precambrian Era was the *Paleozoic Era*, which lasted 293 million years. Scientists think that at the beginning of the Paleozoic Era, Earth's landmasses were scattered around the world. By the end of the Paleozoic, these landmasses had collided to form the supercontinent Pangaea. This tectonic activity created new mountain ranges and lifted large areas of land above sea level. The *Cambrian Period* is the first period of the Paleozoic Era and marks an important point in the history of life on Earth; it is the time when most of the major groups of animals first appear in the fossil record. This event is sometimes called the "Cambrian Explosion," because of the relatively short time over which this diversity of life-forms appeared. Familiar life-forms such as fish, land plants, insects, amphibians, and reptiles evolved during the Paleozoic.

Following the Paleozoic Era was the *Mesozoic Era*, which lasted about 186 million years, from 251–65 million years ago. During the Mesozoic, Earth's surface changed dramatically. As Pangaea broke into separate continents, the tectonic plates drifted and collided, uplifting great mountain ranges such as the Sierra Nevada in California. Warm and humid conditions during the Mesozoic favored the survival of reptiles. Lizards, turtles, crocodiles, snakes, and dinosaurs flourished during the Mesozoic. So, this era is also known as the *Age of Reptiles*.

Unit VIII Earth History *continued*

Self-Check Identify two major geologic and two major biologic developments of the Mesozoic Era.

The geologic period that began about 65 million years ago and includes present time is called the *Cenozoic Era*. During the Cenozoic, the continents moved to their present-day positions. Dramatic changes in climate also occurred. At times, continental ice sheets covered nearly one-third of Earth's surface. Mammals diversified and became the dominant life-form during the Cenozoic. Thus, the Cenozoic Era is often called the *Age of Mammals*. Cenozoic rocks contain an extremely detailed and diverse fossil record. This abundance of fossil information has allowed scientists to divide the two periods of the Cenozoic Era—the Tertiary and the Quaternary—into shorter time units called *epochs*.

Self-Check List the four major divisions of geologic time—*epoch, eon, period, era*—in order of length from shortest to longest.

REVIEW YOUR UNDERSTANDING

Some questions may require use of the *Earth Science Reference Tables*.

_____ **9.** According to fossil evidence, which set of developments is listed in the correct order from earliest to most recent?
   (1) earliest trilobites, first mammal-like reptiles, earliest insects
   (2) earliest chordates, earliest birds, earliest fish
   (3) peak development of eurypterids, earliest reptiles, extinction of dinosaurs
   (4) earliest grasses, extinction of armored fish, modern coral groups appear

_____ **10.** Which life forms were living on Earth during the Permian Period?
   (1) humans
   (2) birds
   (3) flowering plants
   (4) fish

_____ **11.** Which fossil would most likely be found in the same rock layer as a *Valcouroceras* fossil?
   (1) *Phacops*
   (2) *Stylonurus*
   (3) *Bothriolepis*
   (4) *Lichenaria*

_____12. During which era did the landmass known as
Pangaea first begin to break up?
(1) Cenozoic
(2) Paleozoic
(3) Mesozoic
(4) Late Proterozoic

Notes/Study
Ideas/Answers

ANSWERS TO SELF-CHECK QUESTIONS

• Unless layers have been disturbed, a rock layer is older than the layers above it and younger than the layers below it.

• A fault or igneous intrusion is always younger than the rock layers it cuts through. If a fault or intrusion cuts through an unconformity, the fault or intrusion is younger than all the rocks it cuts through above and below the unconformity.

• Relative age means the age of a rock layer relative to other rock layers (i.e., younger, older). Absolute age means the numerical age of a rock, such as 37 million years old.

• Half-life is the amount of time it takes for one-half of a sample of radioactive parent isotope to decay into its daughter isotope.

• Rock has passed through two half-lives ($20,000 \div 2 = 10,000$). After one half-life: 20 grams (1/2 of original mass); After two half-lives: 10 grams (1/4 of original mass)

• The ancient environment must have been one in which the organisms could have survived. For example, the presence of fish fossils indicates an ocean, lake, or stream.

• The fossil must be distinct, abundant, widespread, and must have existed for only a short span of geologic time.

• If the same index fossil is found in rock layers that are in different locations, the layers are most likely the same age.

• Precambrian rocks are very old and organisms lacked the hard parts that commonly form fossils.

• Major developments of the Mesozoic: earliest birds, dinosaurs flourished, earliest flowering plants, earliest mammals, breakup of supercontinent Pangaea.

• epoch, period, era, eon

Questions for Regents Practice

Earth History

PART A

Some questions may require use of the
Earth Science Reference Tables.

_____ 1. A rock contains a 1:3 ratio (25% to 75%) of original radioisotope uranium-235 to decay product lead-207. If the half-life of uranium-235 is 704 million years, what is the absolute age of the rock?
   (1) 1.4 million years old
   (2) 2.1 million years old
   (3) 1.4 billion years old
   (4) 2.1 billion years old

_____ 2. A newly formed rock contains 16 grams of a radioactive isotope that has a half-life of 1.25 billion years. How much of the isotope will remain after 3.75 billion years?
   (1) 0 grams
   (2) 2 grams
   (3) 4 grams
   (4) 8 grams

_____ 3. Carbon-14 is most useful for determining the age of which fossils?
   (1) eurypterids that lived during the Paleozoic Era
   (2) mastodonts that lived during the Cenozoic Era
   (3) placoderms that lived during the Paleozoic Era
   (4) algae that lived during the Precambrian Era

_____ 4. The fossil record indicates that, in the history of life on Earth,
   (1) most species appeared during the Quaternary Period
   (2) most species became extinct
   (3) most species were preserved in igneous intrusions
   (4) most species appeared during the Permian Period

_____ 5. Which event occurred latest in Earth's history?
   (1) erosion of Taconic Mountains
   (2) initial opening of Atlantic Ocean
   (3) appearance of birds
   (4) extinction of dinosaurs

_____ 6. During which geologic epoch did the most recent continental glaciers retreat from New York State?
   (1) Pleistocene
   (2) Late Pennsylvanian
   (3) Eocene
   (4) Early Mississippian

_____ 7. During which geologic period did North America separate from Africa?
   (1) Jurassic
   (2) Ordovician
   (3) Tertiary
   (4) Silurian

_____ 8. The absolute age of an igneous rock can best be determined by
   (1) observing the rock's position relative to other rocks
   (2) analyzing the ratio of original radioisotope to decay product
   (3) measuring the sizes of the mineral grains
   (4) examining the environment in which the rock is found

| Unit VIII Earth History *continued*

PART B-1

Base your answers to questions 9 through 11 on your knowledge of earth science and the graph below, which shows the decay of radioactive carbon-14.

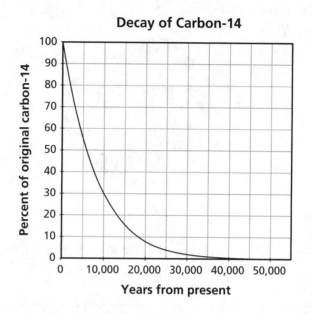

Decay of Carbon-14

_____ **9.** An ancient bone contains 5% radioactive carbon-14. Approximately how old is the bone?
(1) 500 years old
(2) 8,500 years old
(3) 25,000 years old
(4) 50,000 years old

_____ **10.** Based on the graph, the half-life of carbon-14 is closest to
(1) 500 years
(2) 6,000 years
(3) 40,000 years
(4) 50,000 years

_____ **11.** Wood from an ancient building was estimated to be 5,000 years old. Approximately what percentage of radioactive carbon-14 was found in the wood?
(1) 10%
(2) 35%
(3) 40%
(4) 55%

Unit VIII Earth History *continued*

PART B-2

Base your answers to questions 12 through 15 on your knowledge of earth science, the *Earth Science Reference Tables*, and the diagram below, which shows an index fossil found in surface bedrock in New York State.

Eospirifer

12. State the name of the group of invertebrate animals to which this species belongs.

_____

13. Name the geologic time period when this particular species was alive and abundant.

_____

14. How might an *Eospirifer* fossil be used to determine the absolute age of the rock layer in which it was found?

_____

_____

15. Describe the process that scientists would use to radiometrically date an *Eospirifer* fossil.

_____

_____

| Unit VIII **Earth History** *continued*

PART C

Base your answers to questions 16 through 19 on your knowledge of earth science, the *Earth Science Reference Tables*, and the geologic cross-section of bedrock shown below. In the cross section, letters A through F represent different fossil species. Lines X and Y are locations where rock layers have been eroded away. The rock layers have not been overturned.

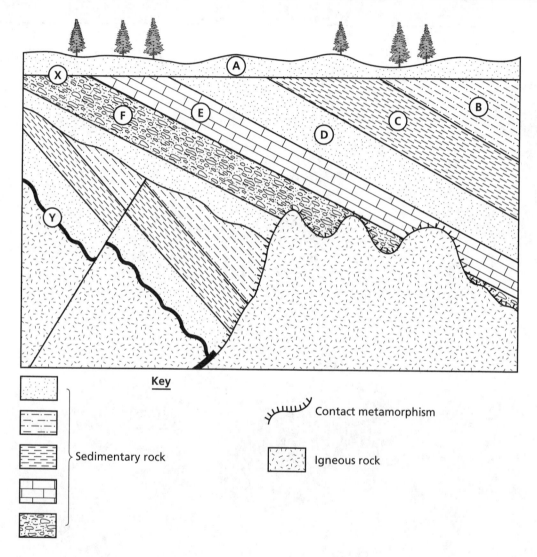

Key

Sedimentary rock

〜〜〜〜 Contact metamorphism

Igneous rock

16. Which fossil is the oldest?

_____

17. Explain your reasoning. Include in your answer the name of the geologic law or principle that supports your answer for question 16.

_____

_____

_____

Earth History *continued*

18. State the name of the geologic feature represented by lines X and Y.

_____

19. Rock layers B, C, and D formed during the Middle Ordovician Period. State the name of one index fossil that might be found in these rock layers.

_____

Oceanography

Nearly three-quarters of Earth's surface lies beneath a body of salt water called the *global ocean*. The presence of liquid water on Earth is the greatest difference between it and other known planets. Only Earth can be called the "water planet."

Ocean Water and Surface Currents

Although scientists do not know how long it took for oceans to form on Earth, evidence of surface water can be found in rocks that date back to very early in Earth's history. Our planet began as a rocky mass without surface water. As the atmosphere developed, Earth cooled enough for liquid water to form. Water vapor in the atmosphere condensed and fell to Earth as rain. This liquid water collected on the newly formed crust to form the first oceans.

Some scientists think that a portion of Earth's water may have come from outer space. As you will learn in Unit 14, comets are composed largely of ice. Comets striking Earth probably contributed some of the water in the oceans.

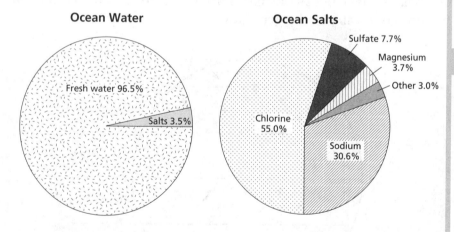

The first ocean was probably made of fresh water. However, we know today that about 3.5% of the mass of ocean water is dissolved salts. Where did all of the salt come from? The kinds of salts found in ocean water are found in the rocks of Earth's crust. Over millions of years, surface runoff and groundwater dissolved some of the rocks on land and carried the chemicals into the oceans. As these chemicals accumulated in the ocean, they combined to form salts. As ocean water evaporated, the salts were left behind. More chemicals were carried to the oceans, and the concentration of salts increased. Additional dissolved substances enter the oceans through deep-sea vents,

What You'll Need to Learn

This topic is part of the Regents Curriculum for the Physical Setting Exam.

Standard 4, Performance Indicator 1.2: *Describe current theories about the origin of the universe and solar system.* Major Understandings: 1.2f

Standard 4, Performance Indicator 2.2: *Explain how incoming solar radiation, ocean currents, and land masses affect weather and climate.* Major Understandings: 2.2b, 2.2c, 2.2d

What Terms You'll Need to Know

abyssal plain
deep-ocean basin
gyre
neap tide
spring tide
surface current
tidal range
tides
trench

Where You Can Learn Even More

Holt Earth Science: The Physical Setting
Chapter 19: The Ocean Basins
Chapter 20: Ocean Water
Chapter 21: Movements of the Ocean

**Notes/Study
Ideas/Answers**

which release water that has circulated through the rocks of the oceans' bottom.

Self-Check Describe the formation of Earth's oceans.

Water in the ocean is constantly moving in giant streams called *currents*. Currents that move on or near the surface and are driven by winds are called **surface currents.** The winds, in turn, result from the sun's uneven heating of Earth's atmosphere. Warm air is less dense than cold air, so cold air tends to sink and warm air tends to rise. In short, the sun provides the energy that drives the winds, and the winds use some of this energy to move large masses of water at the oceans' surface.

Winds and ocean currents follow a curved or circular pattern that is caused by Earth's rotation. As Earth spins on its axis, the Coriolis effect causes ocean currents and wind belts to curve, forming huge moving circles of water, called **gyres.** In the Northern Hemisphere, water in gyres curves to the right. In the Southern Hemisphere, this flow curves to the left. The "Surface Ocean Currents" map in the *Earth Science Reference Tables*, page 227, shows the major surface currents of the world. Look at the map. Can you find a gyre in the North Atlantic Ocean? What surface ocean currents form this gyre? In which direction does the water in the gyre flow?

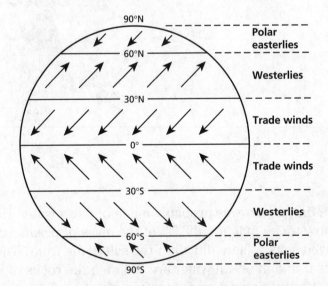

Self-Check Identify the winds that drive surface currents in the middle latitudes (30° to 60° north and south latitudes).

Cold and warm currents also affect coastal temperatures. For example, the cool California current, which flows southward along the California coast, keeps the water temperature too chilly for most swimmers, even during the summer months. By contrast, the warm *Gulf Stream*, which flows northward along the eastern coast of the United States, helps moderate winter temperatures considerably. Winter temperatures in New York City and on Long Island, for example, are far less severe than locations in New York State that are far from the ocean. By looking at the arrows on the "Surface Ocean Currents" map, you can tell where warm or cool ocean currents affect coastal areas. Black arrows show warm currents and white arrows show cool currents.

Self-Check Name two surface currents that warm coastal regions in the Northern Hemisphere.

In recent years, scientists have become more aware of the effects ocean currents have on regional climate. For example, most of the time, cold ocean currents and nutrient-rich water are found off the coast of South America. Good fishing in this region fuels local economies and provides employment for many people. However, in some years, the trade winds in this region weaken, allowing warm surface water to replace the normally cold surface water. This intrusion of warm surface water reduces fish populations and upsets the food chains on which fish, marine mammals, and seabirds depend. Local inhabitants call this phenomenon *El Niño* ("the child").

The increase in coastal surface temperatures during an El Niño event usually ends in a few months. However, every three to eight years large quantities of warm water spread north and south along the coast of the Americas, and surface temperatures remain elevated for more than a year. (Please see Unit X for more discussion of El Niño and the influence of ocean currents on climate.)

REVIEW YOUR UNDERSTANDING

Some questions may require use of the *Earth Science Reference Tables*.

_____ **1.** Earth's ocean surface currents are primarily caused by
(1) river currents
(2) global wind belts
(3) gravity
(4) precipitation

Notes/Study Ideas/Answers

**Notes/Study
Ideas/Answers**

_____ **2.** Ocean surface currents curve to the right in the Northern Hemisphere and to the left in the Southern Hemisphere because of
(1) the moon's rotation on its axis
(2) the moon's revolution around Earth
(3) Earth's rotation on its axis
(4) Earth's revolution around the sun

_____ **3.** Which ocean current likely has a warming effect on the coastal location it flows by?
(1) California Current
(2) Canaries Current
(3) Brazil Current
(4) Peru Current

_____ **4.** The Peru Current along the west coast of South America and the Benguela Current along the west coast of Africa are both
(1) cool currents that flow toward the equator
(2) cool currents that flow away from the equator
(3) warm currents that flow toward the equator
(4) warm currents that flow away from the equator

Tides

Many people who live along ocean coastlines are aware that the sea level periodically rises and falls. The twice-daily change in sea level is known as the **tides.** High tide is when the water level is at its highest; low tide occurs when the water level is lowest. Most locations have two high tides and two low tides every day.

Tides are caused by the gravitational pull of the sun and moon. The force of gravity between two objects depends on their masses and the distance between them. Although the moon is much smaller than the sun, it is much closer to Earth. Consequently, the moon has a greater influence on the tides than does the sun.

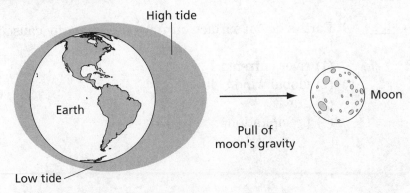

The moon's gravitational pull is greatest on the part of Earth closest to it. As a result, the ocean on the side of Earth closest to the moon bulges slightly, which causes a high tide in locations within the area of the bulge. At the same time, another tidal bulge forms on the opposite side of Earth. This tidal bulge forms because the solid Earth, which acts as though all of its mass were at Earth's center, is pulled more strongly toward the moon than the ocean water on Earth's far side is. Low tides form halfway between the two high tides. The bulges of water are stationary. As Earth spins on its axis, the land rotates through them. That is why most locations have two high tides each day. Because the moon rises about 50 minutes later each day, the cycle of high and low tides occurs about 50 minutes later each day. So, tides are about 12 hours and 25 minutes apart, on average.

Self-Check Explain how the gravitational pull from the moon causes tides.

The difference in water levels between high tide and low tide is called the **tidal range.** Tidal range varies widely, depending on the location. The greatest tidal range in the world occurs in the Bay of Fundy in eastern Canada, where the tidal range reaches nearly 17 m—the height of a four-story building!

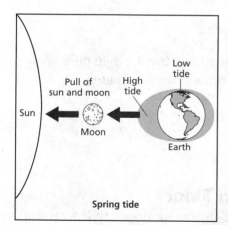

Spring tide

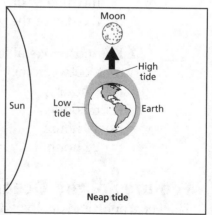

Neap tide

The sun's gravitational pull can affect the tidal range. When the moon, the sun, and Earth are aligned during full moon and new moon, the sun's gravitational pull works together with the moon's gravitational pull. This results in higher high tides and lower low tides. During these two monthly periods, tides are called **spring tides.**

Notes/Study Ideas/Answers

Self-Check Explain how the sun can influence the moon's effect on tides.

When the moon is in its first quarter and third-quarter phases, the sun and the moon are at right angles to each other in relation to Earth. During these times, the gravitational forces of the moon and the sun work against each other. The sun's gravity is pulling water away from the high tide bulges, toward the low tide areas. As a result, the daily tidal range is small, with relatively low high tides and relatively high low tides. Tides that occur during these two periods are called **neap tides.**

REVIEW YOUR UNDERSTANDING

_____ **5.** Which phrase best describes ocean tides?
(1) unpredictable and cyclic
(2) unpredictable and noncyclic
(3) predictable and cyclic
(4) predictable and noncyclic

_____ **6.** It is possible to tell if a coastal area is experiencing a neap tide or a spring tide by knowing
(1) the phase of the moon
(2) the season of the year
(3) the time of day
(4) the day of the week

_____ **7.** For most coastal locations, the average period of time between high tides is approximately
(1) 1 hour
(2) 6 hours
(3) 12 hours
(4) 24 hours

Features of the Ocean Floor

The geography and geology of the ocean floor are the products of crustal changes over the course of Earth's history. The main features of the ocean floor are the evidence for plate motion and the results of plate tectonics.

The ocean floor can be divided into two major areas: the continental margin and the deep-ocean basin. The *continental margins* are the edges of the landmasses presently below the ocean surface and their steep slopes that descend to the deep-ocean floor. A continental margin is composed of the continental shelf, slope, and rise.

Unit IX Oceanography *continued*

The *continental shelf* is a gently sloping land-border of varying width that slopes gently toward the deep-ocean floor. The *continental slope* is a steep slope on the seaward side of the continental shelf. At the base of the continental slope, there may be a gentle slope formed by the accumulation of sediment. This part of the ocean floor is the *continental rise*.

Self-Check Name the three parts of a continental margin.

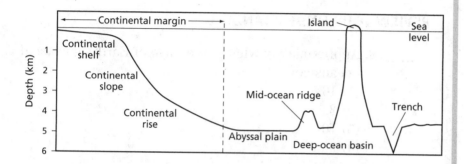

Both the continental shelf and continental slope are often gouged by *submarine canyons*—deep, V-shaped canyons that occur near the mouths of rivers. The force of river water and sediment flowing down from the land to the ocean bottom cuts the valleys.

The **deep-ocean basin,** which occurs at an ocean depth of 4,000–6,000 m (13,000–20,000 ft), covers more of Earth's surface than do the continents. Like the continental margin, distinctive geological features characterize the deep-ocean basin.

An ocean **trench** is a long, narrow depression located in the deep-ocean basin. The Marianas Trench in the western Pacific Ocean is the world's deepest ocean trench. At more than 11,000 m deep, it is the deepest place on Earth. As you recall from Unit VII, trenches form at convergent plate boundaries, where an oceanic plate subducts beneath a continental plate. (See Unit VII for more information about the formation of trenches.)

Self-Check What is an ocean trench, and how does it form?

In many places, the ocean floor is a vast, flat plain known as the **abyssal plain.** Abyssal plains form as sediment deposits and cover the irregular topography of the ocean floor.

Mid-ocean ridges, as you recall from Unit VII, are giant underwater mountain ranges and are the most prominent features of deep-ocean basins. Recall that mid-ocean ridges are found where tectonic plates diverge. A narrow depression, or rift, runs along the center of the ridge. Through this rift, magma reaches the sea floor and cools to form new lithosphere.

Self-Check What is a mid-ocean ridge, and how does it form?

Submerged volcanic mountains that are taller than 1 km are called *seamounts*. Seamounts form in areas of increased volcanic activity, known as hot spots. Seamounts that rise above the ocean surface form *islands*.

REVIEW YOUR UNDERSTANDING

_____ **8.** Approximately what percentage of Earth's surface do oceans cover?
(1) 10%
(2) 3.5%
(3) 70%
(4) 90%

_____ **9.** The continental shelf steepens rapidly at the
(1) continental rise
(2) continental slope
(3) mid-ocean ridge
(4) abyssal plain

_____ **10.** The shallowest portion of the continental margin is the
(1) continental shelf
(2) abyssal plain
(3) continental rise
(4) continental slope

_____ **11.** The vast, flat part of the deep-ocean basin is called the
(1) continental slope
(2) submarine valley
(3) ocean trench
(4) abyssal plain

Unit IX Oceanography *continued*

ANSWERS TO SELF-CHECK QUESTIONS

- The first oceans formed from rainfall. Moving water dissolved salts from rocks, and carried these chemicals to the oceans.

- The westerlies drive surface currents in the middle latitudes.

- The Gulf Stream flows northward along the eastern coast of North America. The Kuroshio Current flows northward along the eastern coast of Asia.

- The moon's gravity causes two high-tide bulges in Earth's oceans: one on the side of Earth nearest the moon and one on the opposite side. Low tides occur between the bulges. As Earth rotates, the land rotates through the bulges.

- The sun can support or oppose the moon's influence. During spring tides, the sun's pull is added to the moon's pull. During neap tides, the sun's pull partly counteracts the moon's pull.

- A continental margin consists of a continental shelf, a continental slope, and a continental rise.

- A trench is a deep canyon in the ocean floor that forms when an oceanic plate subducts beneath a continental plate.

- A mid-ocean ridge is a huge, underwater mountain range formed by diverging tectonic plates.

Questions for Regents Practice

Oceanography
PART A
Some questions may require use of the
Earth Science Reference Tables.

_____ 1. Seamounts, mid-ocean ridges, and trenches owe their existence and particular characteristics to
(1) plate tectonics
(2) erosion and deposition
(3) continental weathering
(4) ocean surface currents

_____ 2. Warm water from tropical oceans is carried to northern Europe by the Gulf Stream and the
(1) Brazil Current
(2) Kuroshio Current
(3) Canaries Current
(4) North Atlantic Current

_____ 3. Which surface ocean current carries cool water toward the equator?
(1) Kuroshio Current
(2) Peru Current
(3) North Atlantic Current
(4) West Wind Drift

_____ 4. In which ocean is the surface current known as the Gulf Stream located?
(1) North Pacific
(2) North Atlantic
(3) South Pacific
(4) South Atlantic

_____ 5. Garbage from New York State has been dumped into the Atlantic Ocean, where surface currents can distribute it. Which coastal region is most likely to become polluted by this garbage?
(1) eastern coast of Asia
(2) western coast of Europe
(3) western coast of South America
(4) eastern coast of Africa

_____ 6. A high tide was recorded on a Monday at 2:00 A.M. The first high tide on Tuesday will occur closest to
(1) 1:00 A.M.
(2) 2:00 A.M.
(3) 3:00 A.M.
(4) 2:00 P.M.

_____ 7. Which statement best describes the difference between spring tides and average tides?
(1) High tides are lower than average and low tides are higher than average.
(2) High tides are higher than average and low tides are lower than average.
(3) Time between high tides is shorter than average and time between low tides is longer than average.
(4) Time between high tides is longer than average and time between low tides is shorter than average.

Unit IX Oceanography *continued*

PART B-1

Base your answers to questions 8 through 10 on your knowledge of earth science and the diagram below, which shows a cross-section of the ocean floor between two continents. Points A through D represent locations on the ocean floor.

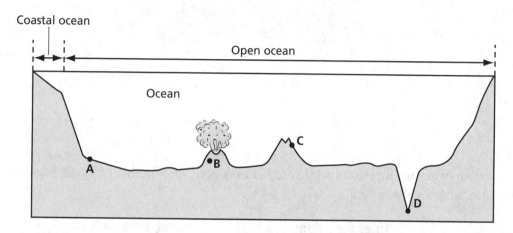

8. Which letter represents a location where tectonic plates are converging?
(1) A
(2) B
(3) C
(4) D

9. Which ocean floor structure is common near mantle hot spots?
(1) A
(2) B
(3) C
(4) D

10. Which letter represents a location where tectonic plates are diverging?
(1) A
(2) B
(3) C
(4) D

PART B-2

Base your answers to questions 11 and 12 on your knowledge of earth science and the diagram below, which shows the positions of the sun, the moon, and Earth on a specific date of the month. Letters A through D represent coastal locations on Earth's surface.

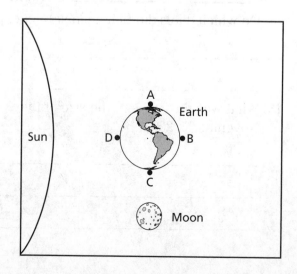

Unit IX Oceanography *continued*

11. Which two locations would be experiencing high tide at this time?

_____

12. Describe the high and low tides that would occur on this date. In your answer discuss how the tides would differ from average tides.

_____

_____

_____

_____

PART C

Base your answers to questions 13 through 15 on your knowledge of earth science and the partial tide table below.

Tides for Shinnecock Inlet, Long Island, New York

Date	% Moon Visible/Moon Phase	High Tide A.M. height above sea level (feet)	Low Tide A.M. height above sea level (feet)
10/6/04	54 (third quarter)	2.4	0.9
10/14/04	0 (new moon)	3.6	0.0
10/21/04	50 (first quarter)	2.7	0.6
10/28/04	99 (full moon)	3.5	0.0
11/5/04	53 (third quarter)	2.3	0.9

13. On which date was the tidal range the greatest? What was the tidal range?

_____

_____

14. On which dates did Shinnecock Inlet experience neap tides?

_____

_____

15. What was the cause of the size of the tidal range that occurred at Shinnecock Inlet on November 5, 2004?

_____

_____

_____

Name _____ Class _____ Date _____

The Atmosphere

Holt Earth Science: The Physical Setting

The **atmosphere** is the layer of gases and tiny particles that envelop Earth. The atmosphere protects Earth from the damaging effects of solar radiation and absorbs and redistributes energy from the sun to regulate Earth's temperature.

Structure of the Atmosphere

The most abundant elements in the atmosphere are the gases nitrogen, oxygen, and argon. (See the "Average Chemical Composition of Earth's Crust, Hydrosphere, and Troposphere" table in the *Earth Science Reference Tables* section, page 239. Look at the far-right column; the troposphere is the lowest layer of the atmosphere.) The most abundant compounds in the atmosphere are carbon dioxide and water vapor. In addition, the atmosphere also contains solid particles, such as dust and pollen.

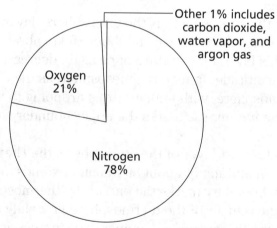

Chemical Composition of Earth's Atmosphere

Other 1% includes carbon dioxide, water vapor, and argon gas

Oxygen 21%

Nitrogen 78%

Self-Check Identify five main chemical components of the atmosphere.

Four distinct layers of Earth's atmosphere have been identified, based on temperature differences and the way solar radiation is absorbed. (See the "Selected Properties of Earth's Atmosphere" table in the *Earth Science Reference Tables* section, page 247.)

The atmospheric layer that is closest to Earth's surface and in which nearly all weather occurs is called the **troposphere.** Most of the atmosphere's carbon dioxide and water vapor is

What You'll Need to Learn

This topic is part of the Regents Curriculum for the Physical Setting Exam.

Standard 4, Performance Indicator 2.1: *Use the concepts of density and heat energy to explain observations of weather patterns, seasonal changes, and the movement of the Earth's plates.* Major Understandings: 2.1a, 2.1b

Standard 4, Performance Indicator 2.2: *Explain how incoming solar radiation, ocean currents, and land masses affect weather and climate.* Major Understandings: 2.2a, 2.2b

What Terms You'll Need to Know

air pressure
atmosphere
aurora
conduction
convection
convection cells
Coriolis effect
global winds
ionosphere
jet streams
mesosphere
ozone layer
radiation
stratosphere

Unit X The Atmosphere *continued*

found within the troposphere. The lower troposphere is warm, heated by energy that radiates from Earth's surface. However, as altitude increases in this layer, temperature steadily decreases. Although it can vary, the rate of decrease averages about 6.5°C per kilometer. At an altitude of about 11 km, the temperature stops decreasing. This zone of constant temperature, called the *tropopause*, marks the upper boundary of the troposphere.

The next highest layer of the atmosphere is the **stratosphere.** In contrast to the troposphere, temperature increases with increasing altitude in the stratosphere. The upper stratosphere is warmer than the lower stratosphere because of the presence of the **ozone layer.** Ozone is a form of oxygen gas that absorbs ultraviolet (UV) radiation in sunlight and filters much of it out before such radiation can reach Earth's surface. The energy absorbed from UV radiation is converted into heat energy, warming the upper stratosphere. Because UV radiation can be harmful to living things, the presence of the ozone layer is extremely important to life on Earth.

Temperature in the stratosphere rises steadily up to an altitude of about 50 km, where it peaks. This high-temperature zone, called the *stratopause*, marks the upper boundary of the stratosphere.

Above the stratosphere is the atmospheric layer called the **mesosphere,** which extends to about 80 km above Earth's surface. In this layer, temperature once again decreases with increasing altitude. In fact, the mesosphere is the coldest layer of the atmosphere, with temperatures dropping to around −90°C. The *mesopause* marks the upper boundary of the mesosphere.

The outermost layer of the atmosphere, the **thermosphere,** begins at an altitude of about 80 km and extends outward into space. No boundary marks the end of the thermosphere. Instead, the thin air of the thermosphere gradually merges with space. In the thermosphere, temperature increases rapidly with increasing altitude, from about −90°C to more than 1,000°C.

The lower part of the thermosphere contains a region of charged particles, or ions, and is called the **ionosphere.** In the ionosphere, molecules of nitrogen and oxygen lose one or more electrons as they absorb solar radiation. The molecules become positively charged ions. These ions are most dense between the altitudes of 80 km and 400 km. At these high altitudes, certain radio waves sent from Earth's surface, such as AM radio waves, bounce off ions and travel back to Earth.

Colorful flashes of light known as **auroras** also occur in the ionosphere. Auroras are produced when charged particles from the sun are attracted to Earth's magnetic poles. There, these particles cause ions in the ionosphere to glow. In the Northern Hemisphere, these displays are called the *aurora borealis*, or "northern lights."

Self-Check Name and describe the four main layers of the atmosphere.

The atmosphere has weight because of Earth's gravity. As a result of this weight, the atmosphere exerts pressure. **Air pressure** is the force exerted by the weight of a column of air on a surface. Air pressure changes with altitude. The atmosphere is densest near Earth's surface and becomes less dense as altitude increases. This is because air can be compressed. Near Earth's surface, a column of air includes the entire depth of the atmosphere, so the pressure and density are high. As altitude increases, the depth of the column of air above decreases, so the pressure decreases. At high altitudes, there is very little air in the column above, so air pressure is lower.

Self-Check Summarize the cause of atmospheric pressure.

REVIEW YOUR UNDERSTANDING

Some questions may require use of the *Earth Science Reference Tables*.

_____ **1.** Atmospheric temperatures decrease with altitude in the troposphere because
(1) solar radiation is less at higher levels
(2) the atmosphere is heated by energy radiated from the surface
(3) air at higher altitudes is less dense
(4) there are more atmospheric gases at higher altitudes

_____ **2.** Which layer of the atmosphere has an average temperature of −10°C and an atmospheric pressure of 10^{-2} atm?
(1) troposphere
(2) stratosphere
(3) mesosphere
(4) thermosphere

Unit X The Atmosphere *continued*

Notes/Study
Ideas/Answers

_____ **3.** What is the average atmospheric pressure at an elevation of 40 km above sea level?
(1) less than 10^{-3} atm
(2) 10^{-3} atm
(3) 10^{-2} atm
(4) 100 atm

_____ **4.** In which layer of Earth's atmosphere is water vapor found?
(1) troposphere
(2) stratosphere
(3) mesosphere
(4) thermosphere

Solar Energy and the Atmosphere

Earth's atmosphere is heated in several ways by the transfer of energy from the sun. A small amount of this energy is transferred directly to the atmosphere when atmospheric gases absorb solar radiation. Most of the energy is transferred to the atmosphere indirectly, as ocean and land surfaces absorb solar radiation and then transfer it to the atmosphere.

Energy from the sun is transferred to the atmosphere through the process of radiation. **Radiation** is the transfer of heat energy in the form of electromagnetic waves. It is the only way that energy can travel through the vacuum of space. All the energy that Earth receives from the sun travels through space as radiation.

Electromagnetic energy includes a wide range of radiant energy. This energy travels in waves, similar to the waves on an ocean or lake. However, we are not able to see electromagnetic waves in the same way that we observe waves on water. Still, they have similar measurable properties. One property common to all energy waves is frequency. *Frequency* is a measure of how many waves pass in a given period of time. Visible light has a frequency of about 600 trillion cycles per second. A second common property is *wavelength.* This is the distance from the top of one wave to the top of the following wave.

The "Electromagnetic Spectrum" chart in the *Earth Science Reference Tables* section, page 247, shows the range of wavelengths of electromagnetic energy. Only a narrow band of this energy is visible as light. Although we cannot see other wavelengths of electromagnetic energy, they are very important to us. Gamma rays and X-rays are the forms of electromagnetic energy with the shortest wavelengths. These highly penetrating radiations have applications in industry and medicine.

Unit X The Atmosphere *continued*

Ultraviolet radiation is longer in wavelength than gamma rays and X-rays, but the wavelength is still too short for the energy to be visible. Most of the sun's energy reaches Earth's surface as visible light that warms our planet and enables us to see. On the other side of the wavelength scale is invisible long-wavelength radiation. This includes infrared and microwaves, which can heat matter. Radio waves are used in communications such as radio and television.

**Notes/Study
Ideas/Answers**

Self-Check Name the different types of electromagnetic waves.

As solar radiation passes through the atmosphere, the atmosphere affects the radiation in several ways. Most short-wavelength radiation, such as X-rays, gamma rays, and ultraviolet rays, is absorbed by the upper atmosphere. Most ultraviolet rays, for example, are absorbed by the ozone in the stratosphere. Radiation may also be *scattered* by clouds, dust, water droplets, and gases in the atmosphere, which means that the solar rays can be reflected and bent in different directions. Scattering is what makes the sky appear blue and makes the sun appear red at sunrise and sunset.

When solar radiation reaches Earth's surface, the surface either absorbs the radiation or reflects it. The kind of surface on which the radiation falls largely determines whether it will be reflected or absorbed. In general, dark or rough-textured surfaces absorb more and reflect less solar radiation than do smooth, shiny, or light-colored surfaces.

The radiation that is absorbed heats the rocks, soil, water, and other materials of Earth's surface. The heated materials then emit that energy in the form of longer-wavelength infrared rays. Some atmospheric gases, especially carbon dioxide and water vapor, absorb these infrared rays, capturing heat energy and preventing it from escaping back into space. The process by which these atmospheric gases trap heat—called the *greenhouse effect*—keeps Earth's atmosphere much warmer than it would be if there were no atmosphere.

Self-Check Describe how light from the sun warms Earth.

Although most atmospheric heating comes from absorption of radiation directly from the sun or indirectly from Earth's surface, a small amount results from conduction and convection. In **conduction,** heat energy is transferred from one substance to another by direct contact. Much of the heating of the lower part of the atmosphere occurs through conduction, when air comes into contact with the heated surface of Earth.

| **Unit X The Atmosphere** *continued*

Convection involves the movement of gases or liquids when they are heated unevenly. As air is heated by conduction or radiation, it becomes less dense, rises, and then cools. Cold air is denser than warm air, so the cold air begins to sink. As the cold air comes closer to the ground, it is warmed, and then it rises again. This continuous cycle of cold air sinking and warm air rising helps warm Earth's atmosphere relatively evenly.

Self-Check How do conduction and convection warm Earth's atmosphere?

REVIEW YOUR UNDERSTANDING

Some questions may require use of the *Earth Science Reference Tables*.

_____ **5.** Which process is primarily responsible for heating the lowest portion of the troposphere?
(1) conduction
(2) reflection
(3) convection
(4) scattering

_____ **6.** Which atmospheric layer absorbs most of the electromagnetic energy traveling in waves that are 10^{-5} cm long?
(1) troposphere
(2) stratosphere
(3) mesosphere
(4) thermosphere

_____ **7.** Electromagnetic energy of which wavelength is likely to be felt as "heat"?
(1) 10^{-5} cm
(2) 10^{-7} cm
(3) 10^{-3} cm
(4) 10^{-2} cm

_____ **8.** As air on the surface of Earth warms, the density of the air
(1) decreases
(2) increases
(3) remains the same

Unit X The Atmosphere *continued*

Global Circulation of Air

The uneven heating of Earth and its atmosphere causes the horizontal movement of air, or **wind.** This uneven heating causes temperature differences that in turn create areas of pressure differences in the atmosphere. Air moving from areas of high pressure to areas of low pressure causes a general circulation of air around the globe. You will learn more about how differences in air pressure cause winds in Unit XI.

Winds that blow over long distances are called **global winds.** These winds are part of a worldwide pattern of air circulation. Global winds are caused by the unequal heating of Earth's surface across a large region.

Global Atmospheric Circulation

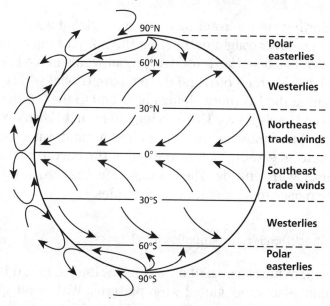

Global winds move in a series of huge bands called **convection cells.** As you can see in the diagram, these bands look like loops from the side. These bands are caused by temperature variations across Earth's surface. At the equator, for example, temperatures tend to be warmer than at other latitudes. Warm air rises at the equator, creating an area of low pressure. This warm air is replaced by cooler air brought by global winds blowing near the surface. Higher in the atmosphere, air blows away from the equator toward the poles. Similar convection cells cover large bands of latitude across Earth. (Please also see the "Planetary Wind and Moisture Belts in the Troposphere" diagram in the *Earth Science Reference Tables* section, page 247.)

The *trade winds* are wind belts just north and south of the equator. In the Northern Hemisphere, they blow from the northeast to the southwest. The *prevailing westerlies* occur between

Notes/Study
Ideas/Answers

Unit X The Atmosphere *continued*

30° and 60° latitude in both hemispheres. These winds generally blow from west to east over much of North America. The *polar easterlies* extend from 60° latitude to the poles in both hemispheres.

Rising and sinking air currents create wet and dry zones at particular latitudes. Where the air is often rising, such as along the equator, the cooling of warm, moist air creates clouds and precipitation. Most of the world's deserts are located approximately 30° north and 30° south of the equator. This is where sinking air currents become warmer as they fall through the atmosphere, and the relative humidity at the surface tends to be low.

Self-Check Name and describe the global wind belts.

If Earth were not rotating on its axis, global winds would move in nearly straight paths from the poles to the equator. However, because Earth rotates, global winds move in curved paths between the poles and the equator. Global winds curve to the right in the Northern Hemisphere and to the left in the Southern Hemisphere. The curving effect that Earth's rotation has on all free-moving objects, such as air and water, is called the **Coriolis effect.** The magnitude of the curvature varies significantly with latitude. The Coriolis effect is zero at the equator and increases to a maximum at the poles.

Self-Check What is the Coriolis effect?

Fast-moving streams of air at high altitudes, called **jet streams,** also affect global wind patterns. With wind speeds that can be greater than 160 km/h (100 mi/h), jet streams circle the globe from west to east, usually in the middle latitudes. Jet streams seldom follow surface winds and usually occur where cold polar air meets warmer air in the mid-latitudes.

The path of the jet stream is changeable as it meanders around the globe. In fact, two jet streams sometimes develop in the Northern Hemisphere. They tend to occur at the northern and southern limits of the zone of prevailing westerly winds. The "Planetary Wind and Moisture Belts in the Troposphere" diagram in the *Earth Science Reference Tables* section, page 247, shows the large convection cells responsible for prevailing surface winds at various latitudes. Notice how the jet streams generally occur in the regions between the circular convection cells.

Unit X The Atmosphere *continued*

REVIEW YOUR UNDERSTANDING

Some questions may require use of the *Earth Science Reference Tables*.

_____ **9.** Wind is caused primarily by
   (1) the rotation of Earth
   (2) humidity differences
   (3) air pressure differences
   (4) the revolution of Earth

_____ **10.** The curvature of planetary winds, called the Coriolis effect, is a direct result of the
   (1) gravitational forces on Earth
   (2) rotation of Earth
   (3) revolution of Earth
   (4) solar radiation that reaches Earth

_____ **11.** Which phrase best describes air blown by the polar easterlies?
   (1) low pressure air moving west
   (2) high pressure air moving west
   (3) high pressure air moving east
   (4) low pressure air moving east

ANSWERS TO SELF-CHECK QUESTIONS

- nitrogen, oxygen, argon, carbon dioxide, and water vapor

- *troposphere:* surface to 11 km above, contains carbon dioxide and water vapor, weather occurs here, temperature decreases with altitude; *stratosphere:* 11–50 km above surface, contains ozone layer, temperature increases with altitude; *mesosphere:* 50–80 km above surface, coldest layer, temperature decreases with altitude; *thermosphere:* hottest layer, temperature increases with altitude, contains ionosphere, layer in which auroras occur

- Air pressure is created by the weight of upper layers of air pressing down on lower layers of air. Air pressure decreases with altitude.

- gamma rays, X-rays, ultraviolet rays, visible light, infrared waves, microwaves, radio waves

Unit X The Atmosphere *continued*

- Solar radiation is absorbed by land and water and converted into heat. These surfaces, in turn, give off heat to the lower atmosphere.

- Conduction warms the atmosphere when air in the lower troposphere is heated by direct contact with warm surface materials. Convection warms the atmosphere when heated air becomes less dense and rises. This air is replaced by colder, denser air. The continuous cycle of cold air sinking and warm air rising helps heat the lower troposphere evenly.

- Trade winds blow toward the equator in both hemispheres between 30° and 0° latitude. North of the equator, trade winds blow northeast to southwest; south of the equator, they blow southeast to northwest. Westerlies blow toward the poles in both hemispheres between 30° and 60° latitude. North of the equator, westerlies blow southwest to northeast; south of the equator, they blow northwest to southeast. Polar easterlies exist in both hemispheres between 60° latitude and the polar regions. North of the equator, polar easterlies blow northeast to southwest; south of the equator, they blow southeast to northwest.

- The Coriolis effect is the curving effect that Earth's rotation has on all free-moving objects, such as air and water. The Coriolis effect causes winds to curve to the right in the Northern Hemisphere and to the left in the Southern Hemisphere.

Questions for Regents Practice

The Atmosphere

PART A

Some questions may require use of the *Earth Science Reference Tables*.

_____ **1.** Energy from the sun is transferred to Earth by which process?
(1) convection
(2) reflection
(3) radiation
(4) conduction

_____ **2.** An object moving through the atmosphere from the mesopause to the stratopause will most likely experience which change in air temperature?
(1) a constant increase
(2) a constant decrease
(3) first an increase and then a decrease
(4) first a decrease and then an increase

_____ **3.** Which layer of Earth's atmosphere contains water vapor, has an atmospheric pressure greater than 10^{-1} atmospheres, and has an air temperature that decreases with altitude?
(1) troposphere
(2) stratosphere
(3) mesosphere
(4) thermosphere

_____ **4.** Wind belts between 40° and 60° north latitude originate from which direction?
(1) southwest
(2) southeast
(3) northwest
(4) northeast

_____ **5.** Which global wind belt blows across the contiguous United States and from which direction?
(1) polar easterlies, from the northeast
(2) trade winds, from the northeast
(3) westerlies, from the southwest
(4) trade winds, from the northwest

_____ **6.** Air over the equator generally rises because the air is
(1) cool and has low density
(2) warm and has high density
(3) cool and has high density
(4) warm and has low density

_____ **7.** Which characteristic of a building material would provide the most energy-absorbing exterior covering for a house?
(1) dark-colored and smooth-textured
(2) dark-colored and rough-textured
(3) light-colored and smooth-textured
(4) light-colored and rough-textured

Unit X The Atmosphere *continued*

PART B-1

Base your answers to questions 8 and 9 on your knowledge of earth science, the *Earth Science Reference Tables*, and the diagram below, which shows how surface winds are deflected in the Northern and Southern hemispheres because of Earth's rotation. Points A, B, C, and D represent different locations on Earth's surface.

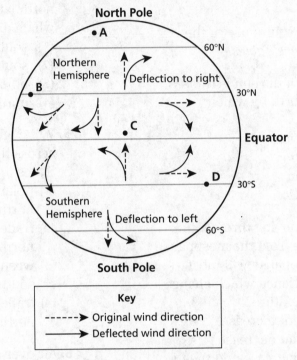

_____ **8.** According to the diagram, Earth's rotation causes winds to be deflected to the
(1) right in both the Northern and Southern hemispheres
(2) right in the Northern Hemisphere and left in the Southern Hemisphere
(3) left in the Northern Hemisphere and right in the Southern Hemisphere
(4) left in both the Northern and Southern Hemispheres

_____ **9.** At which location, A, B, C, or D, is the Coriolis effect at a maximum?
(1) A
(2) B
(3) C
(4) D

| Unit X The Atmosphere *continued*

PART B-2

Base your answers to questions 10 through 13 on your knowledge of earth science, the *Earth Science Reference Tables*, and the diagram below, which represents the different layers of Earth's atmosphere. Measurements indicate distance above Earth's surface. Points A and B represent different altitudes.

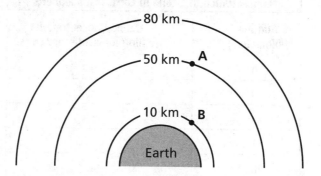

10. Label the diagram with the names of the four different layers of Earth's atmosphere, including the upper boundaries of each layer.

11. State the name of the layer in which the greatest concentration of ozone can be found.

_____

_____

12. A weather balloon measures air pressure as it rises through the atmosphere. Describe the changes in air pressure that the weather balloon would experience as it passes from point B to point A.

_____

_____

_____

13. State the names of two atmospheric gases that are most responsible for regulating surface temperatures on Earth. In which layer of the atmosphere are these gases found?

_____

_____

Unit X The Atmosphere *continued*

PART C

Base your answers to questions 14 through 16 on your knowledge of earth science, the *Earth Science Reference Tables*, and the table below, which shows ozone concentration in the atmosphere at different altitudes.

Concentration of Ozone in Earth's Atmosphere	
Altitude (kilometers)	Ozone Concentration (billion molecules per cm^3)
0	0.7
5	0.6
10	1.1
15	3.0
20	4.9
25	4.4
30	2.6
35	1.4
40	0.6
45	0.2
50	0.1
55	0.0

14. Construct a line graph of the ozone concentration in the atmosphere at different altitudes by plotting the data and connecting the points.

15. What is the name of the atmospheric layer in which ozone concentration is greatest?

_____

16. How does the ozone layer affect incoming solar radiation?

_____

_____

_____

Weather

Everyone is affected by the weather. All of our outdoor activities depend on the weather, people dress for the weather, and people arrange their schedules based on the weather. **Weather** is the condition of the atmosphere at a specific time and place.

Atmospheric Moisture

Driven by the energy of the sun, billions of tons of water evaporate into the atmosphere each year as water vapor. Evaporation from the oceans is the primary source of water vapor in the atmosphere. Water also evaporates from plants, especially from their leaves, in the process known as *transpiration.*

The water vapor content of the air is called **humidity.** Warm air can hold significantly more water vapor than cold air. Because humidity varies with air temperature, scientists often express humidity as relative humidity. **Relative humidity** is a ratio or percentage that compares the actual amount of water vapor in the air with the maximum amount of water vapor air can hold at a given temperature. For example, at 50% relative humidity the air is holding half as much water vapor as it could hold *at the present temperature.*

Of course, adding more water vapor would increase the relative humidity if the temperature stayed the same. But the relative humidity can change even if the amount of water vapor stays the same. For example, if the air temperature increased, the air would be able to hold more water vapor. Therefore, the same amount of water vapor would represent a smaller percentage of the maximum—the relative humidity would be lower.

The *sling psychrometer* is one of the most important instruments used to measure relative humidity. It consists of two thermometers mounted side by side. One thermometer is ordinary and measures the actual air temperature, or *dry-bulb temperature.* The other thermometer has a wet wick covering its bulb and measures the *wet-bulb temperature.* As the psychrometer is moved through the air, water evaporates from the wet wick of the wet-bulb thermometer and cools the thermometer. The dryer the air, the more evaporation from the wet wick and the greater the cooling effect. The difference between the wet-bulb and dry-bulb temperatures is then used with a standard table to find the relative humidity. You can find this table on page 243 in the *Earth Science Reference Tables* section.

What You'll Need to Learn

This topic is part of the Regents Curriculum for the Physical Setting/Earth Science Exam.

Standard 4, Performance Indicator *Use the concepts of density and heat energy to explain observations of weather patterns, seasonal changes, and the movement of the Earth's plates.* Major Understandings: 2.1b, 2.1c, 2.1d, 2.1e, 2.1f, 2.1g, 2.h

What Terms You'll Need to Know

air mass
air pressure
anticyclone
barometer
cloud
cold front
cyclone
dew point
humidity
isobar
isotherm
latent heat
occluded front
precipitation
relative humidity
stationary front
station model
warm front
weather
wind

Unit XI Weather *continued*

As you recall, the maximum amount of water that can exist as a gas is greater at high temperatures than at low temperatures. Therefore, if the air temperature decreases, the air can hold less water vapor. At night, air temperature often decreases, and so the maximum amount of water vapor that the air can hold also decreases. The relative humidity rises, although the amount of water vapor in the air remains the same. Eventually, the air may become saturated with water vapor—that is, 100% relative humidity. The temperature at which air becomes saturated is called its **dew point.** If the temperature drops further, water vapor will condense. Water vapor typically condenses as dew, frost, clouds, or fog. (See the *Earth Science Reference Tables* section, page 242, to learn how psychrometer readings are used to find dew point.)

Self-Check What is the dew point when the dry-bulb temperature is 18°C and the wet-bulb temperature is 13°C?

Water vapor in the atmosphere can lead to the formation of clouds. **Clouds** are visible masses of water droplets or ice particles that are suspended in the atmosphere. Clouds form as warm, moist air rises and water vapor condenses in the atmosphere. Water vapor condenses when air cools to a temperature below its dew point. Such cooling occurs naturally as warm air rises through the atmosphere. As air rises, air pressure decreases. As a result, the air expands and cools, and condensation occurs. Cloud formation, then, is the result of the expansion of the air and the resulting drop in temperature.

For a cloud to form, solid particles such as dust and salt crystals (called *condensation nuclei*) must be present for the water vapor to condense upon. When air is cooled below its dew point, water vapor changes into tiny water droplets or ice crystals on these solid particles.

Precipitation refers to any form of water that falls to Earth's surface from the clouds, such as rain, snow, sleet, or hail. Precipitation occurs when a cloud's droplets or ice crystals become large enough and heavy enough to fall out of suspension. Clouds affect the amount of sunlight that reaches Earth's surface. The amount of cloud cover and types of clouds can help predict the probability of precipitation. Cloud cover is often expressed as the percentage of the sky that is covered.

Unit XI Weather *continued*

REVIEW YOUR UNDERSTANDING

Some questions may require use of the *Earth Science Reference Tables.*

_____ **1.** What is the relative humidity if the dry-bulb temperature is 16°C and the wet-bulb temperature is 10°C?
   (1) 2%
   (2) 14%
   (3) 33%
   (4) 45%

_____ **2.** What is the dew point if the dry-bulb temperature is 6°C and the wet-bulb temperature is 4°C?
   (1) 0°C
   (2) –19°C
   (3) 1°C
   (4) 10°C

_____ **3.** When the air temperature equals the dew point, the relative humidity is
   (1) 0%
   (2) 25%
   (3) 50%
   (4) 100%

Air Pressure and Winds

As you recall from the last unit, **air pressure,** or *atmospheric pressure*, is the force of the air pressing down on Earth's surface. Near sea level, there is more air above you than there would be on the top of Mount Everest. Therefore, air pressure is higher near the sea than it is on the top of a mountain.

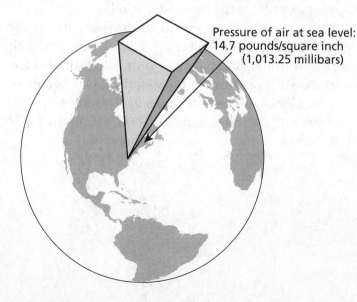

Pressure of air at sea level:
14.7 pounds/square inch
(1,013.25 millibars)

Unit XI Weather *continued*

**Notes/Study
Ideas/Answers**

Air pressure is measured with an instrument called a **barometer.** There are two kinds of barometers. A mercury barometer measures air pressure in inches or millimeters of mercury. Normal air pressure at sea level is 29.92 inches of mercury, which is equivalent to 760 mm of mercury.

An aneroid barometer measures atmospheric pressure in units called *millibars*. Normal, sea-level air pressure is about 1,013 mb. (See page 245 in the *Earth Science Reference Tables* section.)

If you have watched a television weather report, you have probably seen weather maps with large areas marked "H" and "L." These are regional high- and low-pressure systems. A *low-pressure system* is an area where the pressure has been measured to be the lowest relative to its surroundings. A low-pressure system forms where air is rising. As air rises, it cools. As the air cools, water vapor begins to condense into tiny drops of water, or if it's cold enough, into tiny ice crystals. If there is enough water or ice, rain or snow begins to fall. This is why low-pressure systems are associated with bad weather.

Conversely, a *high-pressure system* is an area where the pressure has been measured to be the highest relative to its surroundings. A high-pressure system forms where air is slowly descending. As air descends, it warms, which tends to suppress the formation of clouds. This is why high pressure is generally, but not always, associated with good weather.

Variations in pressure lead to the development of winds, which play a significant role in shaping our daily weather. **Wind** is the flow of air along, or parallel to, Earth's surface. Winds always move from places of higher pressure to places of lower pressure. Wind speed is based on the *gradient* of air pressure. The greater the difference between the high-pressure and low-pressure values, the faster the wind.

Recall from Unit X, differences in air pressure are caused by the unequal heating of Earth's surface. As you've learned, the atmosphere is warmed largely by the reradiation of heat from Earth's surface. As air is heated, it expands. As air becomes less dense, it rises. Cooler, denser air flows in to replace it. This process occurs on both local and global scales, producing local and global winds.

| Unit XI Weather *continued*

REVIEW YOUR UNDERSTANDING

Some questions require use of the *Earth Science Reference Tables*.

_____ **4.** If atmospheric pressure is 1004.0 millibars, what is the air pressure in inches of mercury?
   (1) 29.60   (3) 29.70
   (2) 29.65   (4) 29.75

_____ **5.** Winds always blow from
   (1) high-temperature areas to low-temperature areas
   (2) low-temperature areas to high-temperature areas
   (3) high-pressure areas to low-pressure areas
   (4) low-pressure areas to high-pressure areas

_____ **6.** Air near a low-pressure system will usually
   (1) evaporate into a liquid
   (2) blow away from the center of the low
   (3) rise to form clouds
   (4) compress to form a high-pressure system

Storms and Fronts

You learned that air moves from areas of high pressure to areas of low pressure, creating winds.

   In areas where pressure differences are small, air remains relatively stationary and takes on the characteristic temperature and humidity of that region. A large body of air with uniform temperature and moisture content is called an **air mass.** For example, air masses that form over frozen polar regions are very cold and dry, with high pressure. Air masses that form over tropical oceans are warm and moist and have low pressure. As the table shows, there are four main types of air masses that influence the weather in North America.

North American Air Masses

Air Mass	Symbol	Source Location	Movement	Characteristics
Continental Polar	cP	polar regions in Canada	south-southeast	cold and dry
Maritime Polar	mP	Polar Pacific Polar Atlantic	Pacific: southeast Atlantic: south-southwest	cold and moist
Continental Tropical	cT	U.S. southwest	north-northeast	warm and dry
Maritime Tropical	mT	Tropical Pacific Tropical Atlantic	Pacific: northeast Atlantic: north-northwest	warm and moist

Unit XI Weather *continued*

When winds begin moving air masses, the air masses come into contact with one another. The place where air masses meet is called a *front*. Fronts are often the scene of the most dramatic weather changes. Meteorologists recognize four types of fronts. Three of these fronts are shown in the diagram.

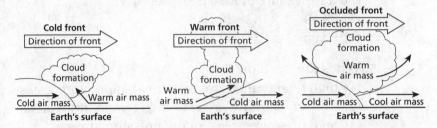

A **cold front** forms when a cold air mass overtakes a warm air mass. The moving cold air is denser than the warm air, so the cold air sinks beneath the warm air, forcing the warm air to rise rapidly. If the warm air is moist, clouds will form quickly, producing short, violent storms with thunder and lightning.

A **warm front** forms when a warm air mass overtakes a cooler air mass. The less dense, warm air rises gradually over the denser, cooler air. The resulting precipitation develops slowly and falls over a large area.

Sometimes, when two air masses collide, neither is displaced. The two air masses move parallel to the front between them. This type of front is called a **stationary front,** because the boundary stays in the same place. The weather around a stationary front is similar to that produced by a warm front. An **occluded front** forms when a warm air mass is caught between two cooler air masses. The cooler air masses force the warm air mass to rise, cutting it off, or *occluding* it, from the ground. As this warm air rises and cools, its water vapor typically condenses. As a result, occluded fronts are generally associated with cloudy skies and precipitation.

Self-Check Compare and contrast the weather associated with the four main types of fronts.

Fronts are normally parts of larger weather systems that are organized around either a center of low air pressure or a center of high air pressure. A weather system with a center of low pressure is called a **cyclone,** or sometimes simply a *low*. As the warm air at the center of a cyclone rises, pressure decreases, causing surrounding air to spiral around and in toward the central low-pressure region. In the Northern Hemisphere, this air spirals in a counterclockwise direction, due to the Coriolis effect. Because air is converging in a cyclone, air masses collide and fronts develop.

Notes/Study Ideas/Answers

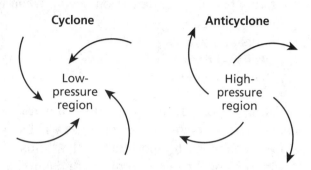

Cyclone   Anticyclone

Low-pressure region   High-pressure region

Cyclones don't stay in one place. A cyclone generally moves in the direction of global winds, and the weather of the cyclone moves along with it. In the middle latitudes, between 30° and 60°, the global winds are the westerlies. The westerlies typically cause fronts and cyclones to move across the United States from west to east.

A cyclone draws much of its energy from the latent heat in Earth's atmosphere. **Latent heat** is energy that is absorbed or released when matter, such as water in the atmosphere, changes state. When water changes state, a great deal of energy is involved. This is shown in the "Properties of Water" table in the *Earth Science Reference Tables* section, page 221. As the table shows, water gains 80 calories of energy per gram of matter (either ice or liquid water) during melting and vaporization. Water releases 540 calories of energy per gram of matter (either liquid water or water vapor) during freezing and condensation.

Cyclones also draw energy from high-speed winds in the upper atmosphere. After a cyclone starts, the winds can pull in more cold air and warm air, enhancing the temperature contrasts and keeping the cyclone going.

A weather system with a swirling center of high air pressure is called an **anticyclone,** or a *high.* Winds in an anticyclone circulate clockwise in the Northern Hemisphere. Because the center of an anticyclone has high pressure, air blows away from that center. As air flows away from the center, dense, colder air descends and replaces it. When air descends, it warms, and its relative humidity decreases. Consequently, the weather associated with an anticyclone includes clear skies, very little precipitation, and generally calm conditions.

Unit XI Weather *continued*

Notes/Study
Ideas/Answers

REVIEW YOUR UNDERSTANDING

_____ **7.** Weather along a warm front is often cloudy with precipitation because condensation occurs when warm air
(1) sinks and cools
(2) sinks and warms
(3) rises and cools
(4) rises and warms

_____ **8.** A maritime polar air mass overtakes a maritime tropical air mass. Which weather changes will likely result?
(1) increasing air temperature with storms
(2) increasing air temperature with clear skies
(3) decreasing air temperature with storms
(4) decreasing air temperature and clear skies

_____ **9.** Around a cyclone in the Northern Hemisphere, air
circulates
(1) clockwise toward the center of the low
(2) clockwise away from the center of the low
(3) counterclockwise toward the center of the low
(4) counterclockwise away from the center of the low

Weather Maps and Forecasting

High-speed computers prepare weather maps—the basic tools
of weather forecasting—at the weather centers where weather
data are received. Weather observations from the stations
reporting to the center are first translated into internationally
recognized symbols. On a weather map, clusters of symbols are
plotted around each weather station, showing the conditions at
that station. Such a cluster of symbols is called a **station
model.** Common weather symbols on a station model describe
temperature, cloud cover, wind speed, wind direction, and
weather conditions such as type of precipitation. Other information in the station model is air temperature, dew point, and
atmospheric pressure. An example of a station model is shown
on page 245 in the *Earth Science Reference Tables* section.

Self-Check What is a station model and how is it used?

Unit XI Weather *continued*

Although the weather maps in newspapers or on television are useful to the general public, meteorologists need additional information on weather maps. For example, temperature might be plotted and analyzed on a map using isotherms. An **isotherm** is a line on a weather map that connects points of equal temperature. Lines that connect points of equal pressure are called **isobars.** The spacing and shape of the isobars help meteorologists interpret their observations about the wind. Closely spaced isobars indicate a large air pressure gradient and high-speed winds. Widely spaced isobars indicate a small air pressure gradient and low-speed winds. Isobars that form circles indicate centers of high or low air pressure.

The weather map is completed by marking in the location of fronts and areas of precipitation. The standard symbols that are used to label fronts on weather maps are shown on page 245 of the *Earth Science Reference Tables* section. For example, a cold front moving south is represented by triangular points on the south side of the front line.

To forecast the weather, meteorologists study current weather maps and compare them with maps of the past few days. Accurate forecasts can be made for several days, but accuracy decreases with each additional day. Extended forecasts of 8 to 14 days are made by computers, which apply the laws of physics directly to the weather data at thousands of points at many altitudes.

Notes/Study Ideas/Answers

Unit XI Weather *continued*

REVIEW YOUR UNDERSTANDING

_____ **10.** On a weather map, station models are used to indicate weather conditions
   (1) in the upper atmosphere
   (2) at the surface
   (3) over the oceans
   (4) around a storm system

_____ **11.** When a station model shows a wind-direction line pointing east, it indicates that the wind is coming from the
   (1) east
   (2) west
   (3) north
   (4) south

_____ **12.** On a weather map, closely spaced isobars indicate
   (1) rapid increases in air temperature
   (2) slow winds
   (3) fast winds
   (4) a fast-moving cold front

ANSWERS TO SELF-CHECK QUESTIONS

- The dew point temperature is 9°C.

- Cold front: decreasing temperatures, storms, rapidly developing precipitation; warm front: increasing temperatures, clouds, and slowly developing precipitation; occluded front: decreasing temperatures, cloudy skies, and precipitation; stationary front: decreasing temperatures, cloudy weather, precipitation

- A station model is a summary of weather conditions around an observation station. Station models are used on weather maps.

Questions for Regents Practice

Holt Earth Science: The Physical Setting

Weather

PART A

Some questions may require use of the *Earth Science Reference Tables.*

_____ **1.** What is the relative humidity if the wet-bulb temperature is 14°C and the dry-bulb temperature is 22°C?
(1) 4%
(2) 25%
(3) 40%
(4) 64%

_____ **2.** The dry-bulb temperature is 20°C and the wet-bulb temperature is 16°C. The air would be saturated with water vapor if the temperature were colder by
(1) 4 Celsius degrees
(2) 6 Celsius degrees
(3) 14 Celsius degrees
(4) 16 Celsius degrees

_____ **3.** If the difference between the air temperature and the dew point decreases, the
(1) amount of cloud cover decreases
(2) likelihood of precipitation decreases
(3) air pressure increases
(4) relative humidity increases

_____ **4.** Which weather changes are likely to occur as a cold air mass overtakes a warm air mass?
(1) sudden storms over a small area
(2) clouds and precipitation over a large area
(3) decreasing air temperature and increasing air pressure
(4) decreasing air temperature and strong winds

_____ **5.** Winds around high-pressure systems in the Northern Hemisphere generally circulate
(1) counterclockwise, toward the center of the high
(2) counterclockwise, away from the center of the high
(3) clockwise, toward the center of the high
(4) clockwise, away from the center of the high

_____ **6.** Which weather map symbol is used to indicate a cold front?
(1) a line with triangles only
(2) a line with semicircles only
(3) a line with alternating triangles and semicircles
(4) a line with triangles on one side and semicircles on the other

_____ **7.** How many feathers should be drawn on a station model to represent a wind speed of 52 miles per hour?
(1) 1
(2) 1.5
(3) 3
(4) 4.5

Unit XI Weather *continued*

PART B-1

Base your answers to questions 8 through 10 on your knowledge of earth science, the *Earth Science Reference Tables*, and the graph below, which shows variations in air temperature and relative humidity in a city over a 12-hour period. Assume that the air mass was stationary over the city.

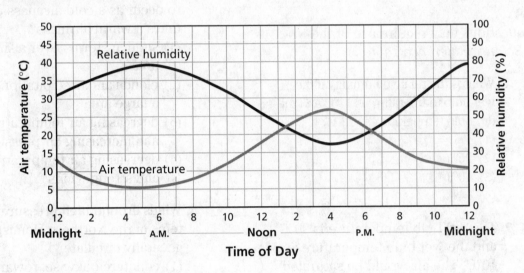

_____ **8.** What were the relative humidity and air temperature at 5:00 P.M. on this day?
- (1) 60% and 15°C
- (2) 47% and 18°C
- (3) 39% and 6°C
- (4) 50% and 25°C

_____ **9.** What was the average rate of temperature change from 9:00 A.M. to 3:00 P.M. on this day?
- (1) about 1°C/hour
- (2) about 2.5°C/hour
- (3) about 4°C/hour
- (4) about 6.5°C/hour

_____ **10.** At which time would the rate of evaporation most likely be greatest?
- (1) 2:00 A.M.
- (2) 8:00 A.M.
- (3) 4:00 P.M.
- (4) 6:00 P.M.

| Unit XI Weather *continued*

PART B-2

Base your answers to questions 11 and 12 on your knowledge of earth science, the *Earth Science Reference Tables*, and the chart below, which shows weather conditions observed at 9:00 A.M. and 12:00 P.M. at a weather station in upstate New York on a day in January.

Weather Conditions

Time	Air Temperature	Dew Point	Precipitation	Air Pressure	Cloud Cover	Wind
9:00 A.M.	4°C	–1°C	none	1032.5 mb	clear	westerly, at 5 knots
12:00 P.M.	–1°C	–1°C	snow	1019.6 mb	100% cloud cover	westerly, at 10 knots

11. Draw a station model diagram that reflects the weather conditions at 9:00 A.M.

12. What might have happened between 9:00 A.M. and 12:00 P.M. to cause the changes in the weather conditions?

_____

_____

_____

Unit XI Weather *continued*

PART C

Base your answers to questions 13 through 16 on your knowledge of earth science, the *Earth Science Reference Tables*, and the map below, which shows a weather system that is affecting part of the United States.

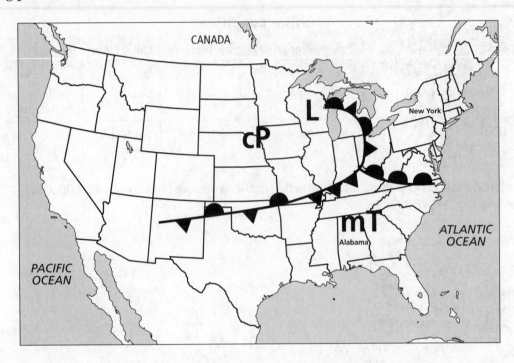

13. Identify by name the types of weather fronts shown on the map.

_____

14. Compare in terms of temperature and humidity the air mass centered over Alabama to the air covering the northwest of the United States.

_____

_____

_____

15. Name the type of weather front that is moving north along the eastern coast of the United States toward New York.

_____

16. Describe the weather conditions associated with the front moving toward New York.

_____

_____

_____

Climate

If you travel around the world or even around the United States, you will experience a variety of climates—from the hot and humid weather conditions in the rain forests of Africa to the dry, icy conditions of northern Canada. **Climate** is the characteristic weather of a region, measured over many years.

Classifying Climates

Scientists divide the world's climates into three major types: tropical climates, temperate climates, and polar climates. Scientists further divide the major climate types into many different specific climates, or *subclimates*.

In their study and classification of climates, scientists consider many factors, including soil type, vegetation, and animal life. Two factors, however, are most important: temperature and precipitation. Scientists consider average temperature and average precipitation over the year, as well as how these factors vary from day to day and from season to season.

Self-Check What is climate, and how is it different from weather?

Tropical climates are found in the warm zone that surrounds the equator. These climates have an average monthly temperature of 18°C or higher, even during the coldest month of the year. Tropical climates receive the most solar radiation, and are affected by large continental and marine air masses that develop close to the equator. *Polar climates* occur in the high latitude regions of both hemispheres, between 55° and 90° north and south latitudes. Hyper-cooled air masses affect these regions. *Temperate climates* exist between the tropics and the polar regions in both hemispheres. Typically, they will experience average monthly temperatures no warmer than 18°C in the winter and no cooler than 10°C in the summer. The weather is quite variable in temperate climate zones, because it is influenced by both tropical and polar air masses.

Factors Influencing Climate

A region's pattern of temperature depends on several factors, including latitude, distance from large bodies of water, ocean currents, and altitude.

A region's latitude is perhaps the most influential factor affecting temperature. Latitude determines the amount and

What You'll Need to Learn

This topic is part of the Regents Curriculum for the Physical Setting/Earth Science Exam.

Standard 4, Performance Indicator 2.2: *Explain how incoming solar radiation, ocean currents, and land masses affect weather and climate.* Major Understandings: 2.2a, 2.2c, 2.2d

Which Terms You'll Need to Know

climate
El Niño
global warming
ice age
insolation
rain shadow
specific heat

Where You Can Learn Even More

Holt Earth Science: The Physical Setting
Chapter 25: Climate

Unit XII Climate *continued*

intensity of incoming solar radiation, or **insolation,** a region receives. This depends on two factors: the angle at which the insolation strikes the region and the number of daylight hours the region receives.

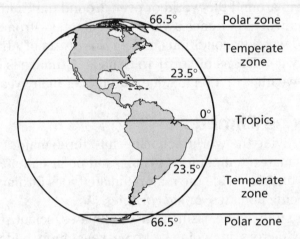

Tropical regions, between 23.5° north and south latitudes, receive the most intense insolation, because the sun shines almost directly overhead. When the sun appears high in the sky, insolation strikes the ground at a greater angle. Because of this angle, the light rays are spread over a smaller area as they reach Earth's surface. A given amount of energy confined to a smaller area results in sunlight that is more intense. On the other hand, the polar zones, extending from the poles to 66.5° north and south latitudes, receive the least intense insolation. Solar radiation hits the polar zones at a lesser angle, spreading the same amount of energy over a wider area. Polar ice also reflects some of this incoming radiation.

Self-Check How does latitude influence intensity of insolation?

Another important factor affecting the temperature of a region is its distance from a large body of water. For example, the Atlantic Ocean and Long Island Sound moderate the climate of New York's Long Island. Therefore, on Long Island winters are usually warmer and summers cooler than in other parts of the state.

One reason why large bodies of water have a great effect on climate is because different substances have different specific heats. **Specific heat** is a measure of the ability of a substance to warm as it absorbs energy or cool as it gives off energy. The "Specific Heats of Common Materials" table in the *Earth Science Reference Tables* section, page 221, lists the specific heats of seven common substances. Notice that the metals copper and lead have low specific heat values, as do the rocks basalt and granite. Water has a very high specific heat. This means that when the same amount of energy is absorbed by equal masses of water and these other substances, water has the least temperature change. It also means that when equal amounts of these substances cool, water releases the most energy. When water and land receive equal solar energy, the land heats more than the ocean. Large bodies of water change relatively little in temperature.

Self-Check Describe the influence of large bodies of water on regional climate.

Global wind patterns also affect the temperature of a region. New York State, for example, has greater extremes of climate than other coastal states, such as California. In fact, California is known for having a mild climate. The reason for this difference is the wind direction. Both states are in the global belt of prevailing west and southwest winds. However, those winds come off the Pacific Ocean in California. In most of New York State, the winds come from inland areas, where temperatures are highly changeable. As a result, the nearby Atlantic Ocean has relatively little effect on the climate of most of New York State.

Global wind belts cause ocean currents, which influence the temperature of many coastal regions. For example, in some parts of the British Isles, palm trees are able to grow because temperatures are relatively mild. The "Surface Ocean Currents" map in the *Earth Science Reference Tables* section, page 227, shows why this is. The Gulf Stream and the North Atlantic Current—two warm water currents—transport warm ocean water from the southern Atlantic Ocean to the area surrounding Great Britain. The British Isles experience more moderate temperatures than does New York State. The British Isles have damp and mild winters in which hard frosts are uncommon. This is true even though Great Britain is roughly 10° of latitude north of New York State.

Self-Check How can a nearby ocean current affect the climate of a region?

Surface features of the land may also influence climate. The *elevation*, or height of land above sea level, produces distinct temperature changes. Typically, temperature decreases by nearly 1°C for every 100 m of elevation. This explains why the tops of high mountain ranges at the equator, in the warmest zone on the planet, can still be covered with snow.

Notes/Study Ideas/Answers

Factors that affect a region's precipitation include its latitude, the direction of prevailing winds, and the existence of a mountain barrier.

Latitude affects patterns of precipitation worldwide, which are a result of Earth's rotation acting on global winds. Recall from Unit XI that instead of one big convection cell in each hemisphere, the Coriolis effect forms three convection cells in each hemisphere. The three convection cells are shown on the "Planetary Wind and Moisture Belts" diagram in the *Earth Science Reference Tables* section on page 247. Notice in the diagram that air rises along the equator and at about 60° north and south latitudes, forming low-pressure regions that circle Earth. The rising air causes cloud formation and generous precipitation at these latitudes. However, at 30° north and south latitudes and at the North and South Poles, regions of high pressure form where sinking cold air warms and gets drier. These latitudes have relatively little precipitation.

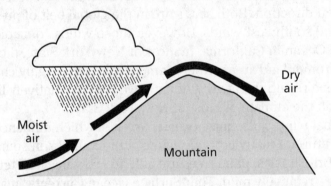

Mountains can also influence the temperature and moisture content of air masses. For example, moist winds off the Pacific Ocean cross California and rise into the Sierra Nevadas. As the mass of air rises over the mountains, the air expands and cools below its dew point. Clouds and precipitation develop, creating cool, damp weather conditions on the western side (windward side) of the Sierra Nevadas. The process by which the temperature of an air mass decreases as the air mass rises and expands is called *adiabatic cooling.*

The climate on the eastern side of the Sierra Nevadas is very different from that on the western side. When the air mass descends on the eastern side of the mountains, the air compresses and becomes warmer without picking up additional moisture, so the relative humidity of the air decreases. This effect, in which mountain barriers rob the air of its moisture before the air descends into the valleys, is sometimes called the **rain shadow** effect.

| Unit XII Climate *continued*

REVIEW YOUR UNDERSTANDING

Some questions may require use of the *Earth Science Reference Tables*.

_____ **1.** Which latitude has the warmest average climate?
   (1) 65°S
   (2) 1°N
   (3) 90°N
   (4) 33°S

_____ **2.** On a clear summer day, the land is usually warmer than the surface of a nearby body of water because the water
   (1) receives less insolation
   (2) reflects less insolation
   (3) has a higher density
   (4) has a higher specific heat

_____ **3.** Which statement best explains why regions like Canada, at higher, northern latitudes, have cold climates?
   (1) Insolation angle is lower in northern latitudes.
   (2) Land absorbs heat more slowly in northern latitudes.
   (3) Insolation angle is higher in northern latitudes.
   (4) There is more moisture in the air at northern latitudes.

Climate Change

Although some years are warmer, colder, drier, or wetter than others, Earth's climate remains fairly constant over the short term. However, over the long term, climates can and do change. For example, today, continental glaciers are located at latitudes near the North and South Poles. However, thousands of years ago, glaciers covered much more of Earth's surface. An **ice age** is a long period of climatic cooling during which the continents are glaciated repeatedly.

In addition to long-term climate changes, such as ice ages, there are short-term natural variations in climate patterns. One such variation that happens every three to eight years is **El Niño,** the periodic warming of the water in the central and eastern Pacific Ocean.

Unit XII Climate *continued*

**Notes/Study
Ideas/Answers**

Human activities may also change climate over time. One possible climate change is caused by the burning of fossil fuels, such as coal and natural gas. How does this occur? Recall from Unit X that sunlight heats the materials on Earth's surface and that these heated materials reflect energy back into the atmosphere in the form of infrared radiation (heat). Carbon dioxide and water vapor in the atmosphere absorb the heat, thereby preventing it from escaping into space. The process by which gases in the atmosphere absorb and re-radiate infrared radiation is known as the **greenhouse effect.** The greenhouse gases, CO_2 and water vapor, allow sunlight to enter and prevent heat from escaping—just like the panes of glass in a greenhouse.

Greenhouse Effect

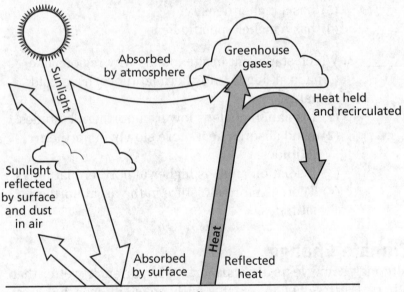

Normally, the greenhouse effect helps to keep Earth's heat budget in *equilibrium*—that is, Earth's inflow of heat is balanced by its outflow of heat. There have been times in Earth's history, however, when Earth's heat budget was not in equilibrium. For example, the ice ages occurred when Earth radiated more energy than it received from the sun. This imbalance led to colder temperatures and the development of glaciers. Today, scientists are concerned that the burning of carbon-based fossil fuels, which releases large quantities of CO_2 into the air, is also creating an imbalance in Earth's heat budget.

Evidence suggests that a greater amount of CO_2 will increase the greenhouse effect and cause the temperature of Earth to rise, a process called **global warming.** Over the last 100 years, average global temperatures have risen approximately 1°C, and scientists have predicted a further increase of 2–4°C over the next century. While these temperature increases appear small, they could have a significant impact on Earth. An increase of only a few degrees could melt the polar ice caps, causing sea levels to rise. Since half the world's population lives near coastlines, a sea level rise of 1 m could have catastrophic consequences for millions of people around the world, as well as a wide variety of plant and animal species.

Notes/Study
Ideas/Answers

Self-Check How might an increase in atmospheric CO_2 lead to global warming?

Volcanic eruptions are also responsible for some changes in the atmosphere. The addition of sulfur and ash can decrease temperature worldwide by blocking sunlight from reaching Earth's surface. These changes last from a few weeks to several years, depending on the strength of the eruption.

REVIEW YOUR UNDERSTANDING

_____ **4.** Carbon dioxide and methane are called *greenhouse gases* because
(1) they are good reflectors of heat
(2) they are good absorbers of heat
(3) they are found in varying amounts in Earth's atmosphere
(4) they are found in fixed amounts in Earth's bedrock

_____ **5.** Scientists are concerned that the burning of fossil fuels is causing an increase in
(1) ice ages around the world
(2) the greenhouse effect
(3) the frequency of El Niño events
(4) volcanic eruptions in South America

_____ **6.** The periodic warming of water in the central and eastern Pacific Ocean is called
(1) global warming
(2) an ice age
(3) El Niño
(4) the greenhouse effect

ANSWERS TO SELF-CHECK QUESTIONS

- Climate refers to the average weather conditions over a long period of time. Weather refers to the conditions in the atmosphere at a particular time.

- Latitude determines the angle at which sunlight strikes Earth. For example, the angle of insolation is high in the tropics, because the sun is almost directly overhead. This causes the light rays to be spread over a small area, resulting in sunlight that is more intense.

- A large body of water helps moderate the temperature of a region, because water heats up and cools down more slowly than does land.

- If the ocean current is warm, it can help keep the temperature of a coastal region warmer than more inland locations. If the current is cold, it can chill coastal locations more than inland locations.

- Carbon dioxide is a greenhouse gas. It traps and absorbs heat emitted from Earth's surface. An increase in carbon dioxide can increase the greenhouse effect, leading to global warming.

Questions for Regents Practice

Climate

PART A

Some questions may require use of the *Earth Science Reference Tables.*

_____ **1.** Which statement explains why Long Island beaches have a narrower yearly temperature range than inland areas at the same latitude?
   (1) Land is a poor absorber and a poor conductor of heat energy.
   (2) Land changes temperature rapidly, due to its high specific heat.
   (3) Ocean water is a good absorber and a good conductor of heat energy.
   (4) Ocean water changes temperature slowly, due to its high specific heat.

_____ **2.** Which latitude receives the greatest intensity of insolation?
   (1) 66.5°S
   (2) 90°S
   (3) 0°
   (4) 23.5°N

_____ **3.** Which climate conditions are typical of regions near the North Pole and the South Pole?
   (1) low temperature and low precipitation
   (2) low temperature and high precipitation
   (3) high temperature and low precipitation
   (4) high temperature and high precipitation

_____ **4.** Many scientists believe that an increased concentration of carbon dioxide in the atmosphere contributes to global warming. This belief is based on the fact that carbon dioxide is a
   (1) good absorber of infrared radiation
   (2) poor absorber of infrared radiation
   (3) good absorber of ultraviolet radiation
   (4) poor absorber of ultraviolet radiation

_____ **5.** A high air pressure, dry climate belt is located at which Earth latitude?
   (1) 0°
   (2) 15°N
   (3) 30°N
   (4) 60°N

_____ **6.** Liquid water can store more heat energy than an equal amount of almost any other naturally occurring substance because liquid water
   (1) covers 71 percent of Earth's surface
   (2) has its greatest density at 4°C
   (3) has a high specific heat
   (4) can be changed into a solid or a gas

_____ **7.** What typically happens to a warm, moist air mass moving over a mountain range?
  (1) It can gain moisture moving downslope.
  (2) It can lose moisture moving downslope.
  (3) It can gain moisture moving upslope.
  (4) It can lose moisture moving upslope.

_____ **8.** The average temperature at the North Pole is colder than the average temperature at the equator because the equator
  (1) receives less ultraviolet radiation
  (2) receives more intense insolation
  (3) has more cloud cover
  (4) has a thicker atmosphere

PART B-1

Base your answers to questions 9 and 10 on your knowledge of earth science, the *Earth Science Reference Tables*, and the graph below. The graph shows the average monthly temperatures for two cities, A and B, which are both located at 41°N.

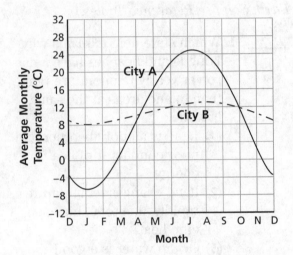

_____ **9.** The climate differences shown on the graph might be explained by the fact that City B
  (1) is located at a higher elevation
  (2) receives less yearly precipitation
  (3) receives more intense solar insolation
  (4) is located near a large body of water

_____ **10.** Based on the annual temperature range, what is the likely climate type of City A?
  (1) tropical climate
  (2) temperate climate
  (3) polar climate
  (4) subtropical climate

Unit XII Climate *continued*

PART B-2

Base your answers to questions 11 and 12 on your knowledge of earth science, the *Earth Science Reference Tables*, and the diagram below, which shows a cross-section of a coastal mountain range. The arrows represent the direction of a moisture-rich air mass from the ocean.

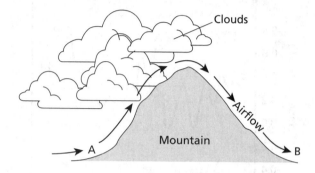

11. Describe the changes that occur to the air mass as it moves up the windward side of the mountain range.

   _____

   _____

   _____

12. Compare and contrast the temperature and humidity conditions at location A to those at location B.

   _____

   _____

   _____

   _____

❚ Unit XII Climate *continued*

PART C

Base your answer to questions 13 and 14 on your knowledge of earth science and the graph below, which shows the global mean temperature change for 1990–2000, following the eruption of Mount Pinatubo in June 1991.

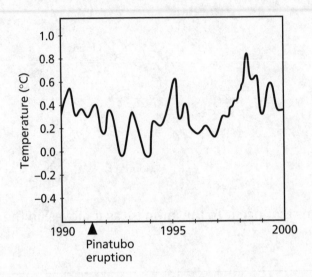

13. According to the graph, by approximately how many degrees did global temperature decrease overall in the one and a half years following the eruption of Mount Pinatubo?

_____

14. Explain how the eruption of Mount Pinatubo could have caused the global temperature drop shown on the graph.

_____

_____

_____

_____

UNIT XIII

Holt Earth Science: The Physical Setting

Movements of Earth and Its Moon

Understanding the basic motions of Earth and its moon helps scientists understand the motions of other bodies in our solar system and elsewhere in the universe. Earth's movements provide a basis for measuring time and are also responsible for the seasons and the changes in weather that accompany them.

Movements of Earth

Earth may seem motionless, but it is actually hurtling around the sun at an average speed of 106,000 km/hr. The movement of Earth around the sun is called **revolution.** Each complete orbit around the sun takes 365.24 days and constitutes one year.

Earth's orbit of the sun lies in a flat plane called the *orbital plane.* Earth's orbit is slightly oval-shaped; therefore, Earth is not always the same distance from the sun. When Earth reaches its annual closest point to the sun in early January, Earth is said to be at *perihelion.* At its annual farthest point, which it reaches in early July, Earth is said to be at *aphelion.*

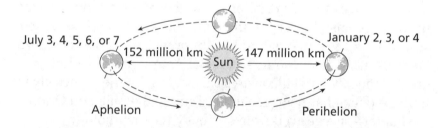

July 3, 4, 5, 6, or 7   152 million km   Sun   147 million km   January 2, 3, or 4

Aphelion   Perihelion

As Earth revolves, it also spins on its axis. This movement is called **rotation.** Earth's rotational axis is tilted 23.5° to a line perpendicular to the plane of its orbit, with the North Pole aligned with Polaris, the North Star. As Earth revolves around the sun, Earth's axis always points toward Polaris. Thus during each revolution, the North Pole sometimes tilts toward the sun and sometimes tilts away from the sun, as shown in the diagram.

Each complete rotation takes about 24 hours, or one day. Because Earth rotates from west to east, the sun appears to rise in the east and set in the west. At any given moment, the side of Earth facing the sun is experiencing daytime. At the same time, the opposite side is experiencing nighttime.

Self-Check Distinguish between Earth's revolution and its rotation.

What You'll Need to Learn

This topic is part of the Regents Curriculum for the Physical Setting Exam.

Standard 4, Performance Indicator 1.1: *Explain complex phenomena, such as tides, variations in day length, solar insolation, apparent motion of the planets, and annual traverse of the constellations.* Major Understandings: 1.1a, 1.1b, 1.1d, 1.1e, 1.1f, 1.1g, 1.1h

Standard 4, Performance Indicator 2.2: *Explain how incoming solar radiation, ocean currents, and land masses affect weather and climate.* Major Understandings: 2.2a

What Terms You'll Need to Know

eclipse
equinox
International Date Line
lunar eclipse
phases of the moon
revolution
rotation
solar eclipse
solstice
time zone

Unit XIII Movements of Earth and Its Moon *continued*

In 1851, French scientist Jean-Bernard-Leon Foucault became famous when he devised an experiment with a huge pendulum that demonstrated that Earth was spinning. Foucault suspended a large iron ball on a steel wire more than 200 ft long from the ceiling of the Pantheon in Paris, France. He attached a needle to the bottom of the ball, which would draw the path of the swinging ball in a ring of damp sand on the floor. At the start of the experiment, the ball was drawn to the side and held in place by rope. The rope was burned to start the ball swinging in a perfect plane. As the ball swung back and forth, its path appeared to change slightly with each swing. The pendulum appeared to be rotating with respect to the floor. Foucault concluded that the floor (which is rigidly attached to Earth) must have been moving, because there was no force acting on the pendulum that would cause it to change its swing.

The Coriolis effect, a second proof of Earth's rotation, was discussed in Unit X. Due to the Coriolis effect, winds and ocean currents curve to the right in the Northern Hemisphere and to the left in the Southern Hemisphere. The apparent curvature is actually a result of the winds and ocean currents trying to follow a straight path on a rotating planet.

Evidence of Earth's rotation, as well as its revolution around the sun, can also be seen in the motion of constellations. A *constellation* is a group of stars that are organized into a recognizable pattern. In 1930, the International Astronomical Union divided the sky into 88 constellations. Many of the names given to these constellations—including Taurus, the bull, and Orion, the hunter—are derived from ancient Greek mythology.

Constellations appear to move in the night sky. For example, if you happen to gaze up at a constellation over a period of several hours, you may notice that the constellation appears to have changed its position in the sky. The apparent movement of the constellation is due to Earth's rotation; the constellation does not actually move.

A constellation's position in the sky will also change because of Earth's revolution around the sun. For example, if you observe a constellation at the same time of the evening over a period of several weeks, you will notice that the position of the constellation appears to have changed. Again, the apparent movement of the constellation is due to Earth's movement. As Earth revolves around the sun, the night side of Earth faces a different direction in space; consequently our "window" on space changes as well.

Unit XIII Movements of Earth and Its Moon *continued*

Self-Check Explain how Foucault's pendulum provided evidence of Earth's rotation.

Earth movements provide the basis for measuring time. For most observers on Earth, the sun rises in the eastern part of the sky. The sun reaches its greatest angular altitude at *solar noon.* It then moves down to dip below the western horizon. Thus, using the sun as the basis for measuring time, 12:00 noon is defined as the time when the sun is at its highest point in the sky. Because the sun appears highest over different locations at different times, Earth's surface has been divided into 24 standard **time zones.** In each zone, noon is set as the time when the sun is highest over the center of the time zone.

Because Earth is nearly spherical, its circumference equals 360°. If you divide 360° by the 24 hours needed for one complete rotation, you find that Earth rotates 15° every hour. Therefore, each of Earth's 24 time zones covers about 15° of longitude. (See Unit II for more information about longitude.) The time in each zone is one hour earlier than the time in the zone to the east.

There are 24 standard time zones and 24 hours in a day. But there must be some point on Earth's surface where the date changes from one day to the next. This point is called the **International Date Line.** The International Date Line runs from north to south approximately along the 180° meridian in the middle of the Pacific Ocean. Traveling east across the line, the time is set back 24 hours; traveling west, the time is set forward 24 hours. The line is drawn so that it does not cut through islands or continents in the Pacific Ocean. Thus, all of the people living within one country have the same date.

REVIEW YOUR UNDERSTANDING

_____ **1.** An Earth year is determined by the time required for approximately one
  (1) Earth revolution around the sun
  (2) Earth rotation on its axis
  (3) sun revolution around Earth
  (4) sun rotation on its axis

_____ **2.** An Earth day is determined by the time required for approximately one
  (1) Earth revolution around the sun
  (2) Earth rotation on its axis
  (3) sun revolution around Earth
  (4) sun rotation on its axis

Unit XIII Movements of Earth and Its Moon *continued*

_____ **3.** Predictable changes in the apparent direction of the swing of a pendulum provided Foucault with evidence that
(1) Earth's orbit is oval-shaped
(2) Earth revolves around the sun
(3) Earth rotates on its axis
(4) an Earth year equals 365.24 days

_____ **4.** Units of time are based on Earth's motion relative to other objects in space. The year is best defined as Earth's motion relative to the
(1) moon
(2) sun
(3) planets
(4) poles

Seasons

As you've learned, Earth's axis is tilted 23.5° from a line perpendicular to its orbital plane. This tilt causes the *seasons*. One effect of Earth's tilt is that the length of daylight changes as Earth revolves around the sun. For example, when the North Pole is tilted toward the sun—as it is during the summer season—the Northern Hemisphere has longer periods of daylight because the sun follows a higher path in the sky. Consider the changing path of the sun for an observer in New York Sate on June 21 or 22, the start of the summer season. On that date, the sun rises in the northeast at about 4:30 A.M. standard time (5:30 A.M. daylight saving time). It moves to the right of the observer until it reaches its highest point at noon, at an altitude angle of nearly 72°. The sun sets in the southwest at about 7:30 P.M. standard time (8:30 P.M. daylight saving time), providing about 15 hours of daylight.

As Earth continues to move in its orbit around the sun from its June 21/22 position, sunrise occurs later each day and sunset occurs earlier each day; the length of daylight is becoming shorter. The position of the sunrise along the horizon also shifts more and more to the east each day. By September 22 or 23, at the start of autumn, an observer in New York State would see the sun rise due east at about 6:00 A.M. The sun follows a lower path in the sky, climbing to a noon altitude angle of about 48°. The sun sets due west at about 6:00 P.M., giving 12 hours of daylight.

Unit XIII Movements of Earth and Its Moon *continued*

By December 21 or 22, when the North Pole is tilted away from the sun, length of daylight is the shortest it will be all year. An observer in New York State would see the sun follow a very different path in the sky. At this time, the sun rises in the southeast at about 7:30 A.M. It reaches it highest point in the sky at noon, at an altitude of about 25°, and then sets in the southwest at about 4:30 P.M., giving just 9 hours of daylight.

As Earth continues in its orbit from its December 21/22 position, sunrise occurs earlier each day and sunset occurs later each day; thus the length of daylight is becoming longer. The position of the sunrise shifts more and more to the north. So, by March 20 or 21 the sun follows the same path it took 6 months earlier at the start of autumn. To an observer in New York State, the run rises due east at 6:00 A.M. It moves to the observer's right as it climbs to a noon altitude angle of 48°. In the afternoon, the sun continues to the right, setting due west at 6:00 P.M.

The length of daylight depends on latitude; the day/night cycle described above applies only for an observer in New York State, at around 42° north latitude. The day/night cycle is much different at the North Pole and at the South Pole. As you know, due to Earth's tilt, the North Pole at times is tilted toward the sun. At the same time, the South Pole is tilted away from the sun. This gives the North Pole 24 hours of daylight for about 6 months, while the South Pole is in darkness. The opposite happens when the South Pole is tilted toward the sun.

Another effect of Earth's tilt is that the sun's rays strike the surface in the hemisphere tilted toward it at an angle that is closer to the perpendicular than the other hemisphere. As you recall, incoming solar radiation is known as *insolation*. The greater the angle of insolation, the more concentrated the energy is and the warmer the surface becomes.

Self-Check Explain how Earth's tilt is related to changes in the intensity of insolation at a given latitude.

Unit XIII Movements of Earth and Its Moon *continued*

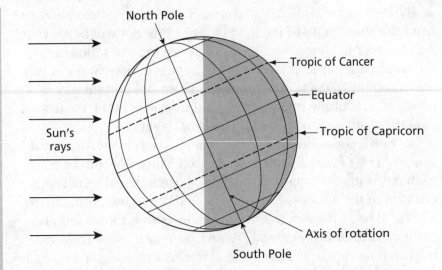

Changes in the angle of insolation and changes in the amount of daylight cause the seasons. For example, when the North Pole is tilted toward the sun, the sun's rays fall on the Northern Hemisphere at a greater angle. As a result, sunlight is more concentrated and intense. This effect, plus the increase in the number of daylight hours, produces the warmer summer temperatures in the Northern Hemisphere. At the same time, the sun's rays strike the surface in the Southern Hemisphere at a lesser angle, and there are fewer hours of daylight. This produces the cooler winter temperatures there.

Self-Check Identify the position of Earth that causes winter in the Northern Hemisphere.

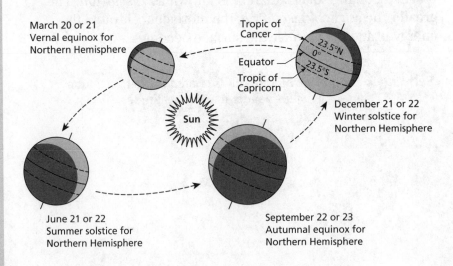

Unit XIII Movements of Earth and Its Moon *continued*

The seasons spring and fall begin on events called equinoxes. During an **equinox,** every location on Earth experiences approximately 12 hours of daylight and 12 hours of darkness. The number of hours of daylight and darkness are approximately equal because Earth's axis is tilted neither toward nor away from the sun.

The *vernal equinox*, which marks the start of spring in the Northern Hemisphere, occurs on March 20 or 21. The *autumnal equinox*, which marks the start of fall in the Northern Hemisphere, occurs on September 22 or 23. It is important to note that equinoxes are not particular days. Rather, they are the exact moments when the sun appears to cross the *celestial equator*, an imaginary line drawn on the sky directly overhead Earth's equator. On both equinoxes, the sun's rays strike Earth's equator at a 90° angle.

The summer and winter seasons begin on moments called **solstices.** In the Northern Hemisphere, the *summer solstice* occurs on June 21 or 22. At the summer solstice, the North Pole is tilted toward the sun, and the sun's rays strike the Tropic of Cancer (23.5° north latitude) at a 90° angle. The sun appears to follow its highest path in the sky and stays above the horizon for its longest period of time. Consequently, the summer solstice is the date that has the most daylight hours. In the Southern Hemisphere, the summer solstice occurs on December 21 or 22, when the South Pole is tilted toward the sun.

By December, Earth is halfway through its orbit, and the North Pole is tilted away from the sun. In the Northern Hemisphere, the *winter solstice* occurs on December 21 or 22. On this date, the North Pole is tilted away from the sun, and the sun's rays strike the Tropic of Capricorn (23.5° south latitude) at a 90° angle. The sun follows its lowest path in the sky. Consequently, the winter solstice is the date that has the fewest daylight hours. In the Southern Hemisphere, the winter solstice occurs on June 21 or 22, when the South Pole is tilted away from the sun.

Self-Check Explain how the sun's apparent path through the sky varies with the seasons.

Unit XIII Movements of Earth and Its Moon *continued*

REVIEW YOUR UNDERSTANDING

_____ **5.** The diagram below represents Earth at four different positions, A, B, C, and D, in its orbit of the sun.

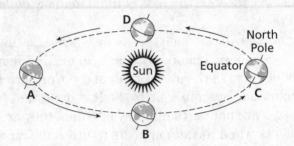

Between which two positions would people in New York State be experiencing the winter season?
(1) A and B
(2) B and C
(3) C and D
(4) D and A

_____ **6.** Summer days in New York State are likely to be hotter than winter days because in summer
(1) Earth is closer to the sun
(2) Earth is farther from the sun
(3) Earth's North Pole is tilted toward the sun
(4) the sun gives off more energy

_____ **7.** On which date would an observer in New York State see the sun follow the higher path in the sky?
(1) March 21
(2) June 21
(3) December 21
(4) September 22

Movements of the Moon

Earth's nearest neighbor in space is its very own satellite, the moon. The moon appears large in the night sky, but that is because it is so close to Earth—an average distance of only 384,000 kilometers. (Please see the "Solar System Data" table in the *Earth Science Reference Tables*, page 249, for more information about Earth's moon.)

Just as Earth rotates on its axis and revolves around the sun, the moon rotates on its axis and revolves around Earth. The moon rotates on its axis once every 27.3 days. It takes the same amount of time to revolve once around Earth. Because these two motions take the same amount of time, the same side of the moon always faces Earth.

The moon shines by reflecting sunlight from its surface. Just as half of Earth experiences day as the other half experiences night, half of the moon is lighted while the other half is dark. As the moon revolves around Earth, different portions of the side facing Earth are illuminated. Thus, the moon appears to change "shape" as the month proceeds. These varying shapes, lighted by reflected sunlight, are called the **phases of the moon.**

Notes/Study
Ideas/Answers

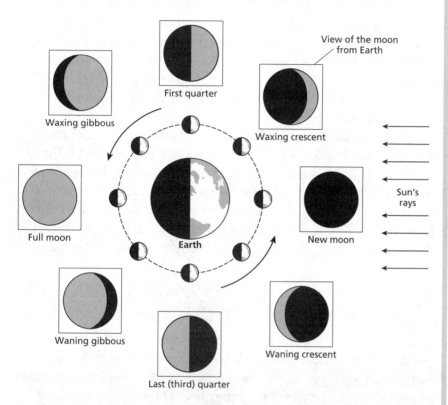

Self-Check Explain why the moon appears to change shape throughout the month.

When the moon is between the sun and Earth, the side of the moon facing Earth is unlighted. The moon is in the sky, but it can't be seen. At these times, the moon is in the *new moon* phase.

As the moon continues to move around Earth, more and more of the side facing Earth becomes illuminated. When the visible portion of the moon increases in size, the moon is said to be *waxing.* When a sliver of the moon becomes visible, the moon is in the *waxing crescent* phase.

About one week after the new moon, when the moon has moved through one-quarter of its orbit, one-half of the side facing Earth is illuminated. The moon looks like a semicircle. This phase is called *first quarter.*

Unit XIII Movements of Earth and Its Moon *continued*

**Notes/Study
Ideas/Answers**

When the visible portion of the moon is larger than a semicircle and still increasing, the moon is in the *waxing gibbous* phase.

The moon continues to wax until it appears as a full circle. At *full moon*, as this phase is called, Earth is between the sun and the moon. Consequently, the entire half of the moon facing Earth is lit up.

After the full moon phase, the amount of the moon's visible side becomes smaller. The moon is said to be *waning*. The *waning gibbous* phase occurs just after a full moon. In this phase, the moon is still larger than a semicircle, but is decreasing in size. When the visible portion of the moon becomes a semicircle again, the moon is in the *last* (or third) *quarter* phase. When only a sliver of the moon is visible, it is in the *waning crescent* phase.

The complete cycle of moon phases takes about 29.5 days. Recall that it takes about 27.3 days for the moon to orbit Earth. The reason it takes longer than one revolution of the moon to observe a full cycle of phases is that Earth is also moving in its orbit around the sun. The moon has moved through one complete revolution of Earth. However, the moon must continue in its orbit another 2.2 days to reach the new moon phase again.

Self-Check Describe the relative positions of the moon, the sun, and Earth during the new moon phase.

In addition to moon phases, the moon's movements create another astronomical phenomenon that can be seen from Earth—the eclipse. An **eclipse** occurs when one planetary body passes through the shadow of another. The moon is involved in two kinds of eclipses, the solar eclipse and the lunar eclipse.

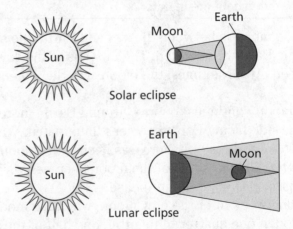

Solar eclipse

Lunar eclipse

Unit XIII Movements of Earth and Its Moon *continued*

When the moon is directly between Earth and the sun, the shadow of the moon falls on Earth, causing a **solar eclipse.** A solar eclipse happens only when the moon is in the new moon phase. To a person on Earth, the moon is observed to move in front of the sun and then move away. If part of the sun is visible throughout the eclipse, it is called a *partial solar eclipse.* During a *total solar eclipse*, the sky becomes much darker than usual, because the moon covers the entire disk of the sun. The sun is visible only as a ring of light surrounding the dark moon.

A **lunar eclipse** occurs when Earth is positioned between the sun and the moon. From Earth, the moon is seen to move into Earth's curved shadow. The moon becomes relatively dark and takes on a reddish glow, due to a small amount of light that is refracted through Earth's atmosphere. The eclipse may continue for an hour or more until the moon moves out of Earth's shadow. A lunar eclipse can occur only when the moon is in its full moon phase.

Solar and lunar eclipses do not occur during every lunar orbit. This is because the moon's orbit of Earth is not in the same plane as Earth's orbit of the sun. The moon crosses the plane of Earth's orbit only twice in each revolution around Earth. Only if this crossing occurs when the moon is between Earth and the sun will a solar eclipse occur. If this crossing occurs when Earth is between the sun and the moon, a lunar eclipse will occur.

Self-Check What conditions must be present for a solar eclipse to occur?

REVIEW YOUR UNDERSTANDING

_____ **8.** The same side of the moon always faces Earth because
  (1) the moon's gravity is greater than Earth's gravity
  (2) Earth's gravity attracts only that side of the moon
  (3) the moon rotates and revolves in the same period of time
  (4) Earth rotates and revolves in the same period of time

Unit XIII Movements of Earth and Its Moon *continued*

_____ **9.** The diagram below represents the moon at four different positions, A, B, C, and D, in its orbit around Earth.

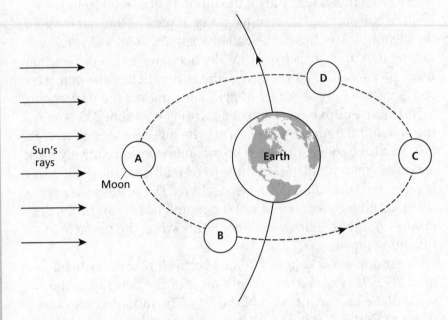

A lunar eclipse is most likely to occur when the moon is in which position?
- (1) A
- (2) B
- (3) C
- (4) D

_____ **10.** In which phase is the moon when the entire side of the moon facing Earth can be seen?
- (1) new moon
- (2) full moon
- (3) first quarter
- (4) last quarter

Unit XIII Movements of Earth and Its Moon *continued*

ANSWERS TO SELF-CHECK QUESTIONS

- Earth's travel around the sun is called revolution. The spinning of Earth on its axis is called rotation.

- The path of the Foucault pendulum appeared to change as it moved back and forth. No force caused the pendulum to change its path; so, Foucault concluded that it was the floor (attached to the spinning Earth) that was moving.

- When one hemisphere is tilted toward the sun, the sun's rays strike the surface at a greater angle, causing the energy to be more concentrated and intense. At the same time, the sun's rays strike the hemisphere that is tilted away at a lesser angle. Because the energy is spread out over a larger area, it is less concentrated and intense.

- In the Northern Hemisphere, winter occurs when the North Pole is tilted away from the sun.

- In summer in the Northern Hemisphere, the North Pole is tilted toward the sun, which makes the sun appear higher in the sky. In winter in the Northern Hemisphere, the North Pole is tilted away from the sun, which makes the sun appear lower in the sky.

- As the moon rotates, different portions of the side of the moon facing Earth become illuminated.

- During the new moon phase, the moon is between the sun and Earth.

- For a solar eclipse to occur, the moon must cross the plane of Earth's orbit when it is between the sun and Earth.

Questions for Regents Practice

Movements of Earth and Its Moon

PART A

_____ **1.** Units of time are based on Earth's movements. The day is best defined as
  (1) the time it takes Earth to make a complete orbit of the sun
  (2) the time it takes the moon to make a complete orbit of Earth
  (3) the time it takes Earth to make one complete rotation on its axis
  (4) the time it takes the moon to make one complete rotation on its axis

_____ **2.** In New York State, between May 21 and June 21,
  (1) the intensity and duration of insolation both decrease
  (2) the intensity and duration of insolation both increase
  (3) the intensity of insolation decreases and the duration of insolation increases
  (4) the intensity of insolation increases and the duration of insolation decreases

_____ **3.** What is the approximate length of time for one complete cycle of the moon's phases?
  (1) one day
  (2) one week
  (3) one month
  (4) one year

_____ **4.** Which statement best explains why a solar eclipse does not happen every month?
  (1) Earth is not directly between the sun and the moon every month.
  (2) The moon does not pass into Earth's shadow every month.
  (3) The sun is not directly between the moon and Earth every month.
  (4) The moon does not cross the plane of Earth's orbit every month.

_____ **5.** The apparent daily path of the sun changes with the seasons because
  (1) the sun rotates
  (2) the sun revolves around Earth
  (3) Earth's axis is tilted
  (4) Earth's distance from the sun changes

_____ **6.** Which observation is a direct result of the 23.5° tilt of Earth's rotational axis?
  (1) Summer occurs in the Northern Hemisphere at the same time as winter occurs in the Southern Hemisphere
  (2) Locations on the equator have 12 hours of sunlight each day
  (3) The diameter of the sun appears to change in a predictable way
  (4) A Foucault pendulum shows predictable shifts in the direction of its swing

Name _____ Class _____ Date _____

Unit XIII Movements of Earth and Its Moon *continued*

PART B-1

Base your answers to questions 7 through 9 on your knowledge of earth science and the diagram below, which shows the altitude of the sun in the sky at local noon on different dates. An observer at 42° north latitude measured the positions of the sun, labeled A and B.

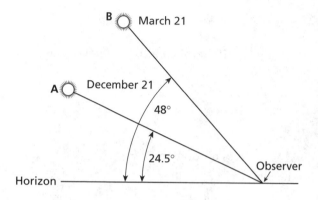

_____ **7.** Which factor is a cause of the difference in the noontime height of the sun on December 21 and March 21?
(1) Earth's rate of revolution
(2) the tilt of Earth's axis
(3) Earth's changing distance from the sun
(4) Earth's rate of rotation

_____ **8.** On what other date of the year could the noontime sun be observed at position B?
(1) December 22
(2) June 21
(3) September 22
(4) June 22

_____ **9.** On March 21, when the sun can be observed at position B,
(1) the sun rises in the east at 6:00 A.M. and sets in the west at 6:00 P.M.
(2) the sun rises in the northeast at 6:00 A.M. and sets in the northwest at 6:00 P.M.
(3) the sun rises in the southeast at 7:30 A.M. and sets in the southwest at 4:30 P.M.
(4) the sun rises in the northeast at 7:30 A.M. and sets in the southwest at 4:30 P.M.

PART B-2

Base your answers to questions 10 and 11 on your knowledge of earth science and on diagrams A, B, and C below. The diagrams represent the length and direction of the shadow of a telephone pole measured at noon on three different dates in New York City.

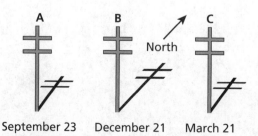

September 23   December 21   March 21

10. What is the cause of the difference in the length of the shadow of the telephone pole between September 23 and December 21?

_____

_____

11. Describe the length of the telephone pole shadow that will most likely be observed at noon in New York City on June 21.

_____

_____

_____

Name _____ Class _____ Date _____

Unit XIII Movements of Earth and Its Moon *continued*

PART C

Base your answers to questions 12 through 14 on your knowledge of earth science and the diagram below, which represents Earth at a specific position in its orbit around the sun. The shaded area represents night. Points A and B are locations on Earth's surface.

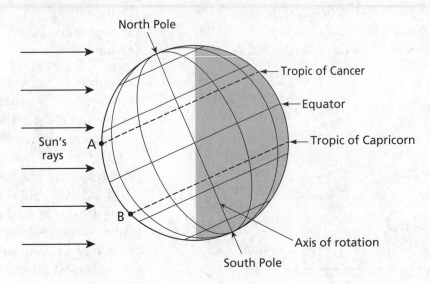

North Pole

Tropic of Cancer

Equator

Sun's rays

Tropic of Capricorn

A

B

Axis of rotation

South Pole

12. Which latitude receives the most intense insolation when Earth is at this position?

_____

13. Compare the number of daylight hours at locations A and B.

_____

_____

_____

14. Draw a diagram, similar to the one above, showing Earth in its orbit six months later. Include and label the sun's rays and all labeled parts that appear in the diagram above.

The Solar System

Holt Earth Science: The Physical Setting

The **solar system** consists of the sun and all of the planets and other bodies that revolve around it. **Planets** are any of the nine primary bodies that orbit the sun. How the solar system formed was once considered an unanswerable question, relegated to the imaginations of mythmakers. Through careful observations, today's astronomers have found clues that help explain how our solar system may have formed.

Models of the Solar System

Greek astronomer Claudius Ptolemy proposed one of the earliest models of the solar system about 2,000 years ago. Ptolemy proposed a geocentric (Earth-centered) model of the solar system. According to the **geocentric model,** the sun, the stars, and the planets all move around Earth. The geocentric model made sense to early scientists; after all, they could not feel the ground moving, and their observations of the sky fit the idea that the sun and other celestial objects circle Earth. However, as is common in the sciences, the geocentric model underwent scrutiny and testing by other scientists in the decades and centuries that followed, and was eventually proved to be incorrect.

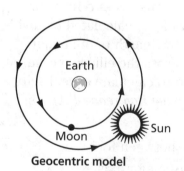

Geocentric model

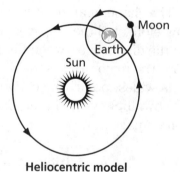

Heliocentric model

In 1543 the Polish astronomer Nicolaus Copernicus proposed a heliocentric (sun-centered) model of the solar system. According to the **heliocentric model,** the sun is at the center of planetary motion and it is mainly the motions of Earth that cause the apparent motions of celestial objects.

Self-Check Compare and contrast the geocentric and heliocentric models of the solar system.

What You'll Need to Learn

This topic is part of the Regents Curriculum for the Physical Setting Exam.

Standard 4, Performance Indicator 1.1: *Explain complex phenomena, such as tides, variations in day length, solar insolation, apparent motion of the planets, and annual traverse of the constellations.* Major Understandings: 1.1a, 1.1b

Standard 4, Performance Indicator 1.2: *Describe current theories about the origin of the universe and solar system.* Major Understandings: 1.2c, 1.2d

What Terms You'll Need to Know

aphelion
asteroid
asteroid belt
comet
eccentricity
ellipse
gas giant
geocentric model
heliocentric model
inertia
meteor
meteorite
meteoroid
nebular theory
perihelion

Unit XIV The Solar System *continued*

planet
planetisimal
solar system
terrestrial planet

Where You Can Learn Even More

Holt Earth Science: The Physical Setting
Chapter 27: Planets of the Solar System
Chapter 28: Minor Bodies of the Solar System

In 1609, just as the first telescopes came onto the scene and a wealth of new observations became available, a German astronomer named Johannes Kepler set out to explain the motions of the solar system in mathematical terms. He created three laws of planetary motion that revolutionized astronomy.

Kepler's first law, *the law of ellipses*, states that each planet orbits the sun in a path called an ellipse. An **ellipse** is an oval whose shape is determined by two points within the ellipse. Each of these points is called a *focus* (plural, *foci*). For example, the sun is at one focus of the orbit of planet Earth.

Self-Check Define and describe an ellipse.

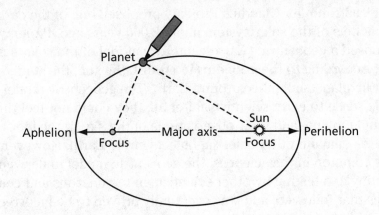

The shape of an orbit is described by its **eccentricity,** or how elongated the ellipse is. Eccentricity is calculated by dividing the distance between the foci by the length of the major axis. The major axis is the distance across the ellipse measured at its widest point. The equation used to calculate eccentricity is shown below and in the *Earth Science Reference Tables* section on page 221.

$$\text{eccentricity} = \frac{\text{distance between foci}}{\text{length of major axis}}$$

In the diagram, the distance between the foci is 4.0 cm. The length of the major axis is 6.1 cm. Therefore,

$$\text{eccentricity} = \frac{4.0 \text{ cm}}{6.1 \text{ cm}} = 0.66$$

Eccentricity is always a number less than 1, with no units of measure. An eccentricity of zero would indicate a circle—the two foci are at the same point, the center. An eccentricity of 1 would indicate a shape that is stretched into a straight line connecting the foci.

Unit XIV The Solar System *continued*

Kepler's second law describes the speed at which planets travel at different points in their orbits. The orbits of the planets are ellipses; therefore, a planet's distance from the sun varies. The point where an orbit is closest to the sun is the **perihelion.** The point where it is farthest away from the sun is the **aphelion.** Because a planet is not always the same distance away from the sun, the sun's gravitational tug will not always be the same. This means that the speed of a planet around the sun varies—faster when the planet is closer to the sun, slower when the planet is farther away.

Self-Check At which point would a planet achieve its greatest orbital speed, at perihelion or at aphelion?

Kepler's third law, the *law of periods*, describes the relationship between a planet's average distance from the sun and its orbital period (period of revolution). The *orbital period* is the time required for a planet to make a single orbit. Because a planet's distance from the sun and its orbital period are proportional, scientists can calculate how far away the planets are from the sun simply by watching the sky and measuring the orbital periods of the planets.

A planet's orbit around the sun is determined by two factors: inertia and gravity. **Inertia** is the tendency of an object at rest to remain at rest or an object in motion to move at a constant speed in a straight line unless acted on by an outside force. For example, if you roll a ball across a flat floor, the ball will continue in a straight line until some force causes it to change its speed or its direction. That force could be friction with the floor, causing the ball to slow down. It could be a force applied by an object or a wall as the ball collides with it. It could also be a force applied by someone pushing the ball to one side, causing the ball to change direction. Similarly, a planet moving through space will move in a straight line unless some force causes it to change its speed or its direction.

Planets follow curved paths around the sun. This tells us that a force must be acting on them. That force is *gravity*, the force of attraction between all objects. The motion of Earth or any celestial object in its elliptical orbit can be thought of as a combination of two kinds of motion. While gravity pulls the objects inward, their inertia keeps them moving forward fast enough so that, as they fall inward, they keep missing the sun— that is, they fall around it. The more distant a planet is from the sun, the weaker the sun's gravitational attraction. Thus, the outer planets don't have to move as fast as the inner planets to balance gravity with their inertia in order to stay in orbit.

Notes/Study Ideas/Answers

Unit XIV The Solar System *continued*

REVIEW YOUR UNDERSTANDING

Some questions may require use of the *Earth Science Reference Tables*.

_____ 1. Which object would orbit Earth in both the Earth-centered and sun-centered models of the solar system?
   (1) Earth's moon
   (2) Mars
   (3) the sun
   (4) the North Star

_____ 2. What is the eccentricity of an ellipse if the distance between foci on a scale diagram of the ellipse is 27.0 cm and the length of the major axis is 82.0 cm?
   (1) 0.33 cm
   (2) 3.04 cm
   (3) 0.33
   (4) 3.04

_____ 3. A planet's orbital speed around the sun varies because of variations in the
   (1) planet's rate of rotation
   (2) planet's distance from the sun
   (3) eccentricity of the planet's orbit
   (4) tilt of the planet's axis of rotation

_____ 4. The greatest distance across a planet's orbit is 299,200,000 km. The distance from the sun to the location in space that is the other focus of the planet's orbit is 5,086,400 km. What is the eccentricity of the planet's orbit?
   (1) 0.017
   (2) 58.82
   (3) 0.017 km
   (4) 58.82 km

Planets and Minor Bodies of the Solar System

The planets are often separated into two groups. Mercury, Venus, Earth, and Mars are the closest planets (in that order) to the sun. All four planets are solid, rocky bodies surrounded by a relatively thin atmosphere or no atmosphere at all. This group of planets is known as the **terrestrial planets,** because they are similar to Earth in their rocky composition.

Unit XIV The Solar System *continued*

The next four planets out from the sun—Jupiter, Saturn, Uranus, and Neptune (in that order)—are called **gas giants,** because they are large planets made mostly of gas. The gas giants are also known as *Jovian planets*, because of their similarity to Jupiter. All the gas giants are encircled by rings of small particles of dust and ice. None of the four inner planets have such rings.

Pluto, the most distant planet from the sun, is somewhat of an oddball. Pluto is neither a terrestrial planet nor a gas giant. It is a ball of ice and rock that is smaller than some moons, including Earth's moon. Some astronomers believe that Pluto was a moon of Uranus that was knocked into an orbit around the sun by a passing object. Others suggest it is one of many smaller objects beyond the orbits of the other planets and should not be listed as a planet.

Notes/Study Ideas/Answers

Self-Check Compare and contrast the characteristics of the terrestrial planets and the gas giants.

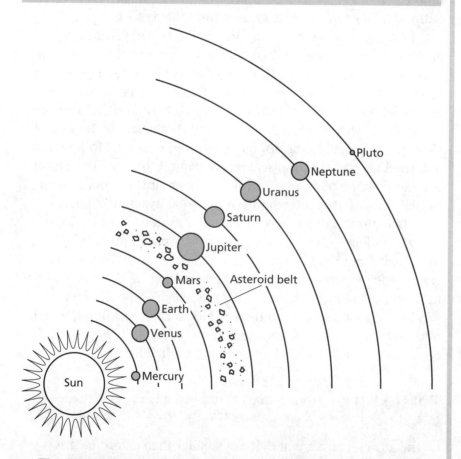

The "Solar System Data" table in the *Earth Science Reference Tables* section, page 249, offers a variety of information about the planets, including each planet's diameter, average distance

Unit XIV The Solar System *continued*

from the sun, orbital and rotational periods, eccentricity, mass, and density. The planets are listed in order of their average distance from the sun. Similar data for the sun and Earth's moon is also listed in this table.

Self-Check Use the *Earth Science Reference Tables* to compare the size, density, periods of rotation, and periods of revolution of Earth and Venus.

In addition to the major celestial bodies, the planets, the solar system also contains a number of minor bodies. A body that orbits a larger body is called a *satellite*. The planets are satellites of the sun. Most of the planets also have satellites. These natural satellites are called *moons*. Astronomers are constantly discovering more moons around the outer planets, so some of the moon data in the *Earth Science Reference Tables* may be subject to change. All the planets except Mercury and Venus possess one or more moons. The Jovian planets all have large numbers of moons. As of September 2004, Jupiter had 62 known moons, Saturn had 35, Uranus had 27, and Neptune had 13.

The largest of the minor bodies in the solar system are asteroids. **Asteroids** are irregularly shaped rocky masses that are smaller than planets. Millions of asteroids exist in the solar system. The largest concentration of asteroids resides in the **asteroid belt,** a region between the orbits of Mars and Jupiter.

Another type of minor body that orbits the sun is the comet. **Comets** are small bodies of ice, rock, and dust that follow long, extremely eccentric, elliptical paths around the sun. The highly eccentric shape of comets' orbits means that they spend most of their time in the outer parts of the solar system. When comets enter the inner part of the solar system, they move quickly under the influence of the sun's strong gravitational pull. Heat from the sun causes the comet's ices to change to gas, releasing a sweeping tail of gas and dust millions of kilometers long. The brightest comets are usually visible for several weeks. Perhaps the best known comet is Halley's comet, which returns to the inner solar system about every 75 years. Halley's comet was visible in 1986 and will return in 2061.

Self-Check Why do comets spend most of their time in the outer reaches of the solar system, far away from the sun?

Bits of rock and metal that are smaller than asteroids are called **meteoroids.** Often, these are pieces of debris that have become detached from comets or asteroids. A **meteor** is a streak of light caused by a meteoroid that heats up and burns when it falls through Earth's atmosphere. Meteors are sometimes called "shooting stars," because they give off a bright streak of light as they burn. When a large number of meteoroids enter the atmosphere in a short period of time, a *meteor shower* occurs. Meteor showers occur at the same time each year when Earth passes into the debris trail of a comet. Meteoroids that strike Earth are called **meteorites.** Scientists study meteorites to gain insight into the origin of Earth and the solar system, because nearly all of them are about 4.5 billion years old.

Impact craters left by asteroids and meteoroids can be identified in Earth's crust. Many scientists believe that a large asteroid hit Earth about 65 million years ago, causing the extinction of the dinosaurs and many other organisms. It is thought that the violent impact sent large clouds of dust into the air. These clouds would have blocked sunlight from reaching Earth, causing global climate change and eventual extinction of species.

REVIEW YOUR UNDERSTANDING

Some questions may require use of the *Earth Science Reference Tables*.

_____ **5.** Which choice lists the inner planets in order of increasing distance from the sun?
(1) Venus, Earth, Mars, Mercury
(2) Mars, Earth, Venus, Mercury
(3) Earth, Mercury, Venus, Mars
(4) Mercury, Venus, Earth, Mars

_____ **6.** Which planet is approximately 40 times farther from the sun than Earth is?
(1) Jupiter
(2) Pluto
(3) Uranus
(4) Mars

_____ **7.** Which bodies exist in the millions in a wide belt between the orbits of Mars and Jupiter?
(1) meteors
(2) asteroids
(3) comets
(4) moons

_____ **8.** Compared to Jupiter, Earth is
(1) denser, smaller, and more solid
(2) denser, larger, and more solid
(3) less dense, smaller, and more gaseous
(4) less dense, larger, and more gaseous

Unit XIV The Solar System *continued*

Notes/Study
Ideas/Answers

Formation of the Solar System

Scientists have long debated the origin of the solar system. In the 1600s and 1700s, many scientists believed that the sun formed first and "threw off" the materials that later became the planets. Today, the generally accepted explanation for the origin of the solar system is the nebular theory. The **nebular theory** states that the solar system formed from a rotating cloud of gas, ice, and dust, called a *solar nebula*.

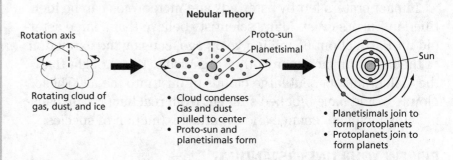

Nebular Theory

Rotation axis

Rotating cloud of gas, dust, and ice

Proto-sun
Planetisimal

- Cloud condenses
- Gas and dust pulled to center
- Proto-sun and planetisimals form

Sun

- Planetisimals join to form protoplanets
- Protoplanets join to form planets

According to the nebular theory, shock waves from an exploding star caused the solar nebula to contract. The nebula most likely began with a slight overall rotation. As the nebula contracted, it began to spin faster and flatten out into a disk-shaped cloud called a *protoplanetary disk*. About 99.9% of the mass of the solar nebula became concentrated near the center of the disk, where the sun would eventually form. The planets would eventually form from the outer parts of the disk. As the nebula continued to contract, the enormous density at the center of the disk increased until the temperature reached a few million degrees. When the temperature at the center became high enough, nuclear reactions began to fuse hydrogen into helium. This was the beginning of the sun becoming a star.

The nebular model also explains how the planets could have formed. Not all the material in the solar nebula was captured by the young sun's gravity. Remaining gas, ice, and dust particles collided and stuck together, forming larger bodies called **planetisimals.** Planetisimals grew by *accretion*, the process of adding mass by colliding with other planetisimals. Eventually, planetisimals joined to form larger bodies, called *protoplanets*. When the protoplanets became large enough, they condensed to form planets and moons.

Self-Check How were temperatures distributed across the protoplanetary disk that formed our solar system?

The composition and sizes of the planets are also explained by the nebular theory. In the inner solar system, where the ter-

Unit XIV The Solar System *continued*

restrial planets formed, the temperature was too high for ice to exist. Thus, the solid particles that made up the inner proto-planets were mostly rocky or metallic. In contrast, ice could form in the outer solar system, where it was much colder. Therefore, much more material was available in the outer solar system, allowing some of the outer planets to grow to many times the size of Earth. As these planets grew, their gravity increased, and they were able to capture the extremely abundant hydrogen and helium gas from the surrounding space. These planets became the gas giants Jupiter, Saturn, Uranus, and Neptune.

Self-Check Why are gas giants so much larger than terrestrial planets?

The nebular material that remained after the planets formed makes up less than 1% of the total mass of the solar system but accounts for all the other minor bodies that populate space. This material became the icy, rocky planet Pluto as well as a host of similar bodies, such as asteroids, meteoroids, and comets.

Several lines of scientific evidence support the nebular theory. Astronomers have been able to observe protoplanetary disks around newborn stars. Observations also show that all the planets revolve in the same direction that the sun rotates. Most of their moons also revolve in this direction. In addition, the spacing of the planets is ordered. Most planets are about twice as far from the sun as is their neighbor closer to the sun. The planets also orbit the sun in nearly the same plane. All of this evidence suggests that a single event formed the solar system.

REVIEW YOUR UNDERSTANDING

_____ **9.** Several lines of scientific evidence suggest that the solar system originated from a
  (1) protoplanet
  (2) planetisimal
  (3) star
  (4) nebula

_____ **10.** Most of the mass of the solar system is contained in
  (1) the sun
  (2) the inner planets
  (3) the outer planets
  (4) minor bodies, such as moons

Unit XIV The Solar System *continued*

_____ **11.** According to the nebular theory, the planets formed
(1) from material "thrown off" by the sun
(2) when the temperature in the center of the disk became hot enough for hydrogen to fuse into helium
(3) in the center of the protoplanetary disk, where most of the mass was concentrated
(4) in the outer parts of the protoplanetary disk, where planetisimals grew by accretion

_____ **12.** The main difference between the four innermost planets and the next four planets is that the inner planets
(1) formed from protoplanets
(2) originated in the solar nebula
(3) are solid and rocky
(4) are huge and of low density

ANSWERS TO SELF-CHECK QUESTIONS

- The geocentric model states that the sun, planets, moons, and other bodies revolve around Earth. The heliocentric model states that planets, moons, and other bodies revolve around the sun.

- An ellipse is an oval. All ellipses have two foci. Eccentricity describes how different an ellipse is from a circle.

- perihelion

- Terrestrial planets are small, rocky, and dense. Gas giants are large, gaseous, and of low density.

- Earth and Venus have nearly the same size and density. Earth's period of rotation is much shorter than Venus's (Venus's "day" is 243 Earth days). Venus's period of revolution is shorter than Earth's (Venus's "year" is about 225 Earth days).

- Comets have long, extremely eccentric orbits.

- Temperature was very hot near the center of the disk, which eventually became the sun. Temperature was much colder in the outer parts of the disk, far away from the developing sun.

Unit XIV The Solar System *continued*

- Due to the colder temperatures, more material, including ice, was available in the outer solar system. This allowed the outer protoplanets to grow larger than the inner planets. As the outer planets grew, their gravity increased, and they were able to capture the abundant hydrogen and helium gases from surrounding space.

Notes/Study Ideas/Answers

Questions for Regents Practice

The Solar System

PART A

Some questions may require use of the
Earth Science Reference Tables.

_____ 1. Which planet originated from one
of the five protoplanets farthest
from the sun?
(1) Uranus
(2) Mercury
(3) Venus
(4) Mars

_____ 2. The main difference between the
geocentric and heliocentric models of the solar system is that
(1) the geocentric model is sun-
centered and the heliocentric
model is Earth-centered
(2) the geocentric model is Earth-
centered and the heliocentric
model is sun-centered
(3) the heliocentric model is
based on scientific evidence,
while the geocentric model
is not
(4) the geocentric model is based
on scientific evidence, while
the heliocentric model is not

_____ 3. Compared to the terrestrial planets, the Jovian planets
(1) are smaller, on average
(2) are less dense, on average
(3) have fewer moons
(4) orbit the sun faster

_____ 4. Which two planets are most similar in size?
(1) Earth and Mars
(2) Uranus and Saturn
(3) Earth and Venus
(4) Pluto and Mercury

_____ 5. Compared to Earth's density and
period of rotation, Mars is
(1) denser and has a shorter
period of rotation
(2) denser and has a longer
period of rotation
(3) less dense and has a shorter
period of rotation
(4) less dense and has a longer
period of rotation

_____ 6. Compared to Pluto, Mercury has
a greater average orbital speed
because Mercury
(1) is larger
(2) is closer to the sun
(3) is more dense
(4) has a more eccentric orbit

_____ 7. Which planet's orbit is most similar in shape to the moon's orbit
of Earth?
(1) Mercury
(2) Neptune
(3) Jupiter
(4) Saturn

_____ 8. Which planet's orbital shape is
closest to a perfect circle?
(1) Pluto
(2) Mercury
(3) Earth
(4) Venus

PART B-1

Base your answers to questions 9 and 10 on your knowledge of earth science and the diagram below, which shows a planet revolving in an elliptical orbit around a star. Letters A through D represent different points along the orbit.

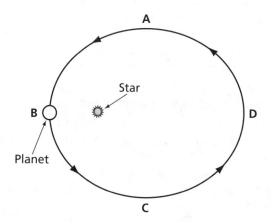

_____ **9.** Starting at the position shown, how will the gravitational attraction between the planet and the star change as the planet makes one complete orbit around the star?
   (1) It will remain the same.
   (2) It will continually decrease.
   (3) It will increase, then decrease.
   (4) It will decrease, then increase.

_____ **10.** At which position is the planet's orbital speed greatest?
   (1) A
   (2) B
   (3) C
   (4) D

PART B-2

Base your answers to questions 11 through 13 on your knowledge of earth science, the *Earth Science Reference Tables*, and the information and data table below.

   Scientists have discovered two large extrasolar (outside our solar system) planets that orbit Gliese 876, a star located 15 light-years from Earth. The two planets are called planet GJ876b and planet GJ876c. Information about the planets is shown in the table below. The period of revolution for planet GJ876b has been left blank.

Characteristics of Two Planets Orbiting the Star Gliese 876

Planet	Mass	Distance from Gliese 876 (AU)	Period of Revolution
GJ876b	1.9 times the mass Jupiter	0.21	
GJ876c	0.6 the mass of Jupiter	0.13	30 Earth days

1 AU = 149.6 million kilometers (average distance from the Earth to Sun)

11. As planet GJ876b orbits star Gliese 876, describe the change in gravitational attraction as the distance between the planet and the star increases.

_____

_____

_____

Unit XIV The Solar System *continued*

12. Describe the mass of planet GJ876c in comparison to the mass of Saturn.

_____

_____

13. If our solar system had a planet located at the same distance from the sun as planet GJ876b is from Gliese 876, what would be its approximate period of revolution?

_____

_____

PART C

Base your answers to questions 14 through 16 on your knowledge of earth science, the *Earth Science Reference Tables*, and the diagram below, which shows the orbit of planet GJ876c around the star Gliese 876. All distances are drawn to scale. Letters A and B represent different points along the orbit of planet GJ876c.

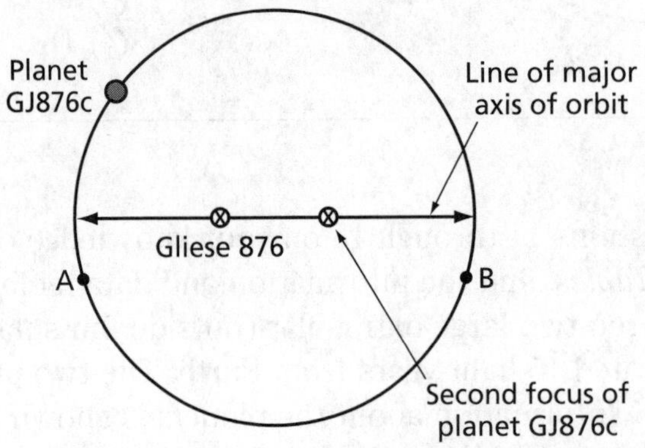

14. Calculate the eccentricity of the orbit of planet GJ876c. Show all work.

15. Compare the shape of planet GJ876c's orbit to the shape of Earth's orbit.

_____

_____

16. Compare the gravitational force between planet GJ876c and the star Gliese 876 at points A and B. Where is the gravitational force greatest? How do you know?

_____

_____

_____

Focus On
The Regents Exam

Stars, Galaxies, and the Universe

Our solar system is centered on the sun, the star nearest to Earth. A **star** is a massive ball of gases in space that creates and radiates energy in the form of light and heat.

Characteristics of Stars

A star's color indicates the temperature of its surface, as shown in the table. The hottest stars, with surface temperatures above 30,000°C, appear blue. The coolest stars are red stars, which have surface temperatures around 3,000°C. Stars with surface temperatures between 5,000°C and 6,000°C appear yellow, like our sun.

Classification of Stars

Color	Surface Temperature
Blue	more than 30,000°C
Blue-White	10,000–30,000°C
White	7,500–10,000°C
Yellow-White	6,000–7,500°C
Yellow	5,000–6,000°C
Orange	3,500–5,000°C
Red	less than 3,500°C

Magnitude is a measure of a star's brightness. The total energy output of a star is called its *absolute magnitude*, or **luminosity.** *Apparent magnitude* is how bright the star looks from Earth. A star that is closer to Earth appears brighter than it would if it were farther away. A good example is the sun. As a medium-sized star, the sun gives off less light than many other stars. However, the sun is so close to Earth that during the day its light washes out the light of the other stars. If it were possible to see the sun at the same distance as the other stars, the sun would be dimmer than most of them. Therefore, the apparent magnitude of a star depends on its absolute magnitude and its distance from the observer.

Self-Check What is the difference between apparent magnitude and absolute magnitude?

What You'll Need to Learn

This topic is part of the Regents Curriculum for the Physical Setting Exam.

Standard 4, Performance Indicator 1.1: *Explain complex phenomena, such as tides, variations in day length, solar insolation, apparent motion of the planets, and annual traverse of the constellations.* Major Understandings: 1.1g

Standard 4, Performance Indicator 1.2: *Describe current theories about the origin of the universe and solar system.* Major Understandings: 1.2a, 1.2b

What Terms You'll Need to Know

big bang theory
black hole
blue shift
cosmic background
    radiation
Doppler effect
galaxy
giant
H-R diagram
light-year
luminosity
main-sequence star
Milky Way galaxy
nebula
neutron star
nuclear fusion

Unit XV Stars, Galaxies, and the Universe *continued*

planetary nebula
red shift
spectrograph
star
supergiant
supernova
white dwarf

Where You Can Learn Even More

Holt Earth Science: The Physical Setting
Chapter 30: Stars, Galaxies, and the Universe

In addition to color and brightness, stars also vary in size and mass. Some stars are less than 20 km in diameter, which is far smaller than Earth. Other stars are more than 1,000 times as large as the sun. The sun is a medium-sized star with a diameter of 1,392,000 km. Most stars visible in the night sky are medium-sized stars. In terms of mass, some stars have only 1/50 of the sun's mass. Others have more than 50 times the sun's mass. Most stars are in the range of 1/5 to 5 times the mass of the sun.

Self-Check Compare the mass of the sun with that of other stars.

Astronomers learn about stars mainly by analyzing the light that they give off. The **spectrograph** is one of the most important tools used. Astronomers use spectrographs to identify the various elements in a star's atmosphere. When starlight passes through the spectrograph, the light is separated into a spectrum of colors (wavelengths), just like a glass prism can separate white light into an array of colors.

Each star produces its own spectrum. The elements within a star's atmosphere absorb light from the star's surface (photosphere). Each element absorbs light of different wavelengths, removing these wavelengths from the star's spectrum. The result is a display of colors and dark lines, called a *spectra*, such as the one shown here. The dark lines, called *absorption lines*, show where light has been absorbed. Just as fingerprints can be used to identify a person, a star's absorption lines can be used to identify different elements in the star. By measuring these fingerprints, astronomers have found that stars like our sun consist mainly of hydrogen and helium. Stars also contain traces of other elements, such as carbon and oxygen. Exactly how much of these elements a star contains reveals details about when and where it was born and how it has changed over time.

Self-Check Describe the chemical composition of a star like the sun.

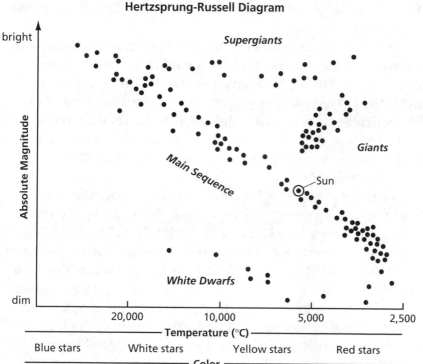

Hertzsprung-Russell Diagram

Notes/Study Ideas/Answers

In the early 1900s, two astronomers working independently, Ejnar Hertzsprung and Henry Norris Russell, discovered that stars could be classified according to their surface temperature (color) and absolute magnitude. Such a graph is called a Hertzsprung-Russell diagram, or **H-R diagram.** The H-R diagram shown here is also presented in the *Earth Science Reference Tables* section, page 248, where it is labeled "Luminosity and Temperature of Stars." Notice on the graph that the horizontal axis shows the surface temperatures of stars. Recall that a star's color is directly related to its surface temperature. The hottest blue stars are on the left side of the graph and the coolest red stars are on the right. The vertical axis shows absolute magnitude, with the brightest stars at the top and the dimmest stars at the bottom.

Most stars fall within a diagonal band running from the hot, bright stars at the upper left to the cool, dim stars at the lower right. Stars within this band are called **main-sequence stars.** The sun and most of the stars that are visible in the night sky are main-sequence stars.

The very bright stars at the upper right of the H-R diagram are called supergiants. **Supergiants** are much brighter than main-sequence stars of the same temperature, because they are much larger than main-sequence stars. In fact, supergiants range in size from 100 to 1,000 times the diameter of the sun. Just below the supergiants on the H-R diagram are the giants.

Unit XV Stars, Galaxies, and the Universe *continued*

Notes/Study
Ideas/Answers

Giants are large, bright stars that are smaller and dimmer than supergiants.

Below the main sequence on the H-R diagram are the smallest stars, called dwarfs. A **white dwarf** is the small, dense remains of a low- or medium-mass star. White dwarfs are hot, but dimmer than main-sequence stars of the same temperature. The smallest stars of all are the *red dwarfs*. They are red in color because they are relatively cool. These stars are so dim that even the relatively close red dwarfs are difficult to see without a telescope.

A **galaxy** is a large collection of stars, gas, and dust that is held together by gravity. Billions of galaxies make up the universe. Our own galaxy is called the **Milky Way.** The Milky Way galaxy has an estimated 200 to 400 billion stars and a diameter of more than 100 light-years. A **light-year** is the distance that light travels in one year. Light travels 300,000 km/sec, so light travels about 9.5 trillion km in one year. As shown in the diagram, the Milky Way galaxy is shaped like a flattened spiral, which is caused by its rotation. Our solar system is located about two-thirds of the way from the center of the Milky Way galaxy.

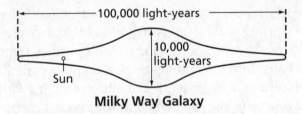

Milky Way Galaxy

REVIEW YOUR UNDERSTANDING
Some questions may require use of the *Earth Science Reference Tables*.

_____ **1.** Which star has about the same surface temperature as the sun?
(1) Rigel
(2) Sirius
(3) Alpha Centauri
(4) Barnard's Star

_____ **2.** Which star is many times more luminous, yet cooler, than the sun?
(1) Procyon B
(2) Betelgeuse
(3) Alpha Centauri
(4) Barnard's Star

Unit XV Stars, Galaxies, and the Universe *continued*

Notes/Study
Ideas/Answers

_____ **3.** The sun is a
   (1) blue supergiant with a temperature of about 20,000°C
   (2) main-sequence star with a temperature of about 6,000°C
   (3) main-sequence star with a temperature of about 4,000°C
   (4) white dwarf with a temperature of about 10,000°C

_____ **4.** Stars that range in temperature from about 7,500°C to 10,000°C and that have very low luminosity are called
   (1) red giants
   (2) blue supergiants
   (3) main-sequence stars
   (4) white dwarfs

Life Cycles of Stars

All stars have life cycles, just as humans do. Stars are born; they undergo a vigorous youth, a middle age, an old age, and eventually death. A typical star's life cycle encompasses billions of years, so no human has ever observed the entire life of a star.

Star formation begins when a cloud of gas and dust, called a **nebula,** starts to contract under the influence of gravity. As the nebula contracts, it heats up and begins to spin rapidly. The shrinking, spinning cloud then begins to flatten into a disk called a *protostar*. As a protostar contracts, its internal pressure and temperature continue to rise.

A star is formed when the protostar becomes so dense and so hot that nuclear fusion begins. **Nuclear fusion** is the process by which lighter elements, such as hydrogen, join to make heavier elements, such as helium. Once nuclear fusion begins in a star, the process continues for billions of years.

Self-Check Describe the process that generates energy in a star's core.

Fusion releases vast quantities of energy and marks the transition of a star into the main-sequence stage. Stars spend about 90% of their lives on the main sequence. In all main-sequence stars, nuclear fusion converts hydrogen into helium at a stable rate. There is an equilibrium between the outward thermal pressure due to fusion and the inward pull of gravity.

A star's mass determines the star's place on the main sequence and how long it will stay there. The most massive stars produce the most energy. High-mass stars become the

Unit XV Stars, Galaxies, and the Universe *continued*

bluest and the brightest main-sequence stars. However, because blue stars burn so brightly, they use up fuel relatively quickly and last only a few million years. Stars similar in mass to the sun occupy the middle of the main sequence. These yellow stars remain stable on the main sequence for about 10 billion years. Small, cool stars are the most long-lived stars. A red main-sequence star may stay on the main sequence for more than 100 billion years.

Stars don't last forever. When a star begins to run out of fuel, gravity gains the upper hand over thermal pressure, and the star's core begins to contract. Soon, the core temperature rises enough to cause the hydrogen in the star's outer shell to begin fusion. The energy flowing outward increases, causing the outer shell of the star to expand. Because the expanding outer shell is moving away from the star's hot core, it begins to cool and glow red. The star becomes a red giant. Eventually, the shrinking core will become hot enough for helium fusion to occur, producing carbon, oxygen, and heavier elements.

Life Cycle of a Star

Stellar nebula
→ Average star ——→ Red giant ——→ Planetary nebula ——→ White dwarf
→ Massive star ——→ Red supergiant ——→ Supernova
    Supernova ↗ Neutron star
    Supernova ↘ Black hole

The end of helium-to-carbon fusion marks the final stage in the life cycles of low-mass and medium-mass stars. Eventually, the star's outer shell of gases will drift away, leaving behind a hot core of carbon shrouded in a cloud of expelled gas. Such a cloud is called a **planetary nebula.** Gravity will eventually cause the carbon core to collapse inward, producing a hot, dense core of matter called a white dwarf. White dwarfs don't undergo fusion, but glow faintly from leftover heat. A white dwarf will glow for billions of years before it cools completely.

Self-Check Sequence the stages that a star like the sun passes through from the beginning to the end of its life cycle.

The life cycle of a high-mass star is very different from the life cycle of a low- or medium-mass star. When the core runs out of hydrogen, these stars fuse helium into carbon just like medium-size stars. However, after the helium is gone, their mass is enough to fuse carbon into heavier elements, the heaviest being iron. As fusion slows, thermal pressure decreases.

Unit XV Stars, Galaxies, and the Universe *continued*

Gravity eventually overcomes the lower pressure, leading to a dramatic collapse of the star's outer layers. This collapse produces a violent explosion called a **supernova.** Supernovas produce enough energy to create elements heavier than iron. These elements, and lighter ones such as carbon and oxygen, are expelled into space by the explosion.

As a supernova ejects material into space, its core continues to collapse. The star may become a neutron star. In a **neutron star,** electrons and protons are smashed together by the star's enormous gravity to form neutrons. Neutron stars are much smaller and denser than white dwarfs. A spoonful of matter from a neutron star would weigh 100 million tons on Earth. Neutron stars rotate very rapidly.

Some massive stars produce leftovers that are too massive to become neutron stars. These stars are so massive that they form an object with gravity so strong that not even light can escape. This is what astronomers call a **black hole.** Black holes cannot radiate energy, but they can be detected because matter that falls into the black hole gives off energy. They can also be located by their gravitational effects on other objects.

REVIEW YOUR UNDERSTANDING

Some questions may require use of the *Earth Science Reference Tables*.

_____ **5.** Stars like the sun produce energy from
  (1) nuclear fusion
  (2) gravitational contraction
  (3) chemical reactions
  (4) nuclear fission

_____ **6.** Which sequence shows the most likely stages of predicted evolutionary changes in the sun?
  (1) sun → white dwarf → main sequence
  (2) sun → red giant → white dwarf
  (3) sun → main sequence → blue supergiant
  (4) sun → red supergiant → white dwarf

_____ **7.** Which star's life cycle is likely to end in a violent explosion called a supernova?
  (1) Rigel
  (2) the sun
  (3) Procyon B
  (4) Barnard's Star

Unit XV Stars, Galaxies, and the Universe *continued*

**Notes/Study
Ideas/Answers**

_____ **8.** A star's place on the main sequence and how long it
will stay there are determined by the star's
(1) color
(2) surface temperature
(3) apparent brightness
(4) mass

The Expanding Universe

Have you ever noticed how a sound or light source appears to
change as it moves toward or away from you? For example, suppose you are standing on a sidewalk near the road. A car is speed-
ing down the street toward you, with its horn sounding. As the car
gets closer and closer, the sound of the horn appears to change.
The horn's pitch (frequency) seems to get higher and higher.
Then, as the car is moving away, the horn's pitch seems to get
lower and lower. The apparent change in the frequency and wavelength of a sound or light source is called the **Doppler effect.**

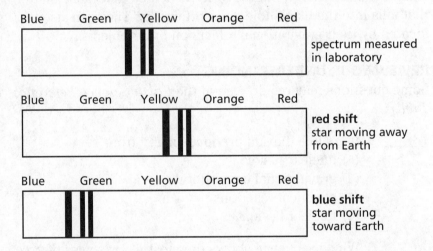

The Doppler effect can be used to determine how fast stars or
galaxies are approaching or moving away from Earth. When a star
or galaxy is approaching Earth, the absorption lines in its spectrum shift toward the shorter (blue) wavelengths, producing what
is called a **blue shift.** When a star or galaxy is moving away from
Earth, the absorption lines shift toward the longer (red) wavelengths, producing a **red shift.** The larger the shift, the faster the
galaxy or star is moving toward or away from Earth.

Unit XV Stars, Galaxies, and the Universe *continued*

Self-Check What is the Doppler effect, and how does it relate to the motion of stars and galaxies?

In the 1920s, American astronomer Edwin Hubble studied many galaxies at different distances from Earth. Hubble found that the light from most galaxies undergoes a red shift, indicating that most galaxies are moving farther away from Earth. Hubble also found that the more-distant galaxies have the greater red shifts. This greater shift means that distant galaxies are moving away from Earth faster than closer galaxies, and that the universe is expanding.

Big Bang

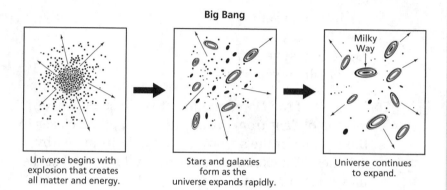

Universe begins with explosion that creates all matter and energy.

Stars and galaxies form as the universe expands rapidly.

Universe continues to expand.

Astronomers theorize that the outward motions of distant galaxies are evidence that the universe came into being in a single moment, in an event called the big bang. The **big bang theory** states that all of the matter and energy in the universe was at one time compressed into an extremely small volume. Then, about 13 or 14 billion years ago, a huge explosion sent all this matter and energy hurtling outward in a giant cloud. As the cloud expanded, some of the matter gathered into clumps and evolved into galaxies. Today, the universe is still expanding, and the galaxies continue to move apart from one another.

The big bang theory suggests that the early universe was a very hot place, and that as it expanded the gas within it cooled. Therefore, the universe should be filled with radiation that is literally the remnant heat left over from the big bang explosion. In 1965 scientists confirmed the existence of this leftover radiation, called **cosmic background radiation.** The radiation was acting as a source of excess noise in a radio receiver they were building.

Unit XV Stars, Galaxies, and the Universe *continued*

Self-Check What evidence supports the big bang theory?

Like any new discovery, the big bang theory must continue to be tested against each new discovery about the universe. As new information about our universe emerges, the big bang theory may be reversed, or a new theory may take its place.

REVIEW YOUR UNDERSTANDING

_____ **9.** According to the big bang theory, a tremendous explosion created all the matter in the universe about
(1) 1 billion years ago
(2) 5 billion years ago
(3) 14 billion years ago
(4) 23 billion years ago

_____ **10.** Because of the Doppler effect, the observed wavelengths of light from distant galaxies appear closer to the red end of the spectrum than light from nearby galaxies. The explanation for this red shift is that the universe is presently
(1) contracting
(2) expanding
(3) remaining constant in size

_____ **11.** Which statement best describes the general pattern of motion that astronomers observe for distant galaxies in the universe?
(1) Most galaxies are moving toward us, and the closer galaxies are generally approaching faster.
(2) Most galaxies are moving toward us, and the more distant galaxies are generally approaching faster.
(3) Most galaxies are moving away from us, and the closer galaxies are generally moving faster.
(4) Most galaxies are moving away from us, and the more distant galaxies are generally moving faster.

Unit XV Stars, Galaxies, and the Universe *continued*

ANSWERS TO SELF-CHECK QUESTIONS

- Absolute brightness is the true brightness of a star. Apparent brightness is how bright the star appears from Earth.

- The sun is a medium-mass star. Some stars have a lower mass than the sun. Some stars have a higher mass.

- Stars like the sun are primarily composed of hydrogen and helium.

- The process is called nuclear fusion. During nuclear fusion lighter elements, such as hydrogen, join to make heavier elements, such as helium. Tremendous amounts of energy are released in the process.

- protostar → main sequence → red giant → white dwarf

- The Doppler effect is the apparent shift in the wavelength and frequency of a light or sound source moving away from or toward an observer. Stars and galaxies that are moving away from us show a red shift of light. Stars that are moving toward us show a blue shift.

- The red shifts of galaxies and cosmic background radiation provide evidence for the big bang theory.

Questions for Regents Practice

Stars, Galaxies, and the Universe

PART A

Some questions may require use of the
Earth Science Reference Tables.

_____ **1.** Stars with surface temperatures
between 5,000°C and 6,000°C
appear
(1) blue
(2) yellow
(3) red
(4) white

_____ **2.** A blue shift of the absorption
lines in the spectrum of light
from a distant star is evidence
that the star
(1) has a surface temperature of
at least 20,000°C
(2) has a surface temperature
that is below 20,000°C
(3) is moving toward Earth
(4) is moving away from Earth

_____ **3.** Which star has about the same
luminosity as Betelgeuse?
(1) the sun
(2) Procyon B
(3) Alpha Centauri
(4) Rigel

_____ **4.** What star color indicates the
coolest surface temperature?
(1) red
(2) blue
(3) yellow
(4) white

_____ **5.** What is the color of a main-
sequence star that gives off about
100 times as much light as the
sun?
(1) blue
(2) yellow
(3) white
(4) red

_____ **6.** Scientists identify Procyon B as a
white dwarf by comparing its
(1) distance and luminosity
(2) color and temperature
(3) size and distance
(4) luminosity and temperature

_____ **7.** One piece of evidence in support
of the big bang theory is the fact
that wavelengths of light in the
spectra of distant galaxies are
(1) longer than normal (red
shifted)
(2) longer than normal (blue
shifted)
(3) shorter than normal (red
shifted)
(4) shorter than normal (blue
shifted)

_____ **8.** The positions of absorption lines
in the spectra of distant galaxies
provide evidence that the universe is
(1) younger than 1 billion years
old
(2) still expanding
(3) less than 100,000 light years
across
(4) uniform in the distribution of
matter

| Unit XV Stars, Galaxies, and the Universe *continued*

PART B-1

Base your answers to questions 9 through 11 on your knowledge of earth science, the *Earth Science Reference Tables*, and the H-R diagram shown below. Letters A through D represent different regions of the H-R diagram.

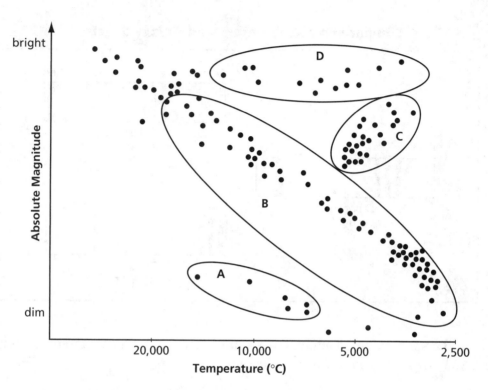

_____ **9.** What type of star is generally located in region B of this diagram?
  (1) white dwarf
  (2) main-sequence
  (3) supergiant
  (4) red giant

_____ **10.** In terms of size and temperature, stars that are in region A of this diagram are generally
  (1) bigger and hotter than the sun
  (2) smaller and hotter than the sun
  (3) bigger and cooler than the sun
  (4) smaller and cooler than the sun

_____ **11.** Which statement correctly compares the color and brightness of stars in region C to the color and brightness of stars in region D?
  (1) Stars in region C are dimmer and mostly have the same color.
  (2) Stars in region C are dimmer and mostly have a different color.
  (3) Stars in region C are brighter and mostly have the same color.
  (4) Stars in region C are brighter and mostly have a different color.

Unit XV Stars, Galaxies, and the Universe *continued*

PART B-2

Base your answers to questions 12 and 13 on your knowledge of earth science and the diagrams below, which represent the spectral lines of hydrogen gas of two galaxies, A and B, and the spectral lines of hydrogen gas observed in a laboratory.

Comparison of Laboratory and Galaxy Spectra

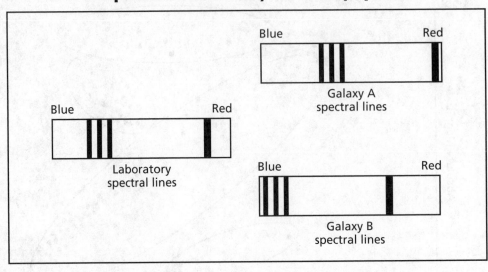

12. Based on the spectral-line diagrams, what inference can be made about the motion of galaxy A? What leads you to this conclusion?

_____

_____

_____

_____

13. Based on the spectral-line diagrams, what inference can be made about the motion of galaxy B? What leads you to this conclusion?

_____

_____

_____

_____

| Unit XV Stars, Galaxies, and the Universe *continued*

PART C

Base your answers to questions 14 through 16 on your knowledge of earth science, the *Earth Science Reference Tables*, and the table below, which presents data for different stars in the universe. Absolute and apparent magnitude are stated as numbers. The greater the number, the dimmer the star. Negative numbers indicate extreme brightness.

Star	Absolute Magnitude	Apparent Magnitude	Light-Years from Earth
The sun	4.8	−26.7	0.000002
Betelgeuse	−5.6	0.4	1,500
Sirius	1.5	−1.4	8.6
Barnard's Star	13.4	9.6	5.9
Rigel	4.4	−0.27	1,400
Polaris	−3.5	2.1	431
Aldebaran	−0.3	0.85	65

14. Which star listed in the table has the greatest overall energy output? How do you know?

_____

_____

_____

_____

15. Compare the absolute and apparent magnitudes of the sun. Why is there such a large difference in these numbers?

_____

_____

_____

_____

16. Using evidence from the table, explain what determines a star's apparent magnitude.

_____

_____

_____

_____

_____

Earth Science Lab Skills

Introduction

Part D of the New York State Regents Examination in Physical Setting/Earth Science consists of hands-on tasks that are designed to measure your ability to use problem-solving and inquiry skills. The tasks are completed at six stations, which are described below. You are given 10 minutes to complete the task at each station.

STATION 1: MINERAL AND ROCK IDENTIFICATION

At this station, you will determine the properties of a mineral and then use the properties to identify the mineral from a flowchart.

To help prepare for this station, you should—

- review Units III and IV of this book
- review the procedures for determining mineral hardness and streak (page 217)
- review the relevant chart in the *Earth Science Reference Tables* (pages 250–251)

STATION 2: LOCATING AN EPICENTER

At this station, you will use seismic data and a travel time graph to determine the location of an earthquake epicenter.

To help prepare for this station, you should—

- review Unit VII of this book
- review the relevant chart in the *Earth Science Reference Tables* (pages 240–241)

STATION 3: ATMOSPHERIC MOISTURE

At this station, you will determine dew point and relative humidity of the air. Students also use an adiabatic lapse rate graph to find the altitude of a cloud base.

To help prepare for this station, you should—

- review Unit XI of this book
- review the procedure for finding dew point and relative humidity (page 219)

STATION 4: DENSITY OF FLUIDS

At this station, you will determine the mass, volume, and density of different fluids.

To help prepare for this station, you should—

- review procedures for determining mass (page 213)
- review procedures for measuring the volume of a liquid (page 214)
- review essential math skills (pages 215–216)
- review the procedure for determining density (page 217)

STATION 5: DATA COLLECTING, GRAPHING, AND PREDICTING

At this station, you will determine the average settling time for each of the three sizes of particles.

To help prepare for this station, you should—

- review essential math skills (pages 215–216)

STATION 6: CONSTRUCTING AND ANALYZING AN ELLIPTICAL ORBIT

At this station, you will construct an ellipse and determine its eccentricity.

To help prepare for this station, you should—

- review relevant sections of Unit XIV of this book
- review essential math skills (pages 215–216)

Using Lab Equipment

USING A TRIPLE-BEAM BALANCE/MEASURING MASS

1. Before determining the mass of the object, slide all the riders back to the zero point. Check that the pointer is pointing to zero. Use the adjustment screws, if necessary.

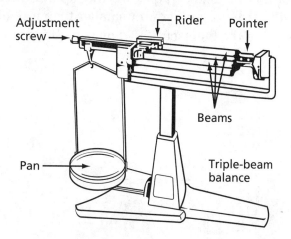

2. Place the object on the pan. Slide the rider with the largest mass along its beam until the pointer drops below zero. Then, move the rider back one notch. Repeat this process on each beam until the pointer swings an equal distance above and below the zero line.

3. The mass of the object will be the sum of the masses indicated on the beams.

Example:

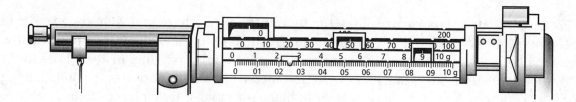

The mass of this object would be read as 59.25 grams.

USING AN ELECTRONIC BALANCE/MEASURING MASS

1. Before using the balance, ensure that it is clean and on a level surface. Turn the balance on.

2. Place a container on the balance, and press the Tare button.

3. Place the object to be massed in the container. Read and record the mass.

Using a Graduated Cylinder/Measuring Volume

A graduated cylinder is a cylindrical container marked with lines from bottom to top. Graduated cylinders are used to determine the volume of a liquid sample. The surface of a liquid when viewed in a graduated cylinder is always curved. This curved surface is called the *meniscus*. Always read a meniscus from the bottom of the curve, viewed along a horizontal line of sight. Do not try to make a reading looking up or down at the meniscus as this will cause the volume reading to appear larger or smaller than it really is. If it is hard to determine the exact position of the meniscus, holding something with a solid color behind the cylinder may help.

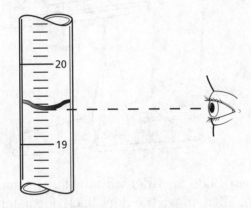

Using a Thermometer/Measuring Temperature

Most laboratory thermometers are made from glass and consist of a glass bulb that is attached to a tube that is marked with a temperature scale. The liquid in the thermometer is usually colored alcohol or mercury. When this liquid becomes warmer, its molecules move faster, causing the liquid to expand inside the tube. The length of the column of liquid indicates the temperature. Temperature is measured in both degrees Celsius (°C) and degrees Fahrenheit (°F).

Measuring air temperature Take the thermometer to where you want to measure the air temperature. Do not hold the thermometer by the bulb because your own body heat will cause the bulb to warm and the thermometer will give a false reading. Instead, hold the thermometer near the 20°C mark. If the thermometer has a loop at one end, you can hang it on a wall or a tree. Keep the thermometer in place for at least five minutes before taking a reading. Return the thermometer to its protective case when you have finished.

214

Math Skills

USING SI UNITS

The metric system is very convenient because unit sizes are based on multiples of 10. Each unit is 10 times larger or 10 times smaller than the next unit. When converting from smaller units to larger units, move the decimal point to the left. When converting from larger units to smaller units, move the decimal point to the right. For example, 32 mm is equal to 3.2 cm.

USING SCIENTIFIC NOTATION

Scientific notation is used to express very large or very small numbers. To convert a large number to scientific notation, move the decimal point to the left until it is located to the right of the number's first nonzero digit. The number of places that you move the decimal point becomes the positive exponent of 10. For example: $13,450,000 = 1.345 \times 10^7$

To write a number less than one in scientific notation, move the decimal point to the right of the number's first nonzero digit. The number of places that you move the decimal point becomes the negative exponent of 10. For example: $0.000474 = 4.74 \times 10^{-4}$

USING SIGNIFICANT DIGITS

In scientific work, measurements always have some degree of uncertainty, based on the precision of the measuring instrument. Significant digits are used to indicate the uncertainty in measurements.

Rules for counting significant digits

1. All nonzero digits are significant. For example, *1.75* has three significant digits.

2. Any zeros between significant digits are also significant. For example, *4,709* has four significant digits.

3. Zeros at the end of a number but to the left of a decimal are significant if they have been measured or are the first estimated digit. Otherwise, they are not significant.

4. If a value has no significant digits to the left of a decimal point, any zeros to the right of the decimal point and also to the left of a significant digit are not significant. For example, *0.0012* has only two significant digits.

5. If a value ends with zeros to the right of a decimal point, those zeros are significant. For example, *0.1200* has four significant digits.

ROUNDING AND SIGNIFICANT DIGITS

When performing mathematical operations with measurements, you must remember to keep track of significant digits.

- If you are adding or subtracting two measurements, your answer can have only as many significant digits as the least precise measurement (the value that has the smallest number of decimal places). For example: $63.642 + 7.1 = 70.742$. The answer to report should be 71, because the least precise measurement (7.1) has only two significant digits.

- If you are multiplying or dividing, your answer can have only as many significant digits as the least precise measurement. For example: $5.78 \times 4.6 = 26.588$. The answer to report should be 27, because the least precise measurement (4.6) has only two significant digits.

Absolute and Relative Error

Scientific measurements can include a certain degree of error. *Error* refers to the "uncertainty" that can happen in an experiment due to unavoidable limitations of the instruments, techniques, and processes used. One way to express error is in terms of accuracy. It is expressed as either an absolute or relative error. *Absolute error* is the actual difference between the measured value and the accepted value. Relative error is expressed as a percentage, and it is therefore often called the *percent deviation of error*, or percent deviation from accepted value. It is calculated as follows:

$$\text{Deviation (\%)} = \frac{\text{difference from accepted value}}{\text{accepted value}} \times 100\%$$

Making a Line Graph

In laboratory experiments, you will usually control one variable, known as the independent variable, and observe how it affects another variable, known as the dependent variable.

For example, suppose you were asked to make a line graph to show how air temperature changes with time. In this experiment, you are controlling the time intervals at which the air temperature is measured. Therefore, time is the independent variable and air temperature is the dependent variable.

**Data for Air Temperature
Versus Time**

Time	Air Temperature (°C)
6:00 A.M.	10
10:00 A.M.	16
2:00 P.M.	21
6:00 P.M.	26

The independent variable is plotted on the x-axis. The x-axis is labeled "Time" and shows the time intervals at which temperature was measured. The dependent variable is plotted on the y-axis. The y-axis is labeled "Air Temperature (°C)" and has a range from 10°C to 26°C.

Think of your graph as a grid that has lines running horizontally from the y-axis and vertically from the x-axis. Notice that each time value has a corresponding air temperature value. To plot a point, find the x value on the x-axis. Follow the vertical line from the x-axis until it intersects the horizontal line from the y-axis at the corresponding y value. Place your point at the intersection of these two lines.

Earth Science Lab Tests

DETERMINING MINERAL HARDNESS AND STREAK

MINERAL HARDNESS

Hardness is the resistance of a mineral to being scratched. Hardness is determined by a scratch test. The Mohs hardness scale classifies minerals from 1 (softest) to 10 (hardest).

A mineral's hardness may be determined by scratching it with minerals from the Mohs scale or with other minerals or common objects of known hardness, such as a fingernail (hardness 2.5), a copper penny (hardness 3.0), a glass plate (hardness 5.5), or a steel file (hardness 6.0).

PRACTICE

1. What is the hardness of a mineral sample that is scratched by a copper penny but not by a fingernail?

2. What is the hardness of a mineral sample that is scratched by a steel file but not by a glass plate?

Mohs Hardness Scale

Mineral	Hardness
Talc	1
Gypsum	2
Calcite	3
Fluorite	4
Apatite	5
Feldspar	6
Quartz	7
Topaz	8
Corundum	9
Diamond	10

MINERAL STREAK

Streak is the color of a mineral in a finely powdered form. The streak shows less variation than the color of a sample; thus, it is more useful in identification.

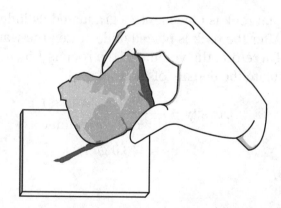

To perform a streak test, rub the mineral sample against a streak plate to determine the color of the mineral in its powdered form. Compare the streak to the color of the mineral.

PRACTICE

Perform a streak test on a variety of minerals. Which minerals have the same color as their streak? Which do not?

Unit XVI Earth Science Lab Skills *continued*

DETERMINING DENSITY OF AN IRREGULAR SOLID

Density is the mass of a mineral sample per unit of volume.

$$\text{Density} = \frac{\text{Mass}}{\text{Volume}}$$

The mass of a mineral sample can be determined by using a balance, such as a triple-beam balance or an electronic balance (see page 213). The volume of an irregular solid, such as a mineral sample, can be determined through the method of water displacement.

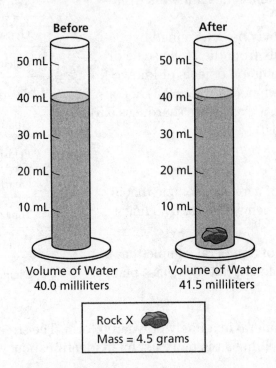

Before	After
50 mL	50 mL
40 mL	40 mL
30 mL	30 mL
20 mL	20 mL
10 mL	10 mL
Volume of Water 40.0 milliliters	Volume of Water 41.5 milliliters

Rock X
Mass = 4.5 grams

In the diagram, a 4.5-gram rock is placed into a graduated cylinder holding exactly 40 mL (40 cm^3) of water. After the rock is placed underwater, the water level rises to 41.5 mL (an increase of 1.5 cm^3). Therefore, the volume of the rock is 1.5 cm^3. Using the formula for density, you can now calculate the density of the rock:

$$\text{Density} = \frac{4.5 \text{ g}}{1.5 \text{ cm}^3} \quad \begin{array}{l}\text{(mass)} \\ \text{(volume)}\end{array}$$

$$\text{Density} = 3.0 \text{ g/cm}^3$$

PRACTICE

1. What is the density of a 6.7-g mineral sample that has a volume of 2.4 cm^3?

2. What is the volume of a 3.5-g mineral sample that has a density of 1.7 g/cm^3?

3. What is the mass of a mineral sample that has a density of 4.1 g/cm^3 and a volume 1.3 cm^3?

| Unit XVI Earth Science Lab Skills *continued*

DETERMINING RELATIVE HUMIDITY

Humidity is a measure of the water vapor content of the air. The amount of water vapor the air can hold varies with air temperature. Warm air can hold more water vapor than cooler air. Therefore, scientists usually express humidity as *relative humidity*. Relative humidity is a ratio that compares the actual amount of water vapor in the air with the maximum amount of water vapor air can hold at a given temperature. For example, when the relative humidity is 75%, the air is holding three-fourths as much water vapor as it could hold at the present temperature.

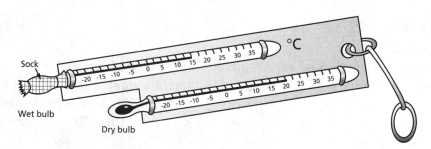

A *sling psychrometer* can be used to measure relative humidity. It consists of two thermometers mounted side by side. One thermometer is ordinary and measures the actual air temperature, or *dry-bulb temperature*. The other thermometer has a wet wick covering its bulb and measures the *wet-bulb temperature*. As the psychrometer is swung though the air, water evaporates from the wet wick of the wet-bulb thermometer, and the evaporation cools the thermometer. The difference between the wet-bulb and dry-bulb temperatures is then used with a chart to find the relative humidity. This chart can be found in the *Earth Science Reference Tables* section on page 243.

EXAMPLE

A sling psychrometer gives a dry-bulb temperature reading of 10°C and a wet-bulb reading of 6°C. What is the relative humidity of the air?

To find relative humidity, first locate the dry-bulb temperature (10°C) in the left-most column of the chart. Place your finger on this temperature. The difference between the dry-bulb and wet-bulb readings is 4°C, so look for the number 4 in the top row of numbers. Slide your finger to the right in the "10" row until you reach the "4" column. The number in the box is the relative humidity of the air.

PRACTICE

1. What is the relative humidity of the air if the dry-bulb temperature is 22°C and the wet-bulb temperature is 11°C?

2. What is the relative humidity of the air if the dry-bulb temperature is 14°C and the wet-bulb temperature is 13°C?

Earth Science Reference Tables

The *Earth Science Reference Tables (ESRT)* is your most important resource for the Earth Science Regents Exam. Understanding the information in the *ESRT* and how to use it on the exam will be of critical importance to your performance.

Physical Constants
RADIOACTIVE DECAY DATA
This table can be used to solve problems involving the calculation of absolute age. *Half-life* is the amount of time it takes for one half of a radioactive sample to change into its decay product. For example, it takes 5.7×10^3 (5,700) years for one half of a given carbon-14 sample to change into its decay product, nitrogen-14 (N^{14}). (See Unit VIII for more information on how this table is used.)

SPECIFIC HEATS OF COMMON MATERIALS
Specific heat is the energy needed to change the temperature of 1 g of a substance by 1°C. Specific heat is important for understanding climate. Water has a higher specific heat than land materials. Because of this, water changes temperature more slowly than does land. (See Unit XII for more information on how this table is used.)

PROPERTIES OF WATER
When water changes state, latent heat is either absorbed or given off. Latent heat is an important reservoir of atmospheric energy. *Melting* is the change from the solid to the liquid state. *Freezing* is the change from liquid to solid. Notice that the same amount of energy is involved in both processes. *Vaporization* is the change from liquid to gas. The opposite process, *condensation*, is the change from gas to liquid. Again, the same amount of energy is involved in both processes, but it is a lot more energy. (See Unit XI for more information on how this table is used.)

Equations
Percent deviation from accepted value   Use this formula to calculate the error of an experiment. (See the Lab Skills section, page 216, for information on how this equation is used.)

Eccentricity of an ellipse   Use this formula to calculate *eccentricity*, the deviation of a planet's orbit from a perfect circle. Eccentricity can range from 0 to 1. (See Unit XIV)

Gradient   Use this formula to calculate the change in a field value (elevation, humidity, temperature, etc.) between two points a certain distance apart. (See Unit II and Unit VI)

Rate of change   Use this formula to calculate how the value of a variable (humidity, temperature, sea level, etc.) changes with time.

Density of a substance   Use this formula to calculate *density*, the ratio of the mass of a substance to its volume. (See Unit III)

Name _____ Class _____ Date _____

The University of the State of New York • THE STATE EDUCATION DEPARTMENT • Albany, New York 12234 • www.nysed.gov

Earth Science Reference Tables

PHYSICAL CONSTANTS

Radioactive Decay Data

RADIOACTIVE ISOTOPE	DISINTEGRATION	HALF-LIFE (years)
Carbon-14	$C^{14} \rightarrow N^{14}$	5.7×10^3
Potassium-40	$K^{40} \rightarrow Ar^{40}$ $\searrow Ca^{40}$	1.3×10^9
Uranium-238	$U^{238} \rightarrow Pb^{206}$	4.5×10^9
Rubidium-87	$Rb^{87} \rightarrow Sr^{87}$	4.9×10^{10}

Specific Heats of Common Materials

MATERIAL		SPECIFIC HEAT (calories/gram • C°)
Water	solid	0.5
	liquid	1.0
	gas	0.5
Dry air		0.24
Basalt		0.20
Granite		0.19
Iron		0.11
Copper		0.09
Lead		0.03

Properties of Water

Energy gained during melting	80 calories/gram
Energy released during freezing	80 calories/gram
Energy gained during vaporization	540 calories/gram
Energy released during condensation	540 calories/gram
Density at 3.98°C	1.00 gram/milliliter

EQUATIONS

Percent deviation from accepted value	deviation (%) =	$\dfrac{\text{difference from accepted value}}{\text{accepted value}} \times 100$
Eccentricity of an ellipse	eccentricity =	$\dfrac{\text{distance between foci}}{\text{length of major axis}}$
Gradient	gradient =	$\dfrac{\text{change in field value}}{\text{distance}}$
Rate of change	rate of change =	$\dfrac{\text{change in field value}}{\text{time}}$
Density of a substance	density =	$\dfrac{\text{mass}}{\text{volume}}$

2001 EDITION

This edition of the Earth Science Reference Tables should be used in the classroom beginning in the 2000–2001 school year. The first examination for which these tables will be used is the January 2001 Regents Examination in Earth Science.

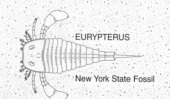

EURYPTERUS

New York State Fossil

cm 1 2 3 4 5 6 7 8 9 10 11 12 13 14 15 16 17 18 19 20 21 22 23 24 25

Name _____ Class _____ Date _____

Generalized Landscape Regions of New York State

This map shows the landscape regions of New York State. A *landscape* is the general shape of the land surface. A *landform* is a single feature of a landscape. Landscapes are generally made of a variety of related landforms, such as mountains, valleys, and rivers.

Most landscape regions can be classified as plains, plateaus, or mountains, based on their relief. *Relief* is the difference in elevation from the highest point to the lowest point on the land.

- *Plains* are relatively flat landscapes, with little relief.
- *Plateaus* have more relief (are less flat) than plains.
- *Mountain* landscapes have the greatest relief.

On the Regents Exam, it may be necessary for you to use this map in conjunction with other sections of the *Earth Science Reference Tables*. This map can be used along with the "Generalized Bedrock Geology of New York State" map (page 225) to locate cities and other geographic features on the landscape map. For example, looking at the landscape map and the bedrock geology map, you can see that Old Forge is located in the Adirondack Mountains, which are underlain by gneiss, quartzite, and marble bedrock.

Practice

1. Locate the approximate latitude and longitude of the following landscape regions:
  (a) Tug Hill Plateau
  (b) Taconic Mountains
  (c) The Catskills

2. Within what landscape region is the island of Manhattan located?

3. Which city is located closest to 43°N, 77°W?

Name _____   Class _____   Date _____

Generalized Landscape Regions of New York State

N ←

NEW ENGLAND PROVINCE (HIGHLANDS)

HUDSON HIGHLANDS

MANHATTAN PRONG

ATLANTIC COASTAL PLAIN

CHAMPLAIN LOWLANDS

TACONIC MOUNTAINS

HUDSON–MOHAWK LOWLANDS

NEWARK LOWLANDS

ST. LAWRENCE LOWLANDS

ADIRONDACK MOUNTAINS

THE CATSKILLS

TUG HILL PLATEAU

GRENVILLE PROVINCE (HIGHLANDS)

INTERIOR LOWLANDS

LAKE ONTARIO

ERIE-ONTARIO LOWLANDS (PLAINS)

ALLEGHENY PLATEAU

APPALACHIAN PLATEAU (UPLANDS)

LAKE ERIE

KEY
— Major Geographic Province Boundary
····· Landscape Region Boundary
—··— State Boundary
—·— International Boundary

Generalized Bedrock Geology of New York State

This map gives the geologic age and rock type for the bedrock in different regions of New York State. Notice the different shading patterns on the map. At the bottom left of the map, you will find a key for the shading patterns. Each shading pattern gives the geologic age and rock type for the bedrock in that region. For example, note that the oldest rocks in New York State are of Precambrian age. These rocks are exposed in the Adirondack Mountains in northern New York State and in the Hudson Highlands between New Jersey and Connecticut. Long Island contains the youngest "bedrock." It is composed of geologically recent sediments of glacial origin.

On the Regents Exam, it may be necessary for you to use this map in conjunction with other sections of the *Earth Science Reference Tables*. For example, the absolute ages of these bedrock regions and the fossils they contain can be determined by using this map along with the "Geologic History of New York State" chart on page 235. You can also use this geology map in conjunction with the "Generalized Landscape Regions of New York State" map to find out about the landforms in which each bedrock is found.

Other information found on this map:

- latitude and longitude coordinates
- city locations
- locations of major rivers and lakes

Practice

1. Where are the oldest rocks in New York State?

2. How old are the oldest rocks in New York State?

3. How old are the oldest sedimentary rocks in New York State?

4. Which New York State landscape region contains bedrock of Devonian age?

5. In which New York State landscape region might you find fossils of the earliest insects?

Generalized Bedrock Geology of New York State

modified from
GEOLOGICAL SURVEY
NEW YORK STATE MUSEUM
1989

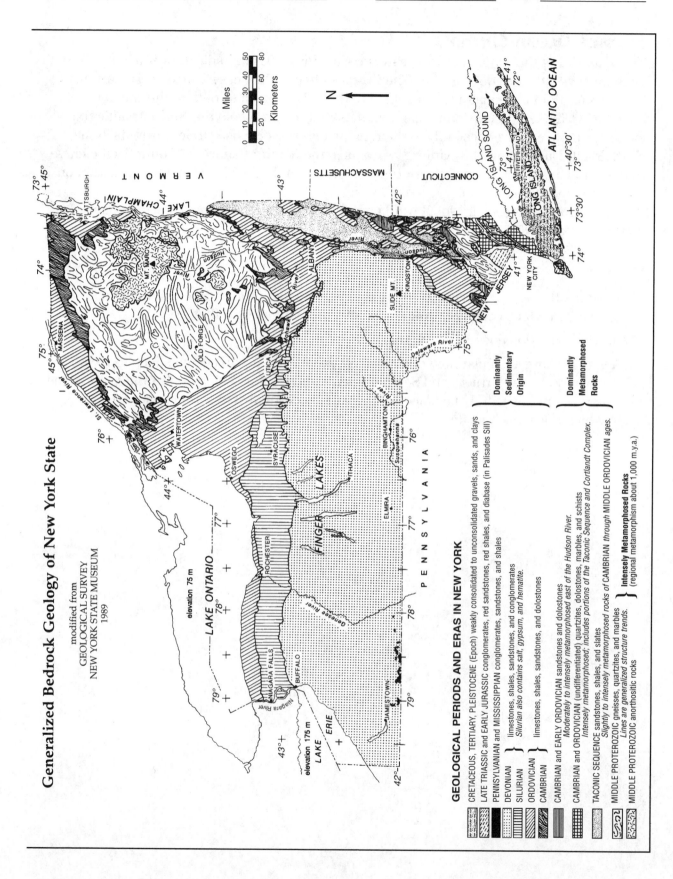

GEOLOGICAL PERIODS AND ERAS IN NEW YORK

CRETACEOUS, TERTIARY, PLEISTOCENE (Epoch) weakly consolidated to unconsolidated gravels, sands, and clays

LATE TRIASSIC and EARLY JURASSIC conglomerates, red sandstones, red shales, and diabase (in Palisades Sill)

PENNSYLVANIAN and MISSISSIPPIAN conglomerates, sandstones, and shales

DEVONIAN { limestones, shales, sandstones, and conglomerates

SILURIAN { limestones, shales, sandstones, and conglomerates
Silurian also contains salt, gypsum, and hematite.

ORDOVICIAN { limestones, shales, sandstones, and dolostones

CAMBRIAN { limestones, shales, sandstones, and dolostones

} Dominantly Sedimentary Origin

CAMBRIAN and EARLY ORDOVICIAN sandstones and dolostones
Moderately to intensely metamorphosed east of the Hudson River.

CAMBRIAN and ORDOVICIAN (undifferentiated) quartzites, dolostones, marbles, and schists
Intensely metamorphosed; includes portions of the Taconic Sequence and Cortlandt Complex.

TACONIC SEQUENCE sandstones, shales, and slates
Slightly to intensely metamorphosed rocks of CAMBRIAN through MIDDLE ORDOVICIAN ages.

MIDDLE PROTEROZOIC gneisses, quartzites, and marbles
Lines are generalized structure trends.

MIDDLE PROTEROZOIC anorthositic rocks

} Dominantly Metamorphosed Rocks

} Intensely Metamorphosed Rocks
(regional metamorphism about 1,000 m.y.a.)

Surface Ocean Currents

This map shows the major surface ocean currents. Black arrows indicate warm currents and white arrows indicate cool currents. The Coriolis effect influences surface ocean currents. Currents north of the equator are deflected to the right. Currents south of the equator are deflected to the left. Notice in the map that most of the currents in the North Atlantic follow a circular path, curving constantly to the right in a great clockwise circle. Currents in the North Pacific also follow this pattern. Currents in the South Atlantic and South Pacific curve to the left in a counterclockwise pattern. (See Unit IX and Unit XII for more information on how this map is used.)

A similar effect is seen in global wind patterns, as seen in the Planetary Wind Belts graphic on page 247.

Practice

1. Describe the ocean current called the Gulf Stream. Is this a warm current or a cool current? In which ocean is it found? In what direction does it flow?

2. In what direction does the California Current flow?

3. A gyre is a large, circular flow of water. Use the surface ocean currents map to locate gyres in both the Northern and Southern hemispheres. For each gyre, list the name of the ocean where it is found, the names of the surface currents that form it, and the direction in which the gyre circulates.

Name _____ Class _____ Date _____

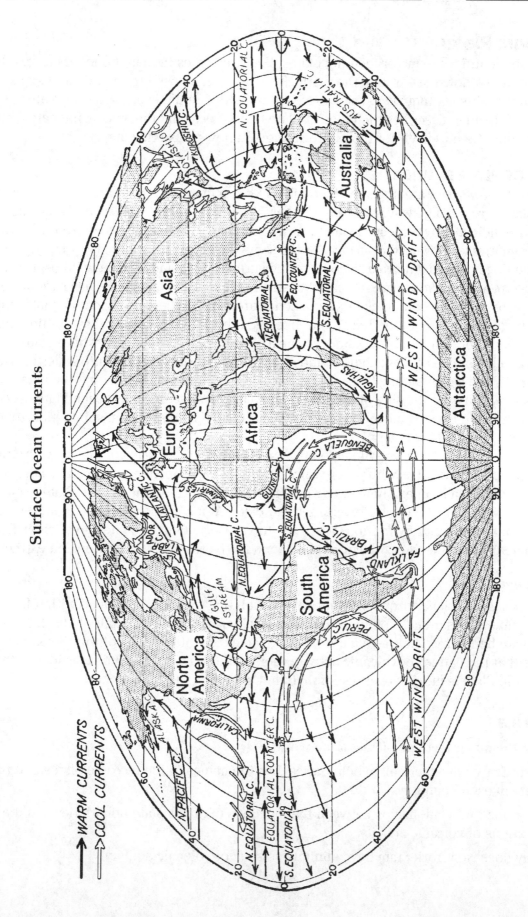

Surface Ocean Currents

→ WARM CURRENTS
⇒ COOL CURRENTS

Tectonic Plates

This map identifies the major tectonic plates, the three types of plate boundaries, and the location of key hot spots around the world. The map can be used to identify and explain plate movements, earthquakes, volcanoes, and related tectonic events. A key located at the bottom of the map describes the types of plate boundaries, and the arrows indicate their relative motion. (See Unit VII for more information on how to use this map.)

TYPES OF PLATE BOUNDARIES

Divergent boundaries are indicated by double lines on the map. These are places where tectonic plates are pulling away from one another. Mid-ocean ridges, such as the Mid-Atlantic Ridge, are indicated by a special symbol. At a mid-ocean ridge, molten rock from Earth's interior (magma) rises toward the surface. At the same time, the lithosphere is spreading away from the ridge, allowing magma to come to the surface, cool, and form new lithosphere.

Convergent boundaries are indicated by lines with black rectangles. These are places where tectonic plates collide. Subduction zones are places where one tectonic plate sinks, or *subducts*, beneath another. Recall that oceanic lithosphere is denser than continental lithosphere and therefore tends to subduct beneath continental lithosphere where plates collide. A good example of this can be found along the western coast of South America. Here, the Nazca Plate is subducting beneath the South American Plate. (Note that the black rectangles are always on the side of the overriding plate.) As the oceanic Nazca Plate descends, it begins to melt, causing magma to rise to the surface. For this reason, subduction zones are regions of volcanic activity.

Transform boundaries are indicated by a single, thin line. These are places where two plates slip past each other without creating or destroying lithosphere. The San Andreas Fault in California is an example of a transform boundary. Here, the Pacific Plate is moving northwest with respect to the North American Plate. At any place along the fault, the plates may be locked together by friction. When the force on the fault becomes great enough to overcome friction, the fault breaks suddenly and the plates move, generating an earthquake.

HOT SPOTS

A *hot spot* is a stationary zone of magma formation that extends from deep within Earth's interior up to the surface. Hot spots are volcanically active areas, commonly far from a tectonic plate boundary. The Hawaiian Islands are an excellent example of this. Scientists believe that the pattern of volcanic activity seen on the Hawaiian Islands is evidence that the Pacific Plate is moving over a stationary hot spot under the lithosphere.

Practice

1. List the major tectonic plates of the world.

2. Identify two divergent plate boundaries. List the names of the tectonic plates that participate in each boundary.

3. Describe the relationships between the locations of major plate boundaries and the locations of volcanic activity.

4. Why does New York State have minimal seismic or volcanic activity?

Tectonic Plates

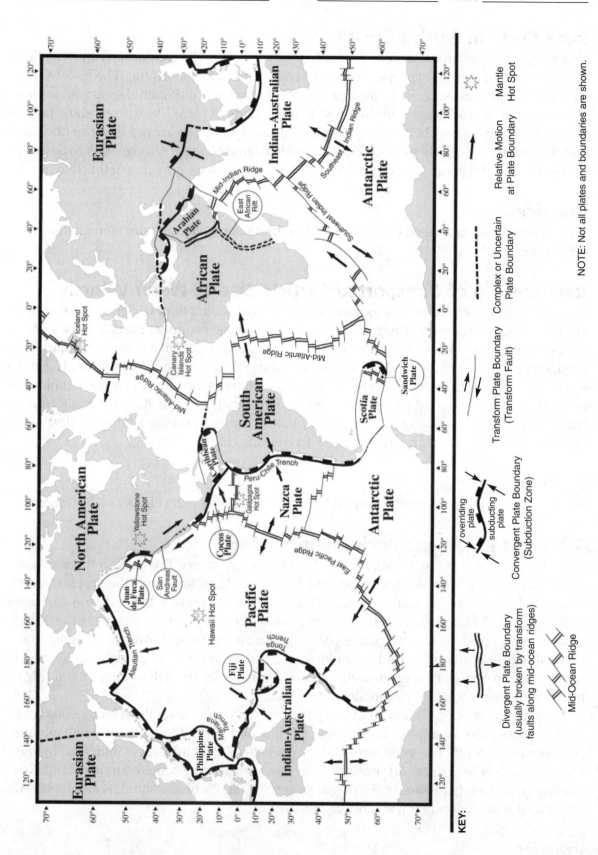

KEY:

Divergent Plate Boundary
(usually broken by transform
faults along mid-ocean ridges)

Convergent Plate Boundary
(Subduction Zone)

overriding plate

subducting plate

Transform Plate Boundary
(Transform Fault)

Complex or Uncertain
Plate Boundary

Relative Motion
at Plate Boundary

Mantle
Hot Spot

Mid-Ocean Ridge

NOTE: Not all plates and boundaries are shown.

Rock Cycle in Earth's Crust

This diagram gives information on how different types of rocks can form. Within the three boxes are the three rock types: sedimentary, igneous, and metamorphic. The in-between stages of magma and sediments are shown in ovals because, although they are important substances in the rock cycle, they are not actually kinds of rock. The arrows show how rock materials change in the rock cycle. The words printed along the arrows describe the changes and the order in which they occur. For example, magma changes into igneous rock by the process of solidification. (See Unit IV for more information on how to use this diagram.)

Practice

What type of rock is formed by the deposition, burial, compaction, and cementation of sediments?

Relationship of Transported Particle Size to Water Velocity

This graph shows the relationship between the size of sediment particles and the minimum stream velocity required to transport them. The larger the sediment particles, the faster a stream must move to keep them in motion. Notice that the graph also gives the particle size (diameter) for the various kinds of sediments (clay, silt, sand, etc.). Sometimes, these sizes are needed in questions that have nothing to do with transport. For example, cobbles are rocks that are between 6.4 cm and 25.6 cm in diameter. The graph shows that a stream must travel at a minimum velocity of about 180 cm/sec in order to transport the smallest cobbles. (See Unit VI for more information on how to use this chart.)

Practice

What sediment particles can be carried by a stream moving at a velocity of 100 cm/sec?

Scheme for Igneous Rock Identification

This chart can help you understand and classify igneous rocks. Rocks with the smallest grains and the finest texture are at the top. As you go down the chart, the grains become larger and the texture becomes coarser. This difference in texture is due to the environment of formation. Extrusive rocks form from magma that cools quickly on or near Earth's surface, resulting in small mineral grains (crystals). Intrusive rocks form from magma that cools slowly underground, resulting in large mineral grains. As you go right on the chart, the rocks become darker, denser, and more mafic. Mafic rocks are rich in magnesium (Mg) and iron (Fe). Felsic rocks are rich in aluminum (Al).

Use the bottom of the chart to identify the percentage of minerals in an igneous rock sample. Notice, for example, that rhyolite, granite, and pegmatite have the same mineral composition, but differ in grain size. The percentage of each mineral is indicated by the scale on each side of the chart. For example, the most felsic granite contains about 73% potassium feldspar, 10% quartz, 8% plagioclase feldspar, 7% biotite, and 2% amphibole. (See Unit IV for more information about igneous rocks.)

Practice

1. How is rhyolite different from granite?

2. Which minerals present in mafic igneous rocks are not present in felsic igneous rocks?

Name _____ Class _____ Date _____

Rock Cycle in Earth's Crust

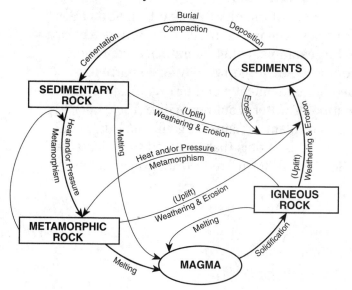

Relationship of Transported Particle Size to Water Velocity

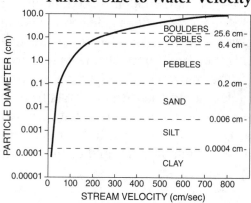

*This generalized graph shows the water velocity needed to maintain, but not start, movement. Variations occur due to differences in particle density and shape.

Scheme for Igneous Rock Identification

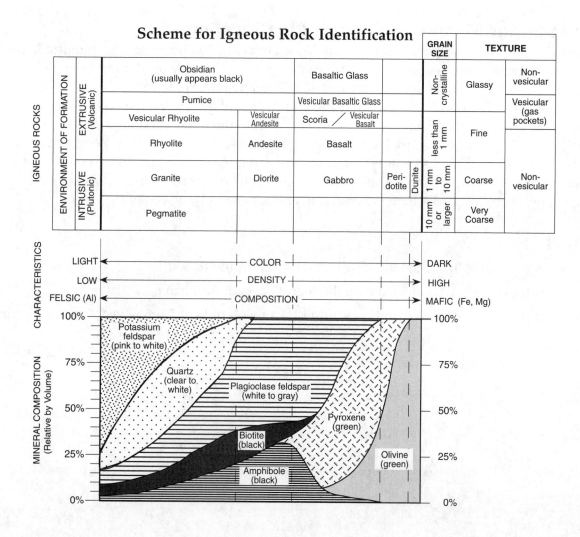

Scheme for Sedimentary Rock Identification

Use this chart to identify sedimentary rocks. The top of the chart gives information about clastic rocks—rocks made from sediment particles. The rocks in this part of the chart are ordered from top to bottom by particle size. For example, conglomerate is composed of large sediment particles, whereas shale is composed of very fine, clay-sized particles.

The bottom of the chart gives information about chemically and/or organically formed rocks. Rocks that form crystals from evaporation of water would be halite (rock salt), gypsum, or dolostone. Rocks that form from fossils or plant remains (organic material) could be coal or limestone. The far-right column show the symbols that are used to indicate each type of rock on maps and exam questions. (See Unit IV for more information about sedimentary rocks.)

Practice

1. What are the two major divisions of sedimentary rocks?

2. How are sandstone, siltstone, and shale different?

3. How is rock gypsum formed?

Scheme for Metamorphic Rock Identification

Use this chart to identify metamorphic rocks. A great way to recognize a metamorphic rock is to look for bands, or *foliation* (organization of minerals into layers), in the sample. The top right section of the chart shows the four foliated metamorphic rocks (slate, phyllite, schist, gneiss), listed in order of increasing grain size and increasing metamorphic changes. The shaded bars in the "Composition" column indicate the mineral composition of these rocks. The four nonfoliated rocks in the bottom right section do not show progressive metamorphic changes. Each has a different grain size and mineral composition. The far-right column shows the symbols that are used to indicate each type of rock on maps and exam questions. (See Unit IV for more information about metamorphic rocks.)

Practice

1. What mineral is found in all four foliated metamorphic rocks?

2. What foliated rock results from the high-grade metamorphism of schist?

3. What fine-grained nonfoliated rock forms as a result of heat from nearby lava or magma?

Scheme for Sedimentary Rock Identification

INORGANIC LAND-DERIVED SEDIMENTARY ROCKS					
TEXTURE	GRAIN SIZE	COMPOSITION	COMMENTS	ROCK NAME	MAP SYMBOL
Clastic (fragmental)	Pebbles, cobbles, and/or boulders embedded in sand, silt, and/or clay	Mostly quartz, feldspar, and clay minerals; may contain fragments of other rocks and minerals	Rounded fragments	Conglomerate	
			Angular fragments	Breccia	
	Sand (0.2 to 0.006 cm)		Fine to coarse	Sandstone	
	Silt (0.006 to 0.0004 cm)		Very fine grain	Siltstone	
	Clay (less than 0.0004 cm)		Compact; may split easily	Shale	

CHEMICALLY AND/OR ORGANICALLY FORMED SEDIMENTARY ROCKS					
TEXTURE	GRAIN SIZE	COMPOSITION	COMMENTS	ROCK NAME	MAP SYMBOL
Crystalline	Varied	Halite	Crystals from chemical precipitates and evaporites	Rock Salt	
	Varied	Gypsum		Rock Gypsum	
	Varied	Dolomite		Dolostone	
Bioclastic	Microscopic to coarse	Calcite	Cemented shell fragments or precipitates of biologic origin	Limestone	
	Varied	Carbon	From plant remains	Coal	

Scheme for Metamorphic Rock Identification

TEXTURE		GRAIN SIZE	COMPOSITION	TYPE OF METAMORPHISM	COMMENTS	ROCK NAME	MAP SYMBOL
FOLIATED	MINERAL ALIGNMENT	Fine	MICA QUARTZ FELDSPAR AMPHIBOLE GARNET PYROXENE	Regional	Low-grade metamorphism of shale	Slate	
		Fine to medium		(Heat and pressure increase with depth)	Foliation surfaces shiny from microscopic mica crystals	Phyllite	
					Platy mica crystals visible from metamorphism of clay or feldspars	Schist	
	BANDING	Medium to coarse			High-grade metamorphism; some mica changed to feldspar; segregated by mineral type into bands	Gneiss	
NONFOLIATED		Fine	Variable	Contact (Heat)	Various rocks changed by heat from nearby magma/lava	Hornfels	
		Fine to coarse	Quartz	Regional or Contact	Metamorphism of quartz sandstone	Quartzite	
			Calcite and/or dolomite		Metamorphism of limestone or dolostone	Marble	
		Coarse	Various minerals in particles and matrix		Pebbles may be distorted or stretched	Metaconglomerate	

Geologic History of New York State

This chart contains much information about Earth's geologic history. You should be familiar with the information provided by this chart. (See Unit VIII for more information about this chart and how to use it.)

Look at the chart and note the following:

- The left-most four columns show the major divisions of geologic time and the absolute age of these divisions in millions of years before the present. For example, the Permian Period began 290 million years ago and ended 251 million years ago.
- The "Life on Earth" column identifies major events in the evolution of life. This information comes from the fossil record. For example, the earliest fish appeared during the late Cambrian Period.
- The "Rock Record in NYS" column indicates the ages of bedrock that can be found in New York State. Spaces between black bars represent unconformities, intervals for which there is no bedrock in New York State.
- The "Time Distribution of Fossils" column indicates when certain fossil organisms lived. Notice the organisms labeled A–Z on the top of the chart are index fossils. The letters that appear on the vertical lines show when these particular organisms were alive. For example, the (Y) on the brachiopod bar indicates that, while there have been brachiopods in New York State since the Cambrian period, the particular brachiopod named *Eospirifer* lived only during the Silurian Period, 443–418 million years ago.
- The "Tectonic Events Affecting Northeast North America" column indicates important interactions between tectonic plates that occurred or are currently occurring. Each tectonic event is shown by a black bar. This information can be used in conjunction with information in the "Important Geologic Events in New York" column to identify the causes of mountain-building events (orogenies) in New York State. For example, the Taconian Orogeny, in which the Taconic Mountains east of the Hudson River Valley formed, occurred early in the Ordovician period. The "Tectonic Events" column reveals that this was the time of a continental collision.
- The maps in the "Inferred Position of Earth's Landmasses" column show how the continents developed and how their positions shifted over millions of years. Specific positions of North America (shown in black) are indicated. For example, notice that 362 million years ago North America was located along the equator. As time passed, North America drifted north and then westward, creating the North Atlantic Ocean.

Practice

1. When did dinosaurs become extinct?

2. During which time period did North America separate from Africa?

3. When was the Acadian Orogeny? What caused it?

GEOLOGIC HISTORY OF NEW YORK STATE

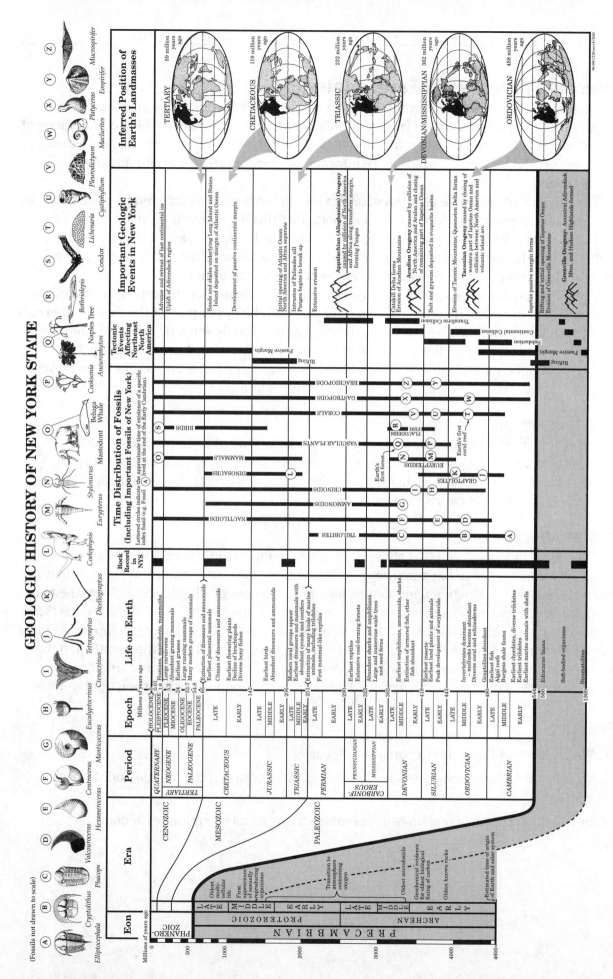

Inferred Properties of Earth's Interior

This figure has three parts: a diagram showing the major layers of Earth's interior, a pressure graph, and a temperature graph. The word "inferred" in the title refers to the fact that much of the information is based on laboratory simulations and other investigations, rather than on direct observations. (See Unit I for more information about Earth's interior and how to use this diagram.)

The top part of the figure illustrates Earth's internal structure, as inferred by seismic wave analysis. The labels and surface features indicate that this diagram represents a region of Earth from the middle of the Atlantic Ocean, across North America, and into the Pacific Ocean. Notice the arrows that show convection currents at the Mid-Atlantic Ridge, and sub-duction of an oceanic plate beneath a continental plate at the trench.

The diagram also shows the major layers of Earth's interior. Earth's top layer is the *litho-sphere*, which includes the crust (shown in black) and the upper part of the mantle. Beneath the lithosphere is the *asthenosphere*, or plastic mantle. The flowing, or "plastic," nature of this layer allows the rigid lithospheric plates to slowly move over Earth's surface. The stiffer, more solid part of the mantle lies above the outer and inner cores. The density range of each layer is provided along the right edge of the diagram.

PRESSURE GRAPH

The middle section is a graph that shows how pressure (in millions of atmospheres) changes with depth. Pressure is caused by the weight of the layers above; therefore, it should not be surprising to see that pressure increases with depth. Vertical dashed lines mark the boundaries between the layers.

TEMPERATURE GRAPH

The lower section is a graph that shows how actual temperature (dark line) changes with depth. The dashed line in the graph represents melting point temperature. When the melting point line is below the actual temperature line, materials are in a liquid state. When the melt-ing point line is above the actual temperature line, materials are in a solid state. Notice that the melting point line ends at the bottom of the mantle and starts again at the top of the outer core. This abrupt change is due to a difference in composition between the mantle and the outer core. Question marks on the melting point line indicate that scientists are not sure about this part of the line. Vertical dashed lines mark the boundaries between the layers.

Practice

1. Which layer of Earth has the greatest density?

2. What is the approximate pressure at the boundary between the mantle and the outer core?

3. In which of Earth's layers does temperature increase most rapidly with depth?

Inferred Properties of Earth's Interior

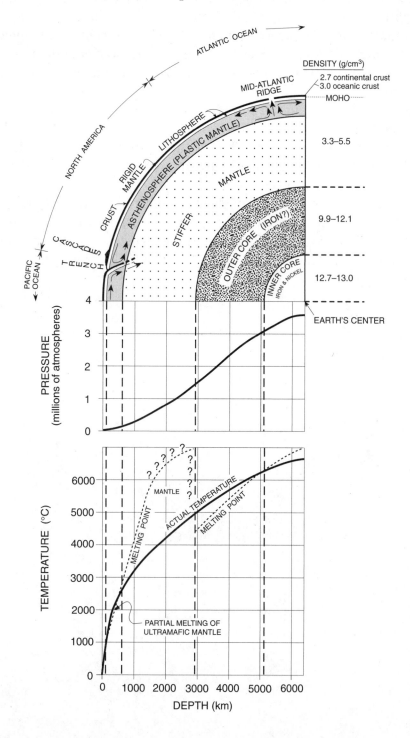

Name _____ Class _____ Date _____

Average Chemical Composition of Earth's Crust, Hydrosphere, and Troposphere

This chart provides information about the chemical makeup of the different parts of Earth.

- The *crust* is the hard, rocky, outer layer of Earth. Notice that the chemical composition of the crust is expressed in two different ways: abundance by mass and abundance by volume. For example, oxygen is by far the most abundant element in Earth's crust by both mass and volume. Silicon is the second most abundant element in Earth's crust by mass. Potassium is the second most abundant element in Earth's crust by volume.

- The *hydrosphere* is the liquid portion of Earth, which includes the salt water in the oceans; the fresh water in lakes, streams, and rivers; and all the water that is frozen in glaciers and in the polar ice caps. The chemical formula for water is H_2O. This explains why the composition of the hydrosphere (by volume) is 66% hydrogen and 33% oxygen.

- The *troposphere* is the lowest layer of Earth's atmosphere; the layer that is closest to Earth's surface. The troposphere contains many gases, but the two most abundant by volume are nitrogen and oxygen. Together, these two gases make up approximately 99% of all atmospheric gases.

Average Chemical Composition
of Earth's Crust, Hydrosphere, and Troposphere

ELEMENT (symbol)	CRUST		HYDROSPHERE	TROPOSPHERE
	Percent by Mass	Percent by Volume	Percent by Volume	Percent by Volume
Oxygen (O)	46.40	94.04	33.0	21.0
Silicon (Si)	28.15	0.88		
Aluminum (Al)	8.23	0.48		
Iron (Fe)	5.63	0.49		
Calcium (Ca)	4.15	1.18		
Sodium (Na)	2.36	1.11		
Magnesium (Mg)	2.33	0.33		
Potassium (K)	2.09	1.42		
Nitrogen (N)				78.0
Hydrogen (H)			66.0	
Other	0.66	0.07	1.0	1.0

Name _____ Class _____ Date _____

Earthquake P-wave and S-wave Travel Time

This graph can be used to determine the distance to an earthquake's epicenter by calculating the difference in arrival times of P-waves and S-waves. P-waves travel faster than S-waves and will always arrive at a seismograph station first. The greater the lag time between the arrival of P-waves and S-waves, the farther away is the epicenter. (See Unit VII for more information about earthquakes and how to use this graph.)

To calculate the distance to an epicenter—

1. Calculate the difference in arrival times between the P-waves and the S-waves. For example, suppose P-waves arrive at a seismograph station at 12:35 and S-waves arrive at 12:40. This is a difference of 5 minutes.

2. Place the edge of a sheet of paper along the y-axis (Travel Time). High on the left edge of the paper, mark a dot at time zero and another at the time corresponding to the difference you calculated in step 1. The distance between the dots represents the difference in arrival times of the P-waves and S-waves.

3. Keeping the lower dot on the lower graph line, and keeping the paper edge straight up and down, slide the paper up the curves until the gap between the lines matches the gap between the dots. When you find this position, read straight down the edge of the paper to the x-axis. The x-axis value is distance from the epicenter.

Practice

1. If P-waves arrive at a seismograph station 5 minutes and 20 seconds before S-waves arrive, what is the distance to the epicenter?

2. An earthquake's epicenter is 3.2×10^3 km from a seismograph station. How long did it take P-waves to arrive at this station?

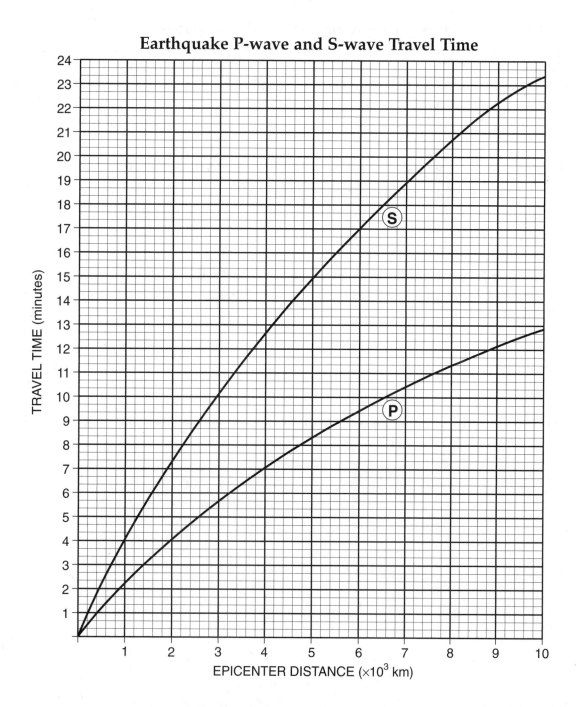

Earthquake P-wave and S-wave Travel Time

TRAVEL TIME (minutes) vs. EPICENTER DISTANCE ($\times 10^3$ km)

Dewpoint Temperatures and Relative Humidity

These charts can be used to determine the dew point and the relative humidity from a set of psychrometer readings. Dew point is the temperature to which the air would have to be cooled (at constant pressure and constant water vapor content) in order to reach saturation—that is, to reach a temperature at which the air is holding all the water vapor it possibly can. The higher the dew point, the greater the water vapor content of the air at a given temperature.

Relative humidity is a ratio that compares the actual amount of water vapor in the air with the maximum amount of water vapor air can hold at a given temperature. For example, when the relative humidity is 30%, it means that the air is holding only 30% of the water vapor it could possibly hold at that temperature.

To determine dew point and relative humidity from psychrometer readings—

1. Find the dry-bulb temperature in the left-most column.

2. Subtract the wet-bulb reading from the dry-bulb reading, and find this difference in the horizontal row at the top of the chart.

3. Move one finger across the row of numbers to the right of the dry-bulb reading and move another finger down the column of numbers below the difference reading at the top. The box where these two lines meet contains the dew point temperature or the relative humidity.

Practice

1. A psychrometer gives a dry-bulb reading of 30°C and a wet-bulb reading of 20°C. What is the dew point?

2. A psychrometer gives a dry-bulb reading of 15°C and a wet-bulb reading of 13°C. What is the relative humidity of the air?

Dewpoint Temperatures (°C)

Dry-Bulb Temperature (°C)	Difference Between Wet-Bulb and Dry-Bulb Temperatures (C°)															
	0	1	2	3	4	5	6	7	8	9	10	11	12	13	14	15
−20	−20	−33														
−18	−18	−28														
−16	−16	−24														
−14	−14	−21	−36													
−12	−12	−18	−28													
−10	−10	−14	−22													
−8	−8	−12	−18	−29												
−6	−6	−10	−14	−22												
−4	−4	−7	−12	−17	−29											
−2	−2	−5	−8	−13	−20											
0	0	−3	−6	−9	−15	−24										
2	2	−1	−3	−6	−11	−17										
4	4	1	−1	−4	−7	−11	−19									
6	6	4	1	−1	−4	−7	−13	−21								
8	8	6	3	1	−2	−5	−9	−14								
10	10	8	6	4	1	−2	−5	−9	−14	−28						
12	12	10	8	6	4	1	−2	−5	−9	−16						
14	14	12	11	9	6	4	1	−2	−5	−10	−17					
16	16	14	13	11	9	7	4	1	−1	−6	−10	−17				
18	18	16	15	13	11	9	7	4	2	−2	−5	−10	−19			
20	20	19	17	15	14	12	10	7	4	2	−2	−5	−10	−19		
22	22	21	19	17	16	14	12	10	8	5	3	−1	−5	−10	−19	
24	24	23	21	20	18	16	14	12	10	8	6	2	−1	−5	−10	−18
26	26	25	23	22	20	18	17	15	13	11	9	6	3	0	−4	−9
28	28	27	25	24	22	21	19	17	16	14	11	9	7	4	1	−3
30	30	29	27	26	24	23	21	19	18	16	14	12	10	8	5	1

Relative Humidity (%)

Dry-Bulb Temperature (°C)	Difference Between Wet-Bulb and Dry-Bulb Temperatures (C°)															
	0	1	2	3	4	5	6	7	8	9	10	11	12	13	14	15
−20	100	28														
−18	100	40														
−16	100	48														
−14	100	55	11													
−12	100	61	23													
−10	100	66	33													
−8	100	71	41	13												
−6	100	73	48	20												
−4	100	77	54	32	11											
−2	100	79	58	37	20	1										
0	100	81	63	45	28	11										
2	100	83	67	51	36	20	6									
4	100	85	70	56	42	27	14									
6	100	86	72	59	46	35	22	10								
8	100	87	74	62	51	39	28	17	6							
10	100	88	76	65	54	43	33	24	13	4						
12	100	88	78	67	57	48	38	28	19	10	2					
14	100	89	79	69	60	50	41	33	25	16	8	1				
16	100	90	80	71	62	54	45	37	29	21	14	7	1			
18	100	91	81	72	64	56	48	40	33	26	19	12	6			
20	100	91	82	74	66	58	51	44	36	30	23	17	11	5		
22	100	92	83	75	68	60	53	46	40	33	27	21	15	10	4	
24	100	92	84	76	69	62	55	49	42	36	30	25	20	14	9	4
26	100	92	85	77	70	64	57	51	45	39	34	28	23	18	13	9
28	100	93	86	78	71	65	59	53	47	42	36	31	26	21	17	12
30	100	93	86	79	72	66	61	55	49	44	39	34	29	25	20	16

Temperature

Use this figure to convert among the three temperature scales: Fahrenheit, Celsius, and Kelvin. For example, to find the Celsius and Kelvin equivalents of 70°F, first find 70° on the Fahrenheit scale. Look to the right to find the equal Celsius (32°C) and Kelvin (305K) temperatures. Note that on the Fahrenheit scale, each small line is 2°. On the Celsius and Kelvin scales, each small line is 1°.

Practice

At what temperature on the Celsius scale does water boil? At what temperature on the Fahrenheit scale does water boil?

Pressure

Use this figure to convert between two barometric pressure scales. One scale shows pressure as measured in millibars (mb). The other scale shows pressure as measured in inches of mercury. Note that on the millibar scale, each line is 1 mb. On the inches of mercury scale, each line is 0.01 inches of mercury. The dotted line shows standard air pressure at sea level—1013.2 mb.

Practice

Convert 30.20 inches of mercury to its equivalent pressure in millibars. Round your answer to the nearest 0.1 mb.

Weather Map Symbols

This figure is a key to the symbols found on weather maps. The top box provides a comprehensive key for interpreting a station model. The bottom box is a key to common weather map symbols.

STATION MODEL

A station model is a summary of the weather conditions near a weather observation station. Notice that in a station model, weather conditions are indicated by numbers and symbols. Read the explanations of the numbers and symbols. Also, pay attention to their positions around the center circle. Real station models may not contain as much detail as the one shown here, but the numbers and symbols will always be found in the same place.

BAROMETRIC PRESSURE

The barometric pressure indicator on a station model can be confusing. The key is to understand that normal pressures range from 950 mb to 1050 mb. Notice that barometric pressure is always shown as a three-digit number. To find the pressure that this represents, do the following:

1. Place a decimal point between the last two digits (for example, 196 becomes 19.6).
2. Place a 9 or 10 to the left of the resulting number to make a number between 950 and 1050. For example, attaching a 9 makes the number 919.6. Attaching a 10 makes the number 1019.6. The correct number to attach is 10, because 1019.6 is in the normal pressure range and 919.6 is not.

Name _____   Class _____   Date _____

Temperature

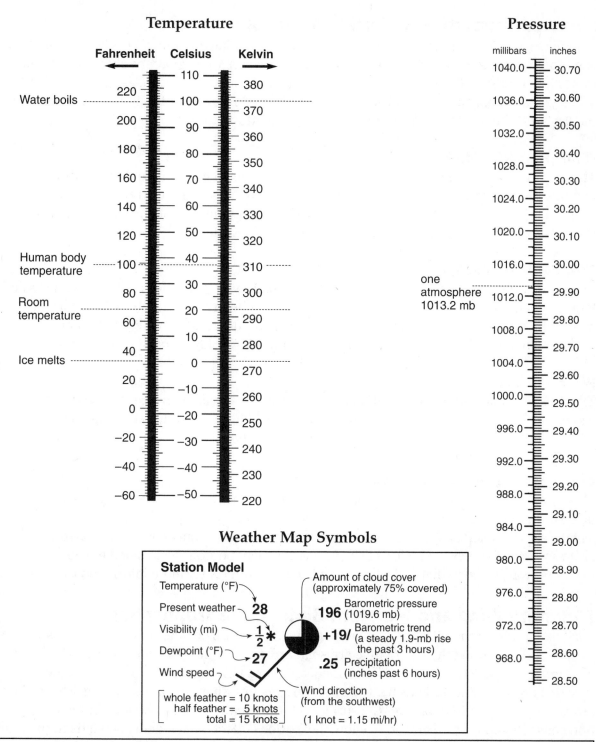

Fahrenheit Celsius Kelvin

Water boils

220 — 110 — 380
200 — 100 — 370
        90 — 360
180 — 80 — 350
160 — 70 — 340
140 — 60 — 330
120 — 50 — 320

Human body
temperature   100 — 40 — 310
                30 — 300
Room   80 — 20 — 290
temperature 60 — 10 — 280
                0 — 270
Ice melts   40 — -10 — 260
             20 —   — 250
              0 — -20 — 240
            -20 — -30 — 230
            -40 — -40 — 220
            -60 — -50

Pressure

millibars   inches

1040.0 — 30.70
1036.0 — 30.60
1032.0 — 30.50
         30.40
1028.0 — 30.30
1024.0 — 30.20
1020.0 — 30.10
1016.0 — 30.00

one
atmosphere 1012.0 — 29.90
1013.2 mb
1008.0 — 29.80
         29.70
1004.0 — 29.60
1000.0 — 29.50
 996.0 — 29.40
 992.0 — 29.30
         29.20
 988.0 — 29.10
 984.0 — 29.00
 980.0 — 28.90
 976.0 — 28.80
 972.0 — 28.70
 968.0 — 28.60
         28.50

Weather Map Symbols

Station Model

Temperature (°F)
Present weather — **28**
Visibility (mi) — ½ ✳
Dewpoint (°F) — **27**
Wind speed

whole feather = 10 knots
half feather = 5 knots
total = 15 knots

Amount of cloud cover
(approximately 75% covered)

196 Barometric pressure
(1019.6 mb)

+19/ Barometric trend
(a steady 1.9-mb rise
the past 3 hours)

.25 Precipitation
(inches past 6 hours)

Wind direction
(from the southwest)

(1 knot = 1.15 mi/hr)

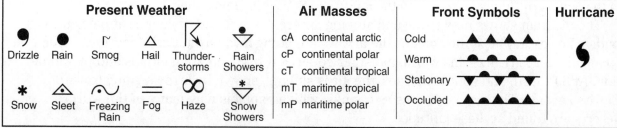

Present Weather						Air Masses	Front Symbols	Hurricane

Present Weather

Drizzle Rain Smog Hail Thunder-storms Rain Showers

Snow Sleet Freezing Rain Fog Haze Snow Showers

Air Masses

cA continental arctic
cP continental polar
cT continental tropical
mT maritime tropical
mP maritime polar

Front Symbols

Cold
Warm
Stationary
Occluded

Hurricane

Selected Properties of Earth's Atmosphere

This figure provides information about the structure of Earth's atmosphere. It can also be used to determine how temperature, pressure, and water vapor content changes with altitude. Note that the altitude scale on the left is used for all three graphs. As you go up the scale, you are going away from Earth's surface. Dotted lines mark the boundaries between the layers of the atmosphere. (See Unit X for more information.)

TEMPERATURE ZONES

The dark line shows the temperature trends of the atmosphere. Notice that as altitude increases, temperature drops in the troposphere; then it rises in the stratosphere, then it drops again in the mesosphere; and then it rises again in the thermosphere. These temperature trends are what scientists use to distinguish between layers.

ATMOSPHERIC PRESSURE

The scale on the bottom is in exponential notation. As you go to the right, the numbers get larger by ten times the amount (i.e., 10^{-1} is ten times the pressure of 10^{-2}). The dark line shows the atmospheric pressure. Notice that pressure decreases steadily with increasing altitude. This is because most of the air exists in the lower layers of the atmosphere.

WATER VAPOR

The dark line shows the concentration of water vapor in the atmosphere. Notice that the water vapor concentration decreases with increasing altitude, and that the atmosphere contains no measurable water vapor content above the tropopause.

Electromagnetic Spectrum

This chart shows the range of wavelengths of electromagnetic energy. Wavelength is the distance from the top of one wave to the top of the following wave. In the chart, shorter wavelengths are to the left and longer wavelengths are to the right. Notice that only a narrow band of electromagnetic energy is visible as light. The visible light portion is expanded to show the range of colors (wavelengths) that make up visible light. (See Unit X for more information.)

Planetary Wind and Moisture Belts in the Troposphere

This diagram is a generalization of wind patterns on Earth. The inner circle represents Earth's surface. Going around the inner circle are solid arrows that show the large convection cells that create the prevailing winds. Notice the jet streams between convection cells. Low pressure occurs where the air is rising. High pressure occurs where the air is sinking. The dashed arrows show wind direction over the surface—these are the surface portions of the convection cells. The arrows are curved to show the Coriolis effect, which deflects winds to the right in the Northern Hemisphere and to the left in the Southern Hemisphere.

The diagram shows how rising and sinking air creates wet and dry zones at particular latitudes. For example, at the equator the arrows are going away from Earth's surface, which means the air is rising. This warm, moist air cools as it rises, creating clouds and precipitation. At 30° north and south latitudes, the air is sinking, shown by arrows going toward Earth's surface. This dry air warms as it sinks, which explains why many of the world's deserts are found at these latitudes.

Selected Properties of Earth's Atmosphere

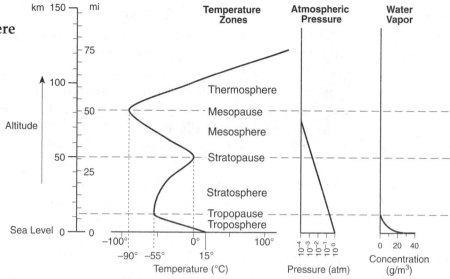

Electromagnetic Spectrum

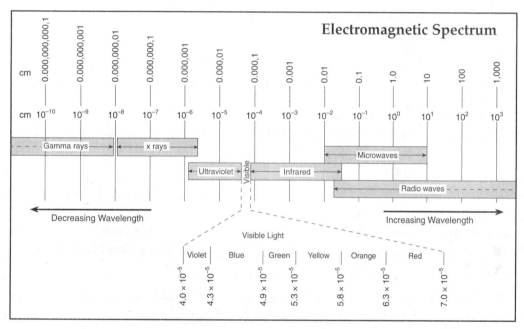

Planetary Wind and Moisture Belts in the Troposphere

The drawing to the left shows the locations of the belts near the time of an equinox. The locations shift somewhat with the changing latitude of the Sun's vertical ray. In the Northern Hemisphere, the belts shift northward in summer and southward in winter.

Luminosity and Temperature of Stars

This graph is also called the Hertzsprung-Russell Diagram, or H-R diagram, in honor of the two astronomers who developed it. It relates a star's absolute luminosity (the amount of light it emits) and its surface temperature (which indicates its color). It is important to understand that the graph shows how the star's luminosity compares to the luminosity of the sun. For example, a star with a luminosity of 100 would look 100 times brighter than the sun, if the two were seen from the same distance.

Notice that most stars fall into distinct groups. Most of the stars are classified as main-sequence stars, which run from the upper left to the lower right of the graph. In all main-sequence stars, nuclear fusion converts hydrogen into helium at a stable rate. Our sun is a main-sequence star. Blue and white stars are the hottest and brightest stars. Some white stars are dim, because they are very small. These are the white dwarfs. Red stars are the coolest stars, so they tend to be dimmer than other stars. If a red star is bright, it must be very large; it must be a red giant or a red supergiant, located in the upper right of the graph. Stars of special significance are labeled by name. (See Unit XV for more information about how stars are classified and how they evolve.)

Practice

1. Approximately how many times brighter is Betelgeuse than our sun?

2. What is the color of Rigel?

3. Which stars are brighter, blue supergiants or red giants?

Solar System Data

This chart provides a tremendous amount of information about the planets in our solar system, including each planet's mass, density, diameter, and average distance from the sun. It includes similar information for the sun and Earth's moon. Planets are listed in order of increasing distance from the sun. (See Unit XIV for more information about the solar system.)

Important facts and relationships to note:

- The four planets closest to the sun are smaller and less massive than the outer planets (except Pluto), yet they are much denser. This is because the inner planets are mainly composed of rock and metal, whereas the outer planets are mainly composed of gas.
- Period of revolution increases with increasing distance from the sun.
- Venus's period of rotation is longer than its period of revolution.
- Neptune has a near circular orbit (eccentricity = 0.009). Pluto has an extremely elliptical orbit (eccentricity = 0.250). Because of this, their orbits cross paths. At times, Neptune is farther from the sun than Pluto.

Practice

1. Which planet has the longest "year"? Which planet has the longest "day"?

2. Which planet has the greatest density?

3. How many times farther from the sun is Pluto than Earth?

Name _____ Class _____ Date _____

Luminosity and Temperature of Stars
(Name in italics refers to star shown by a ⊕)

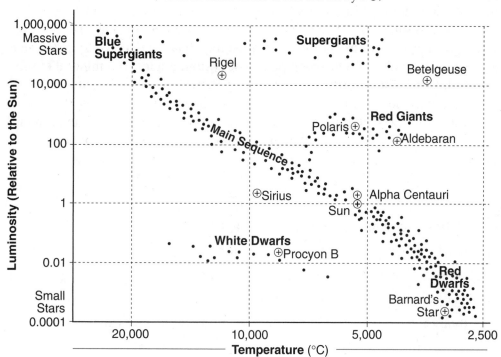

Luminosity is the brightness of stars compared to the brightness of our Sun as seen from the same distance from the observer.

Solar System Data

Object	Mean Distance from Sun (millions of km)	Period of Revolution	Period of Rotation	Eccentricity of Orbit	Equatorial Diameter (km)	Mass (Earth = 1)	Density (g/cm³)	Number of Moons
SUN	—	—	27 days	—	1,392,000	333,000.00	1.4	–
MERCURY	57.9	88 days	59 days	0.206	4,880	0.553	5.4	0
VENUS	108.2	224.7 days	243 days	0.007	12,104	0.815	5.2	0
EARTH	149.6	365.26 days	23 hr 56 min 4 sec	0.017	12,756	1.00	5.5	1
MARS	227.9	687 days	24 hr 37 min 23 sec	0.093	6,787	0.1074	3.9	2
JUPITER	778.3	11.86 years	9 hr 50 min 30 sec	0.048	142,800	317.896	1.3	16
SATURN	1,427	29.46 years	10 hr 14 min	0.056	120,000	95.185	0.7	18
URANUS	2,869	84.0 years	17 hr 14 min	0.047	51,800	14.537	1.2	21
NEPTUNE	4,496	164.8 years	16 hr	0.009	49,500	17.151	1.7	8
PLUTO	5,900	247.7 years	6 days 9 hr	0.250	2,300	0.0025	2.0	1
EARTH'S MOON	149.6 (0.386 from Earth)	27.3 days	27 days 8 hr	0.055	3,476	0.0123	3.3	—

Properties of Common Minerals

This chart lists some of the most useful properties for distinguishing one mineral from another. To identify a mineral, start on the left side of the chart by identifying the luster of your mineral sample. Is the mineral shiny (metallic luster) or dull (nonmetallic luster)? After you have answered this question, look at the columns to the right, checking each of the properties listed (hardness, cleavage, fracture, color, distinguishing characteristics, etc.) *Cleavage* is the tendency of a mineral to split along certain planes at certain angles. If a mineral exhibits cleavage, there is more information (words and/or picture) about how the mineral cleaves in the "Distinguishing Characteristics" column. In addition to these useful properties, the chart also provides information about the chemical composition and common uses of each mineral. The list of chemical symbols at the bottom of the page can be used to decode a mineral's chemical composition.

Practice

1. Name three similarities between quartz and plagioclase feldspar.

2. Which mineral cleaves into sheets and has a dark color?

3. Which mineral is an ore of iron and produces a red streak?

4. List two properties of olivine.

5. Which mineral, commonly used as a food additive, exhibits cubic cleavage?

Name _____   Class _____   Date _____

Properties of Common Minerals

LUSTER	HARD-NESS	CLEAVAGE	FRACTURE	COMMON COLORS	DISTINGUISHING CHARACTERISTICS	USE(S)	MINERAL NAME	COMPOSITION*
Metallic Luster	1–2	✔		silver to gray	black streak, greasy feel	pencil lead, lubricants	**Graphite**	C
	2.5	✔		metallic silver	very dense (7.6 g/cm³), gray-black streak	ore of lead	**Galena**	PbS
	5.5–6.5		✔	black to silver	attracted by magnet, black streak	ore of iron	**Magnetite**	Fe_3O_4
	6.5		✔	brassy yellow	green-black streak, cubic crystals	ore of sulfur	**Pyrite**	FeS_2
Either	1–6.5		✔	metallic silver or earthy red	red-brown streak	ore of iron	**Hematite**	Fe_2O_3
Nonmetallic Luster	1	✔		white to green	greasy feel	talcum powder, soapstone	**Talc**	$Mg_3Si_4O_{10}(OH)_2$
	2		✔	yellow to amber	easily melted, may smell	vulcanize rubber, sulfuric acid	**Sulfur**	S
	2	✔		white to pink or gray	easily scratched by fingernail	plaster of paris and drywall	**Gypsum** (Selenite)	$CaSO_4 \cdot 2H_2O$
	2–2.5	✔		colorless to yellow	flexible in thin sheets	electrical insulator	**Muscovite Mica**	$KAl_3Si_3O_{10}(OH)_2$
	2.5	✔		colorless to white	cubic cleavage, salty taste	food additive, melts ice	**Halite**	$NaCl$
	2.5–3	✔		black to dark brown	flexible in thin sheets	electrical insulator	**Biotite Mica**	$K(Mg,Fe)_3$ $AlSi_3O_{10}(OH)_2$
	3	✔		colorless or variable	bubbles with acid	cement, polarizing prisms	**Calcite**	$CaCO_3$
	3.5	✔		colorless or variable	bubbles with acid when powdered	source of magnesium	**Dolomite**	$CaMg(CO_3)_2$
	4	✔		colorless or variable	cleaves in 4 directions	hydrofluoric acid	**Fluorite**	CaF_2
	5–6	✔		black to dark green	cleaves in 2 directions at 90°	mineral collections	**Pyroxene** (commonly Augite)	$(Ca,Na)\,(Mg,Fe,Al)$ $(Si,Al)_2O_6$
	5.5	✔		black to dark green	cleaves at 56° and 124°	mineral collections	**Amphiboles** (commonly Hornblende)	$CaNa(Mg,Fe)_4\,(Al,Fe,Ti)_3$ $Si_6O_{22}(O,OH)_2$
	6	✔		white to pink	cleaves in 2 directions at 90°	ceramics and glass	**Potassium Feldspar** (Orthoclase)	$KAlSi_3O_8$
	6	✔		white to gray	cleaves in 2 directions, striations visible	ceramics and glass	**Plagioclase Feldspar** (Na-Ca Feldspar)	$(Na,Ca)AlSi_3O_8$
	6.5		✔	green to gray or brown	commonly light green and granular	furnace bricks and jewelry	**Olivine**	$(Fe,Mg)_2SiO_4$
	7		✔	colorless or variable	glassy luster, may form hexagonal crystals	glass, jewelry, and electronics	**Quartz**	SiO_2
	7		✔	dark red to green	glassy luster, often seen as red grains in NYS metamorphic rocks	jewelry and abrasives	**Garnet** (commonly Almandine)	$Fe_3Al_2Si_3O_{12}$

*Chemical Symbols:

Al = aluminum	Cl = chlorine	H = hydrogen	Na = sodium	S = sulfur
C = carbon	F = fluorine	K = potassium	O = oxygen	Si = silicon
Ca = calcium	Fe = iron	Mg = magnesium	Pb = lead	Ti = titanium

✔ = dominant form of breakage

The University of the State of New York

REGENTS HIGH SCHOOL EXAMINATION

PHYSICAL SETTING

EARTH SCIENCE

Wednesday, January 26, 2005 — 1:15 to 4:15 p.m., only

This is a test of your knowledge of Earth science. Use that knowledge to answer all questions in this examination. Some questions may require the use of the *Earth Science Reference Tables*. The *Earth Science Reference Tables* are supplied separately. Be certain you have a copy of the *2001 edition* of these reference tables before you begin the examination.

Your answer sheet for Part A and Part B–1 is the last page of this examination booklet. Turn to the last page and fold it along the perforations. Then, slowly and carefully, tear off your answer sheet and fill in the heading.

The answers to the questions in Part B–2 and Part C are to be written in your separate answer booklet. Be sure to fill in the heading on the front of your answer booklet.

You are to answer *all* questions in all parts of this examination according to the directions provided in the examination booklet. Record your answers to the Part A and Part B–1 multiple-choice questions on your separate answer sheet. Write your answers to the Part B–2 and Part C questions in your answer booklet. All work should be written in pen, except for graphs and drawings, which should be done in pencil. You may use scrap paper to work out the answers to the questions, but be sure to record all your answers on your separate answer sheet and in your answer booklet.

When you have completed the examination, you must sign the statement printed at the end of your separate answer sheet, indicating that you had no unlawful knowledge of the questions or answers prior to the examination and that you have neither given nor received assistance in answering any of the questions during the examination. Your answer sheet and answer booklet cannot be accepted if you fail to sign this declaration.

Notice. . .

A four-function or scientific calculator and a copy of the *2001 Earth Science Reference Tables* must be available for you to use while taking this examination.

DO NOT OPEN THIS EXAMINATION BOOKLET UNTIL THE SIGNAL IS GIVEN.

Answer all questions in this part.

Directions (1–35): For *each* statement or question, write on your separate answer sheet the *number* of the word or expression that, of those given, best completes the statement or answers the question. Some questions may require the use of the *Earth Science Reference Tables*.

1 Which planet's orbit around the Sun is most nearly circular?

(1) Mercury (3) Pluto
(2) Neptune (4) Venus

2 How many times will the Sun's perpendicular rays cross Earth's Equator between March 1 of one year and March 1 of the next year?

(1) 1 (3) 3
(2) 2 (4) 4

3 Which star's surface temperature is closest to the temperature at the boundary between Earth's mantle and core?

(1) *Sirius* (3) the Sun
(2) *Rigel* (4) *Betelgeuse*

4 Which graph best represents the relationship between soil particle size and the rate at which water infiltrates permeable soil?

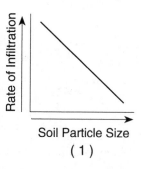
(1)

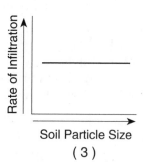
(3)

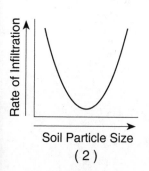
(2)

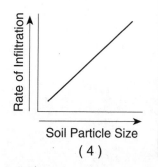
(4)

5 The diagram below shows a standard spectrum compared to a spectrum produced from a distant star.

Standard Spectrum

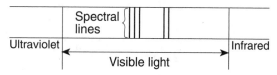

Spectrum from Distant Star

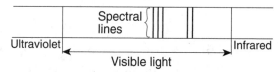

Which conclusion can be made by comparing the standard spectrum to the spectrum produced from this distant star?

(1) The star's spectral lines have shifted toward the ultraviolet end of the spectrum and the star is moving toward Earth.
(2) The star's spectral lines have shifted toward the ultraviolet end of the spectrum and the star is moving away from Earth.
(3) The star's spectral lines have shifted toward the infrared end of the spectrum and the star is moving toward Earth.
(4) The star's spectral lines have shifted toward the infrared end of the spectrum and the star is moving away from Earth.

6 Scientists are concerned about the decrease in ozone in the upper atmosphere primarily because ozone protects life on Earth by absorbing certain wavelengths of

(1) x-ray radiation
(2) ultraviolet radiation
(3) infrared radiation
(4) microwave radiation

7 It is inferred that during the early Archean Era the atmosphere of Earth contained water vapor, carbon dioxide, nitrogen, and other gases in small amounts. These gases probably came from

(1) precipitation of groundwater
(2) volcanic eruptions
(3) evaporation of Paleozoic oceans
(4) convection currents in the mantle

8 Which ocean current flows northeast along the eastern coast of North America?

(1) Gulf Stream   (3) California
(2) North Equatorial   (4) Labrador

9 Which type of land surface would probably reflect the most incoming solar radiation?

(1) light colored and smooth
(2) light colored and rough
(3) dark colored and smooth
(4) dark colored and rough

10 There is evidence that an asteroid or a comet crashed into the Gulf of Mexico at the end of the Mesozoic Era. Consequences of this impact event may explain the

(1) extinction of many kinds of marine animals, including trilobites
(2) extinction of ammonoids and dinosaurs
(3) appearance of the earliest birds and mammals
(4) appearance of great coal-forming forests and insects

11 What is the approximate location of the Canary Islands hot spot?

(1) 32° S 18° W   (3) 32° N 18° W
(2) 32° S 18° E   (4) 32° N 18° E

12 How long would it take for the first S-wave to arrive at a seismic station 4,000 kilometers away from the epicenter of an earthquake?

(1) 5 min 40 sec   (3) 12 min 40 sec
(2) 7 min 0 sec   (4) 13 min 20 sec

13 Which New York State river flows generally southward?

(1) St. Lawrence River   (3) Genesee River
(2) Niagara River   (4) Hudson River

14 The map below shows the stream drainage patterns for a region of Earth's surface. Points A, B, C, and D are locations in the region.

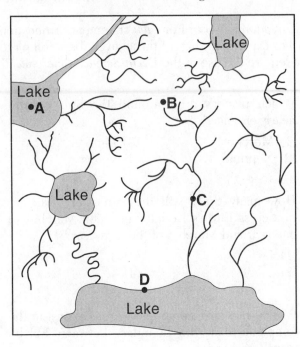

The highest elevation most likely exists at point

(1) A   (3) C
(2) B   (4) D

15 Outwash plains are formed as a result of deposition by

(1) landslides
(2) ocean waves
(3) winds from hurricanes
(4) meltwater from glaciers

16 A stream with a velocity of 100 centimeters per second flows into a lake. Which sediment-size particles would the stream most likely deposit first as it enters the lake?

(1) boulders   (3) pebbles
(2) cobbles   (4) sand

The cross section below shows a soil profile.

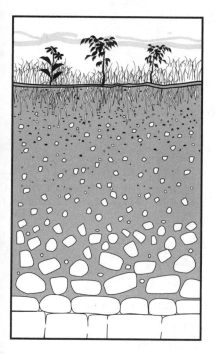

Bedrock

This soil was formed primarily by
(1) erosion by glaciers
(2) erosion by running water
(3) capillarity and human activity
(4) weathering and biological activity

Which type of rock most likely contains fossils?
(1) scoria   (3) schist
(2) gabbro   (4) shale

In which New York State landscape region is most of the surface bedrock composed of metamorphic rock?

(1) Adirondacks
(2) Catskills
(3) Erie-Ontario Lowlands
(4) Newark Lowlands

A human fingernail has a hardness of approximately 2.5. Which two minerals are *softer* than a human fingernail?

(1) calcite and halite
(2) sulfur and fluorite
(3) graphite and talc
(4) pyrite and magnetite

21 The photograph below shows an escarpment (cliff) located in the western United States. The directions for north and south are indicated by arrows. A fault in the sedimentary rocks is shown on the front of the escarpment.

North ←  South →

The photograph shows that the fault most likely formed
(1) after the rock layers were deposited, when the north side moved downward
(2) after the rock layers were deposited, when the north side moved upward
(3) before the rock layers were deposited, when the south side moved downward
(4) before the rock layers were deposited, when the south side moved upward

22 Which mountain range resulted from the collision of North America and Africa, as parts of Pangea joined together in the late Pennsylvanian Period?
(1) Appalachian Mountains
(2) Acadian Mountains
(3) Taconic Mountains
(4) Grenville Mountains

23 Which physical characteristic best describes the rock phyllite?
(1) glassy texture with gas pockets
(2) clastic texture with angular fragments
(3) bioclastic texture with cemented shell fragments
(4) foliated texture with microscopic mica crystals

24 The diagram below represents a part of the crystal structure of the mineral kaolinite.

Structure of Kaolinite

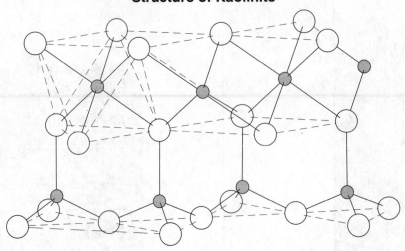

An arrangement of atoms such as the one shown in the diagram determines a mineral's

(1) age of formation
(2) infiltration rate
(3) physical properties
(4) temperature of formation

25 The map below shows the path of a river. The arrow shows the direction the river is flowing. Letters *A* and *B* identify the banks of the river.

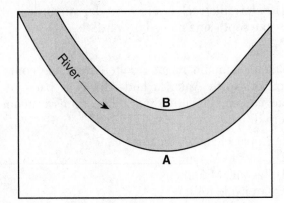

The water depth is greater near bank *A* than bank *B* because the water velocity near bank *A* is

(1) faster, causing deposition to occur
(2) faster, causing erosion to occur
(3) slower, causing deposition to occur
(4) slower, causing erosion to occur

26 Which home-building material is made mostly from the mineral gypsum?

(1) plastic pipes
(2) window glass
(3) drywall panels
(4) iron nails

27 The two most abundant elements by mass in Earth's crust are oxygen and

(1) potassium
(2) hydrogen
(3) nitrogen
(4) silicon

Base your answers to questions 28 through 30 on the diagram below, which represents the planetary wind and moisture belts in Earth's Northern Hemisphere.

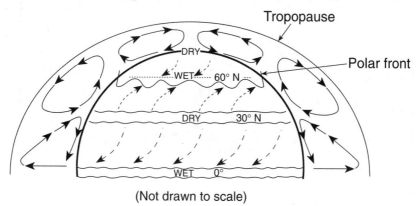

(Not drawn to scale)

28 The climate at 90° north latitude is dry because the air at that location is usually

(1) warm and rising
(2) warm and sinking
(3) cool and rising
(4) cool and sinking

29 The paths of the surface planetary winds are curved due to Earth's

(1) revolution
(2) rotation
(3) circumference
(4) size

30 The tropopause is approximately how far above sea level?

(1) 12 mi
(2) 12 km
(3) 60 mi
(4) 60 km

---

1 The diagram below shows four magnified block-shaped sandstone samples labeled A, B, C, and D. Each sandstone sample contains quartz grains of different shapes and sizes. The quartz grains are held together by hematite cement.

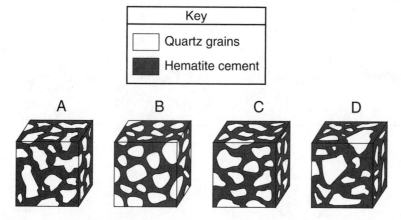

In which sample did the quartz grains undergo the most abrasion during erosional transport?

(1) A
(2) B
(3) C
(4) D

32 On the map below, line *AB* is drawn across several of Earth's tectonic plates in the South Atlantic Ocean.

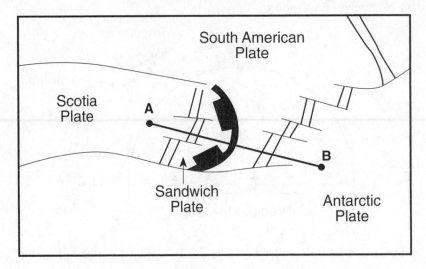

Which cross section best represents the plate boundaries and mantle movement beneath line *AB*?

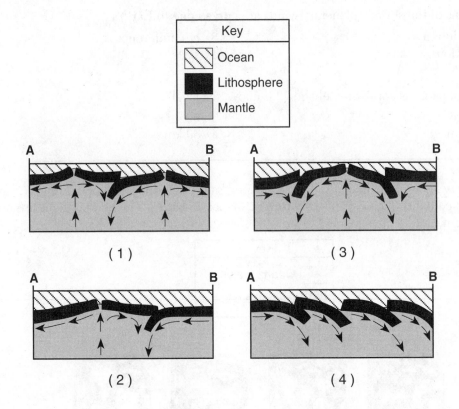

The diagrams below show four major types of fault motion occurring in Earth's crust. Which type of fault motion best matches the general pattern of crustal movement at California's San Andreas fault?

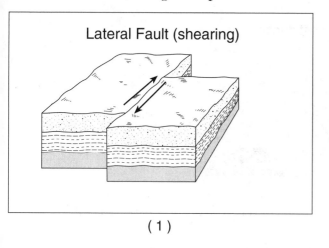

Lateral Fault (shearing)

(1)

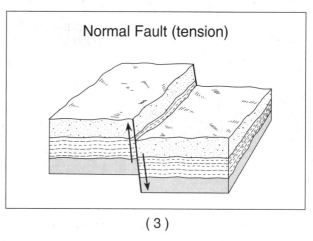

Normal Fault (tension)

(3)

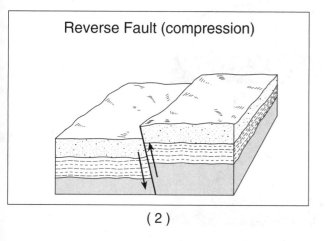

Reverse Fault (compression)

(2)

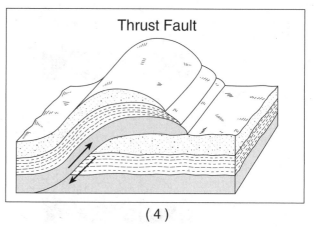

Thrust Fault

(4)

34 The cross section below shows the movement of wind-driven sand particles that strike a partly exposed basalt cobble located at the surface of a windy desert.

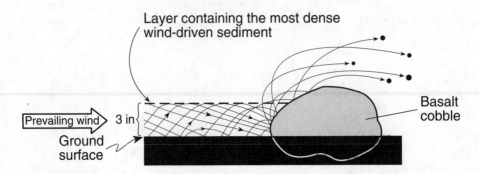

Which cross section best represents the appearance of this cobble after many years of exposure to the wind-driven sand?

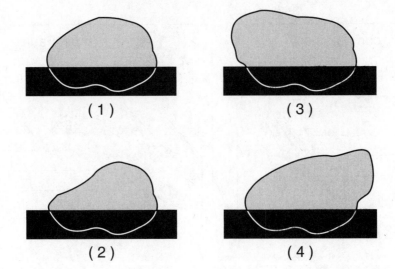

5 Each dot on the graph below shows the result of separate scientific studies of the relationship between the rates of erosion in regions of different relief. Relief is the local difference between the highest and the lowest elevations.

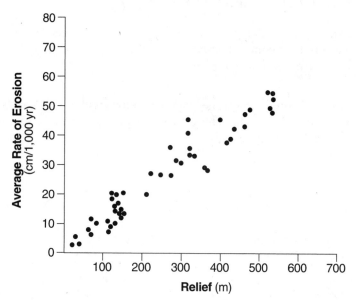

The results of these combined studies indicate that with each 100-meter increase in relief, the rate of erosion generally

(1) decreases at a rate of 10 cm/1,000 years
(2) decreases at a rate of 20 cm/1,000 years
(3) increases at a rate of 10 cm/1,000 years
(4) increases at a rate of 20 cm/1,000 years

Part B–1

Answer all questions in this part.

Directions (36–50): For *each* statement or question, write on your separate answer sheet the *number* of the word or expression that, of those given, best completes the statement or answers the question. Some questions may require the use of the *Earth Science Reference Tables*.

Base your answers to questions 36 through 38 on the diagram below, which represents a model of the sky (celestial sphere) for an observer in New York State. The curved arrow represents the Sun's apparent path for part of one day. The altitude of *Polaris* is also indicated.

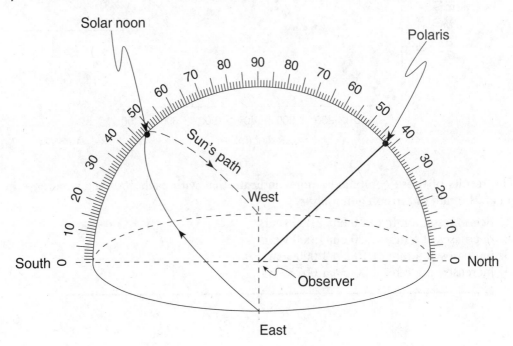

36 According to this diagram, what is the Sun's altitude at solar noon?

(1) 23.5°   (3) 48°

(2) 42°   (4) 90°

37 Where is this observer most likely located?

(1) Massena   (3) Slide Mountain

(2) Oswego   (4) Mt. Marcy

38 On which date could this observation of the Sun's apparent path have been made?

(1) March 21   (3) October 21

(2) July 21   (4) December 21

Base your answers to questions 39 through 42 on the weather map below. The map shows a low-pressure system and some atmospheric conditions at weather stations *A*, *B*, and *C*.

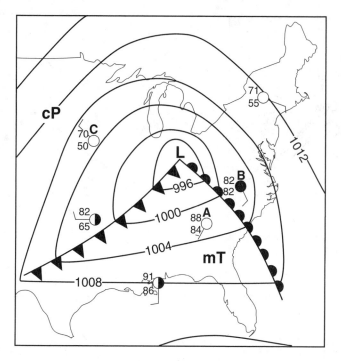

39 Which type of weather is usually associated with a cP air mass, as shown near weather station *C*?

(1) moist and cool   (3) dry and cool

(2) moist and warm   (4) dry and warm

40 Which cross section best represents the air masses, air movement, clouds, and precipitation occurring behind and ahead of the warm front located between stations *A* and *B*?

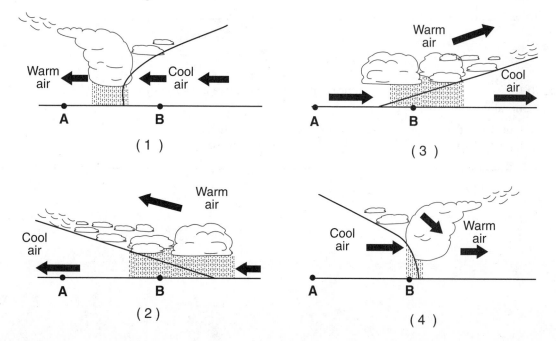

41 The arrows on which map best represent the direction of surface winds associated with this low-pressure system?

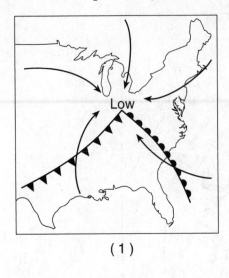

(1)

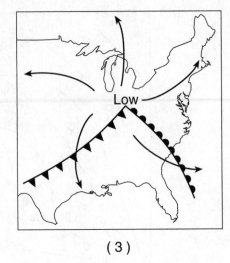

(3)

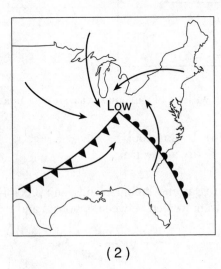

(2)

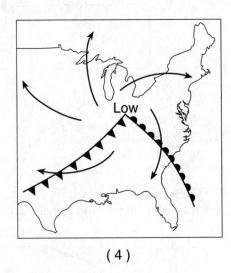

(4)

42 If this weather system follows a normal storm track, the low-pressure center (L) will generally move toward the

(1) northeast   (3) southeast
(2) northwest   (4) southwest

Base your answers to questions 43 and 44 on the bedrock cross section below. The cross section represents part of Earth's crust where natural gas, oil, and water have moved upward through a layer of folded sandstone and filled the pore spaces at the top of the sandstone layer.

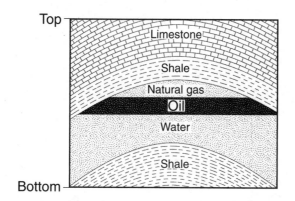

43 The final arrangement of the natural gas, oil, and water within the sandstone was caused by differences in their

(1) density
(2) specific heat
(3) relative age
(4) radioactive half-life

44 The natural gas, oil, and water are trapped within the top of the sandstone and do not move upward through the shale because, compared to the sandstone, the shale has

(1) lower permeability
(2) less foliation
(3) larger pore spaces
(4) larger particles

Base your answers to questions 45 through 47 on the map below, which shows the drainage basin of the Mississippi River system. Several rivers that flow into the Mississippi River are labeled. The arrow at location X shows where the Mississippi River enters the Gulf of Mexico.

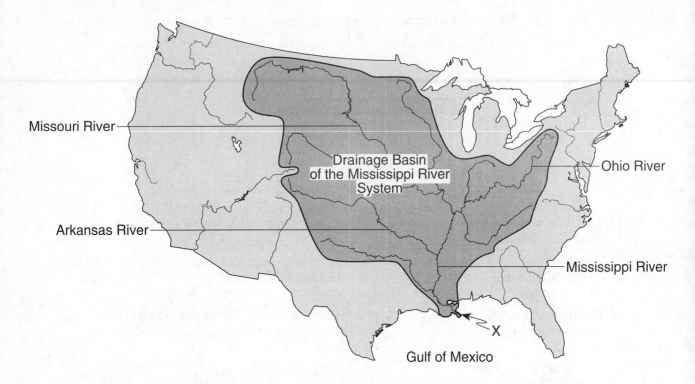

45 The entire land area drained by the Mississippi River system is referred to as a

(1) levee   (3) meander belt
(2) watershed   (4) floodplain

46 Sediments deposited at location X by the Missisippi River most likely have which characteristics?

(1) angular fragments arranged as mixtures
(2) rock particles arranged in sorted beds
(3) rocks with parallel scratches and grooves
(4) high-density minerals with hexagonal crystals

47 The structure formed by the deposition of sediments at location X is best described as a

(1) moraine   (3) delta
(2) tributary   (4) drumlin

Base your answers to questions 48 through 50 on the reading passage and the drawing below and on your knowledge of Earth science.

Fossil With Signs of Feathers Is Cited as Bird-Dinosaur Link

Paleontologists have discovered in China a fossil dinosaur with what are reported to be clear traces of feathers from head to tail, the most persuasive evidence so far, scientists say, that feathers predated the origin of birds and that modern birds are descendants of dinosaurs.

Entombed in fine-grained rock, the unusually well-preserved skeleton resembles that of a duck with a reptilian tail, altogether about three feet in length. Its head and tail are edged with the imprint of downy fibers. The rest of the body, except for bare lower legs, shows distinct traces of tufts and filaments that appear to have been primitive feathers. On the backs of its short forelimbs are patterns of what look like modern bird feathers.

Other dinosaur remains with what appear to be featherlike traces have been unearthed in recent years, but nothing as complete as this specimen, paleontologists said. Etched in the rock like a filigree decoration surrounding the skeleton are imprints of where the down and feathers appear to have been.

The 130-million-year-old fossils were found a year ago by farmers in Liaoning Province in northeastern China. After an analysis by Chinese and American researchers, the fossil animal was identified as a dromaeosaur, a small fast-running dinosaur related to velociraptor. The dinosaurs belonged to a group of two-legged predators known as advanced theropods . . .

excerpted from "Fossil With Signs of
Feathers Is Cited as Bird-Dinosaur Link"
John Noble Wilford
New York Times, April 26, 2001

The drawing below shows an artist's view of the dinosaur, based on the fossilized remains.

48 During which period of geologic time have paleontologists inferred that the feathered dinosaur mentioned in the passage existed?

(1) Cambrian   (3) Paleogene

(2) Cretaceous   (4) Permian

49 This feathered dinosaur is not considered an index fossil because it
  (1) existed too long ago
  (2) was preserved in ash
  (3) was a land-dwelling animal
  (4) was found in only one area

50 The reference to the bird-dinosaur link is most likely referring to the concept of
  (1) plate tectonics
  (2) evolution
  (3) dynamic equilibrium
  (4) recycling

Part B–2

Answer all questions in this part.

Directions (51–62): Record your answers in the spaces provided in your answer booklet. Some questions may require the use of the *Earth Science Reference Tables.*

Base your answers to questions 51 and 52 on the diagram provided *in your answer booklet.* The diagram shows a model of Earth's orbit around the Sun. Two motions of Earth are indicated. Distances to the Sun are given for two positions of Earth in its orbit.

51 On the diagram provided *in your answer booklet,* place an **X** on Earth's orbit to indicate Earth's position on May 21.   [1]

52 Explain why New York State experiences summer when Earth is at its greatest distance from the Sun.   [1]

_____

Base your answers to questions 53 through 55 on the field map provided *in your answer booklet.* The map shows elevations, measured in feet, of a number of points in a certain geographic region. Contour lines have been drawn for the 100-foot and 120-foot elevations. Points A and B represent two spot elevations on the map.

53 On the map provided *in your answer booklet,* draw the 60-foot contour line. Make sure that the contour line extends to the edges of the map.   [1]

54 Toward which general compass direction does Elma Creek flow? [1]

55 Calculate the gradient between points A and B. Label the answer with the correct units.   [2]

_____

56 On the weather map station model provided *in your answer booklet,* using the proper format, record the *six* weather conditions shown below.   [2]

    Wind: from the northwest
    Wind speed: 10 knots
    Barometric pressure: 1022.0 mb
    Cloud cover: 50%
    Visibility: 5 mi
    Precipitation (in the past 6 hours): .45 in

Base your answers to questions 57 and 58 on the map and table below. The map shows the name and location of the volcanic peaks in the Cascade Mountain Range of the northwestern United States west of the Yellowstone Hot Spot. The table shows the major eruptions of each peak over the past 4,000 years.

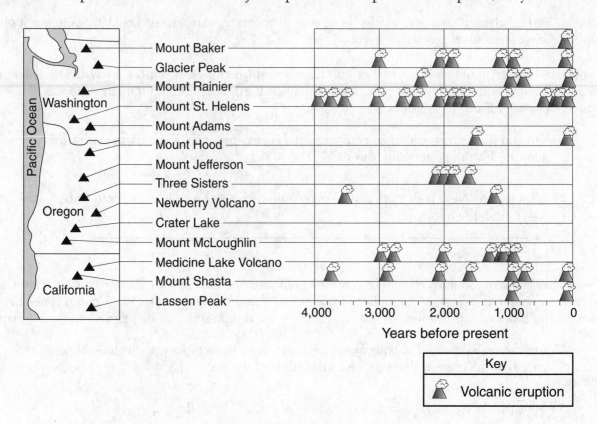

57 During which geologic epoch did the volcanic activity shown on the table occur?   [1]

58 On the cross section provided *in your answer booklet,* place an arrow in the continental crust and an arrow in the oceanic crust to show the relative directions of plate movement.   [1]

59 Which layer of Earth is composed of both the crust and the rigid mantle?   [1]

Base your answers to questions 60 and 61 on the diagram below, which represents a model of the radioactive decay of a particular element. The diagram shows the decay of a radioactive element (☐) into the stable decay element (▓) after one half-life period.

Radioactive Decay Model

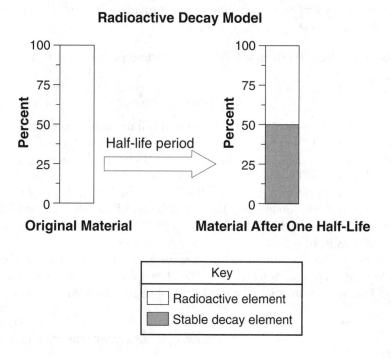

Original Material   **Material After One Half-Life**

Key	
☐	Radioactive element
▓	Stable decay element

60 On the diagram provided *in your answer booklet,* shade in the amount of stable decay element present after the second half-life period.   [1]

61 If the radioactive element in this model is carbon-14, how much time will have passed after one half-life?   [1]

_____

62 The diagram below shows warm, moist air moving off the ocean and over a mountain, causing precipitation between points 1 and 2.

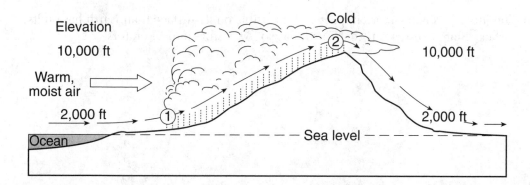

Describe *two* changes that occur to the warm, moist air between points 1 and 2 that would cause cloud formation.   [2]

_____

Part C

Answer all questions in this part.

Directions (63–80): Record your answers in the spaces provided in your answer booklet. Some questions may require the use of the *Earth Science Reference Tables*.

Base your answers to questions 63 through 65 on the reading passage below and on your knowledge of Earth science.

The Blue Moon

A "Blue Moon" is the name given to the second full moon in a calendar month. Because there are roughly 29.5 days between full moons, it is unusual for two full moons to "fit" into a 30 or 31 day month (and impossible to fit into a 28 or 29 day month, so February can never have a Blue Moon). The saying "Once in a Blue Moon" means a rare occurrence, and predates the current astronomical use of the term, which is quite recent. In fact, Blue Moons are not all that rare, on average there will be one Blue Moon every 2.5 years. After 1999, the next Blue Moons will be in November 2001; July 2004; and June 2007. The last one before 1999 was in July 1996.

The term Blue Moon is believed to have originated in 1883 after the eruption of Krakatoa. The volcano put so much dust in the atmosphere that the Moon actually looked blue in color. This was so unusual that the term "once in a Blue Moon" was coined.

"The Blue Moon"
David R. Williams
nssdc.gsfc.nasa.gov/planetary/lunar/blue_moon.html

63 Explain why a Blue Moon never occurs during the month of February.   [1]

64 What is the greatest number of full-Moon phases, visible from Earth, that are possible in a span of 1 year?   [1]

65 In the space provided *in your answer booklet,* draw the relative positions of Earth, the Moon, and the Sun, as viewed from space, so that a full-Moon phase would be visible to an observer on Earth. Label Earth, the Moon, and the Sun in your drawing.   [1]

_____

66 The Moon has many more impact craters visible on its surface than Earth has on its surface. State *two* reasons that Earth has so few visible impact craters.   [2]

Base your answers to questions 67 and 68 on the map and data table shown below. The map shows some tectonic plates and the boundaries between them. Letters *A* and *B* are locations on Earth's surface. The data table shows the depth below Earth's surface of five earthquakes measured from location *A* toward location *B*.

Map

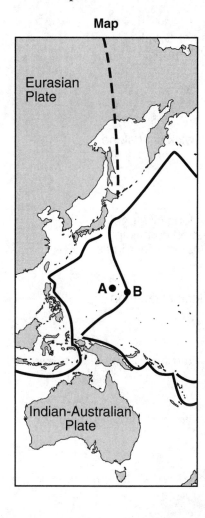

Data Table

Earthquake	Distance from Location *A* Toward Location *B* (km)	Depth Below Earth's Surface (km)
1	100	600
2	200	400
3	250	300
4	300	250
5	400	60

67 On the grid provided *in your answer booklet*, plot the depths of the *five* earthquakes from location *A* toward location *B*.   [1]

68 Identify the type of plate boundary or geologic feature found at location *B*.   [1]

_____

Base your answers to questions 69 through 71 on the cross section below, which shows several rock formations found in New York State. The rock layers have not been overturned.

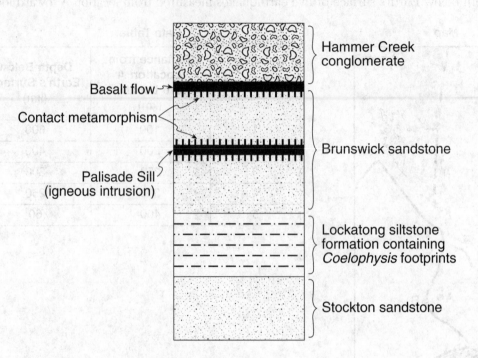

69 How does this cross section indicate that the Stockton sandstone is the oldest rock layer? [1]

70 State one piece of evidence that supports the fact that the Palisade Sill is younger than the Brunswick sandstone. [1]

71 State one tectonic event affecting North America that occurred at the same time as the Palisade Sill intrusion. [1]

Base your answers to questions 72 through 74 on the map below, the graph on the next page, and your knowledge of Earth science. The map shows the length of the growing season in New York State, expressed in days. The growing season is the average number of days between the last frost in spring and the first frost in fall. The graph line shows the relationship between the latitudes of Riverhead, New York; Albany, New York; and Massena, New York; and the length of the growing season at these three locations.

Length of Growing Season (in days)

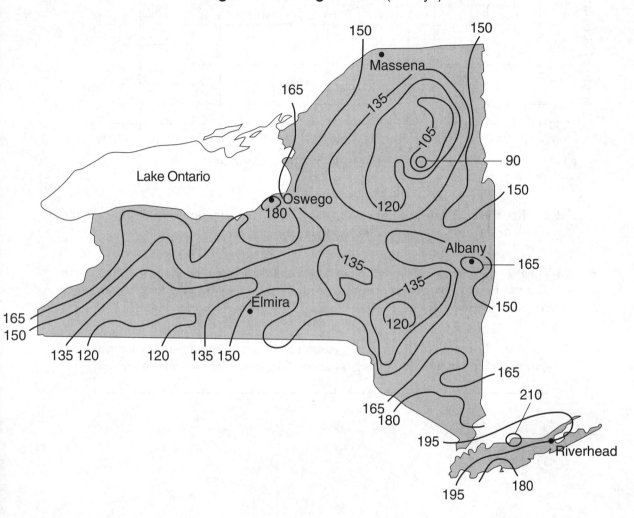

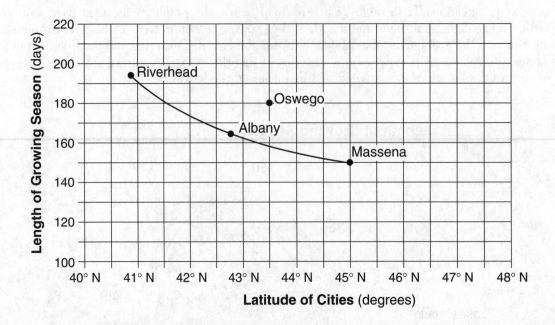

72 For Riverhead, Albany, and Massena, state the relationship between latitude and the length of the growing season shown by the graph.   [1]

73 The data for Oswego, New York, have been plotted separately on the graph. Explain why the location of Oswego causes it to have a growing season longer than other cities at the same latitude.   [1]

74 Compare the length of the growing season in a lowland region with the length of the growing season in a mountain region at approximately the same latitude.   [1]

Base your answers to questions 75 through 77 on the cross section below and on your knowledge of Earth science. The cross section shows a portion of Earth's crust. The age, in millions of years, of each boundary between the different sedimentary rock layers is shown. The age of boundary X between the sedimentary rock and the metamorphic rock is not shown. Assume no overturning has occurred.

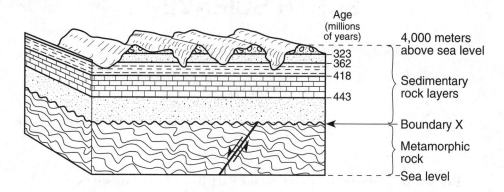

75 Identify the geologic feature represented by boundary X. [1]

76 Describe how the rock type below boundary X was formed. [1]

77 Identify by name one index fossil that existed when the limestone rock shown in the cross section was being formed. [1]

Base your answers to questions 78 through 80 on the diagram and table below. The diagram represents a felsic igneous rock. Letters A, B, and C represent three different minerals in the rock sample. The table describes the physical properties of minerals A, B, and C found in the igneous rock sample.

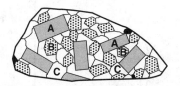

(Actual size)

Mineral	Key	Physical Properties
A		pink, cleaves in two directions at 90°
B		white, cleaves in two directions, striations visible
C		colorless or clear with a glassy luster

78 State the texture of this igneous rock. [1]

79 On the table provided *in your answer booklet*, state the names of minerals A, B, and C. [2]

80 State *two* processes responsible for the formation of an igneous rock. [1]

PHYSICAL SETTING
EARTH SCIENCE

Wednesday, January 26, 2005 — 1:15 to 4:15 p.m., only

ANSWER SHEET

Student .... Sex: ☐ Male ☐ Female Grade ....

Teacher .... School ....

Record your answers to Part A and Part B–1 on this answer sheet.

Part A			Part B–1	
1	13	25	36	44 ....
2	14	26	37	45 ....
3	15	27	38	46 ....
4	16	28	39	47 ....
5	17	29	40	48 ....
6	18	30	41	49 ....
7	19	31	42	50 ....
8	20	32	43	
9	21	33		
10	22	34		
11	23	35		
12	24			

Part B–1 Score

Part A Score

Write your answers to Part B–2 and Part C in your answer booklet.

The declaration below should be signed when you have completed the examination.

I do hereby affirm, at the close of this examination, that I had no unlawful knowledge of the questions or answers prior to the examination and that I have neither given nor received assistance in answering any of the questions during the examination.

_____

Signature

PHYSICAL SETTING
EARTH SCIENCE

Wednesday, January 26, 2005 — 1:15 to 4:15 p.m., only

ANSWER BOOKLET

Student . . . . Sex: ☐ Male ☐ Female

Teacher . . . .

School . . . . Grade . . . .

Answer all questions in Part B–2 and Part C. Record your answers in this booklet.

Performance Test Score
(Maximum Score: 23)

Part	Maximum Score	Student's Score
A	35	
B–1	15	
B–2	15	
C	20	

Total Written Test Score
(Maximum Raw Score: 85)

Final Score
(from conversion chart)

Raters' Initials:

Rater 1 . . . . Rater 2 . . . .

Part B–2

For Raters Only

51

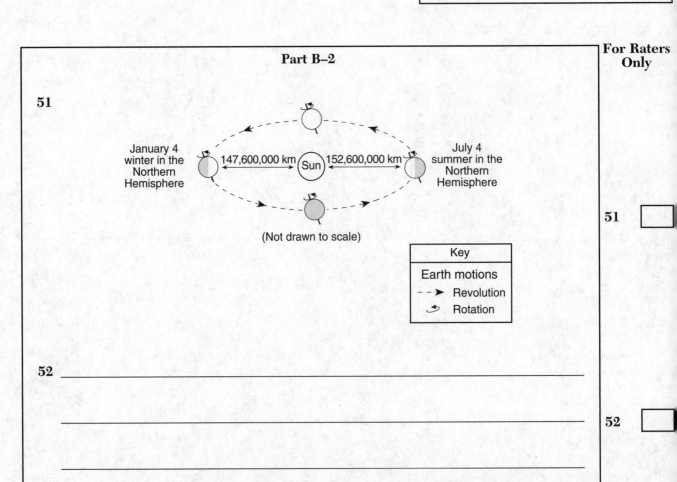

January 4
winter in the
Northern
Hemisphere

147,600,000 km   Sun   152,600,000 km

July 4
summer in the
Northern
Hemisphere

(Not drawn to scale)

Key
Earth motions
– – ➤ Revolution
↲ Rotation

51

52 _____

_____

_____

52

53

Map contents:

A—60

•96   •80   •71   •64   •68   •95   •90

100

•40   •90

•97

•77

•92   •84   •52   •37   •38   •60   •86   100

•78

•83   •78   •60   •49

•65   •51   •85

•58   •34   •28   •59   •75   •91   •80

•40   •18   •20   •40   •77

•43   •17   •60

•38   •25   •11   •10   B   •23   •38   •44   •42

23   •17   •7   •36   •27

•20   0   0   •10   •25   •18

Steeler Bay   •20   •12

Elma Creek

0   1   2   3 miles

N

53 [ ]

54 _____

54 [ ]

55 Gradient = _____

55 [ ]

56

56 [ ]

57 _____ **Epoch**

57 [ ]

[2]

58

Cascade volcanic
mountains

West   **East**

Oceanic crust   Continental crust

Rigid mantle   Rigid mantle

Asthenosphere   Asthenosphere

(Not drawn to scale)

59 _____

60

100

75

Percent   50

25

0

Material After Two Half-Lives

Key	
☐	Radioactive element
▨	Stable decay element

61 _____ **years**

62 (1) _____

   (2) _____

For Raters Only

Part C

63 ____

____ 63 [ ]

64 ____________________ 64 [ ]

65

65 [ ]

66 (1) ____

66 [ ]

(2) ____

67

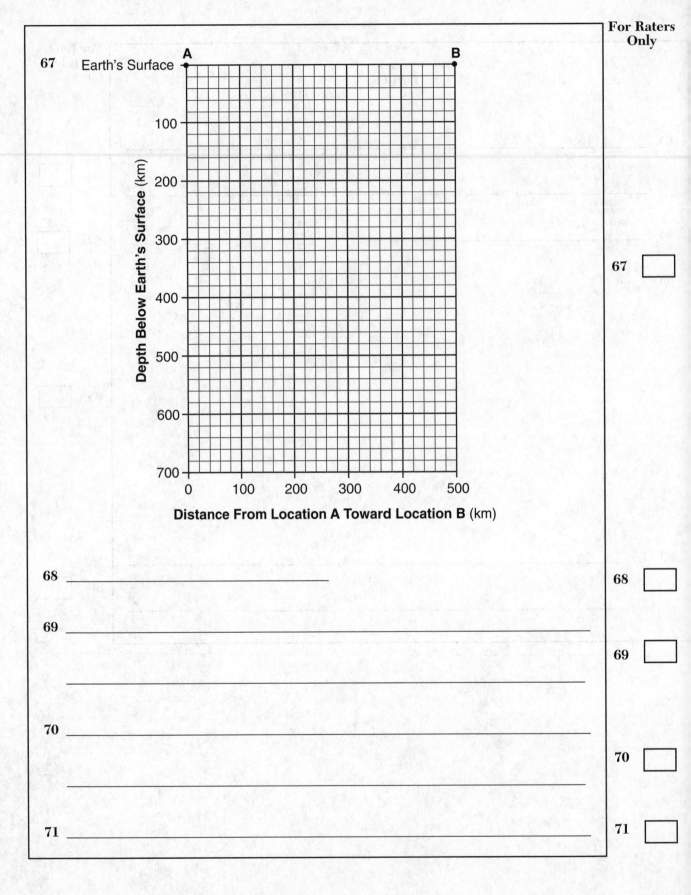

Earth's Surface

Depth Below Earth's Surface (km)

Distance From Location A Toward Location B (km)

68 _____

69 _____

_____

70 _____

_____

71 _____

For Raters Only

72 ____ 72 [ ]

____

73 ____ 73 [ ]

____

74 ____ 74 [ ]

____

75 ____________________ 75 [ ]

76 ____ 76 [ ]

____

77 ____________________ 77 [ ]

78 ____________________ 78 [ ]

79 79 [ ]

Mineral	Name of Mineral
A	
B	
C	

80 ____________________ and ____________________ 80 [ ]

[ ]

Total Score for Part C

The University of the State of New York

REGENTS HIGH SCHOOL EXAMINATION

PHYSICAL SETTING
EARTH SCIENCE

Friday, June 18, 2004 — 1:15 to 4:15 p.m., only

This is a test of your knowledge of Earth science. Use that knowledge to answer all questions in this examination. Some questions may require the use of the *Earth Science Reference Tables*. The *Earth Science Reference Tables* are supplied separately. Be certain you have a copy of the *2001 edition* of these reference tables before you begin the examination.

Your answer sheet for Part A and Part B–1 is the last page of this examination booklet. Turn to the last page and fold it along the perforations. Then, slowly and carefully, tear off your answer sheet and fill in the heading.

The answers to the questions in Part B–2 and Part C are to be written in your separate answer booklet. Be sure to fill in the heading on the front of your answer booklet.

You are to answer *all* questions in all parts of this examination according to the directions provided in the examination booklet. Record your answers to the Part A and Part B–1 multiple-choice questions on your separate answer sheet. Write your answers to the Part B–2 and Part C questions in your answer booklet. All work should be written in pen, except for graphs and drawings, which should be done in pencil. You may use scrap paper to work out the answers to the questions, but be sure to record all your answers on your separate answer sheet and in your answer booklet.

When you have completed the examination, you must sign the statement printed at the end of your separate answer sheet, indicating that you had no unlawful knowledge of the questions or answers prior to the examination and that you have neither given nor received assistance in answering any of the questions during the examination. Your answer sheet and answer booklet cannot be accepted if you fail to sign this declaration.

Notice. . .

A four-function or scientific calculator and a copy of the *2001 Earth Science Reference Tables* must be available for your use while taking this examination.

DO NOT OPEN THIS EXAMINATION BOOKLET UNTIL THE SIGNAL IS GIVEN.

Directions (1–35): For *each* statement or question, write on your separate answer sheet the *number* of the ·d or expression that, of those given, best completes the statement or answers the question. Some questions / require the use of the *Earth Science Reference Tables*.

The motion of a Foucault pendulum provides evidence of

(1) the Sun's rotation   (3) Earth's rotation
(2) the Sun's revolution   (4) Earth's revolution

Which form of electromagnetic radiation has a wavelength of 1.0×10^{-3} centimeter?

(1) ultraviolet   (3) radio waves
(2) infrared   (4) microwaves

The time required for the Moon to show a complete cycle of phases when viewed from Earth is approximately

(1) 1 day   (3) 1 month
(2) 1 week   (4) 1 year

Which planet has an orbital eccentricity most like the orbital eccentricity of the Moon?

(1) Pluto   (3) Mars
(2) Saturn   (4) Mercury

On June 21, where will the Sun appear to rise for an observer located in New York State?

(1) due west   (3) north of due east
(2) due east   (4) south of due east

Which statement best describes sediments deposited by glaciers and rivers?

(1) Glacial deposits and river deposits are both sorted.
(2) Glacial deposits are sorted, and river deposits are unsorted.
(3) Glacial deposits are unsorted, and river deposits are sorted.
(4) Glacial deposits and river deposits are both unsorted.

7 The diagram below shows four different chemical materials escaping from the interior of early Earth.

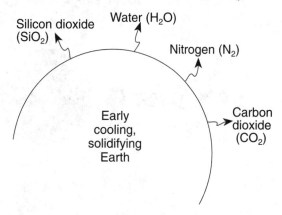

Which material contributed *least* to the early composition of the atmosphere?

(1) SiO_2 (3) N_2
(2) H_2O (4) CO_2

8 The diagram below shows a fossil found in the surface bedrock of New York State.

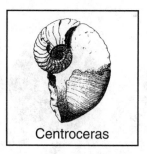

Centroceras

Which other fossil is most likely to be found in the same age bedrock?

(1) *Phacops*   (3) *Coelophysis*
(2) condor   (4) *Tetragraptus*

9 Soil composed of which particle size usually has the greatest capillarity?

(1) silt   (3) coarse sand
(2) fine sand   (4) pebbles

10 Which sequence correctly shows the relative size of the nine planets of our solar system?

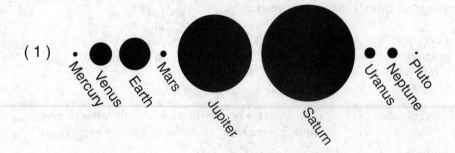

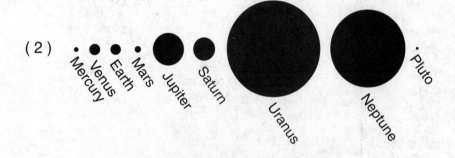

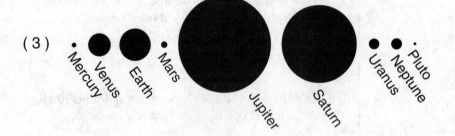

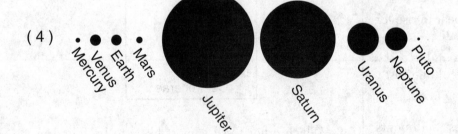

The graph below shows changes in the atmosphere occurring above typical air-mass source regions A, B, C, and D. Changes in air temperature and altitude are shown as the graphed lines. Changes in water-vapor content, in grams of vapor per kilogram of air, are shown as numbers on each graphed line.

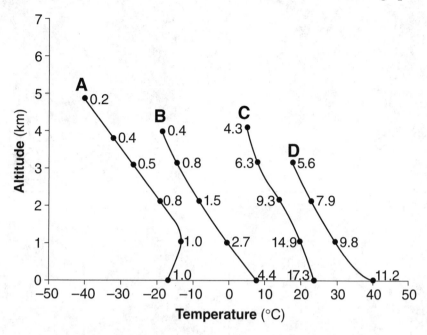

Which list best identifies each air-mass source region?
(1) A — cT, B — cP, C — mP, D — mT   (3) A — mP, B — mT, C — cT, D — cP
(2) A — cP, B — mP, C — mT, D — cT   (4) A — mT, B — cT, C — cP, D — mP

Earth's outer core and inner core are both inferred to be

(1) liquid
(2) solid
(3) composed of a high percentage of iron
(4) under the same pressure

Surface winds on Earth are primarily caused by differences in

(1) air density due to unequal heating of Earth's surface
(2) ocean wave heights during the tidal cycle
(3) rotational speeds of Earth's surface at various latitudes
(4) distances from the Sun during the year

Which nonfoliated rock forms only in a zone of contact metamorphism?

(1) conglomerate   (3) pegmatite
(2) hornfels   (4) quartzite

15 During a dry summer, the flow of most large New York State streams generally

(1) continues because some groundwater seeps into the streams
(2) increases due to greater surface runoff
(3) remains unchanged due to transpiration from grasses, shrubs, and trees
(4) stops completely because no water runs off into the streams

16 The density of Earth's crust is

(1) less than the density of the outer core but greater than the density of the mantle
(2) greater than the density of the outer core but less than the density of the mantle
(3) less than the density of both the outer core and the mantle
(4) greater than the density of both the outer core and the mantle

17 Which map best represents the direction of surface winds associated with the high- and low-pressure systems?

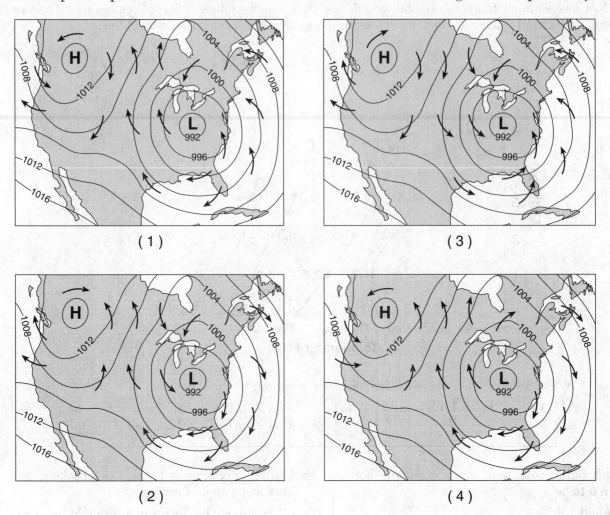

(1) (3)

(2) (4)

18 In each diagram below, the mass of the star is the same. In which diagram is the force of gravity greatest between the star and the planet shown?

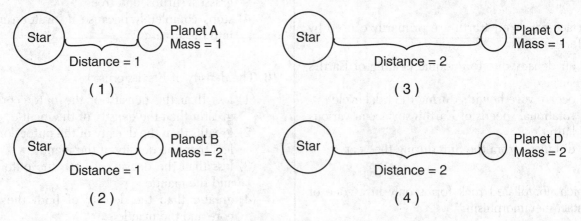

(1) (3)

(2) (4)

The cross section below shows rock layers that underwent crustal movement during an igneous intrusion in the Cretaceous Period.

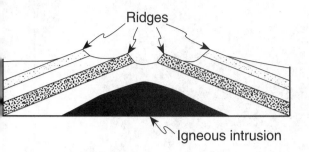
Ridges

Igneous intrusion

Which statement best describes the cause of the ridges shown?

(1) The rock layers were evenly weathered.
(2) Some rock layers were more resistant to weathering and erosion.
(3) The igneous intrusion flowed over the surface.
(4) More deposition occurred at the ridge sites after uplift.

The picture below shows a geological feature in the Kalahari Desert of southwestern Africa.

Which process most likely produced the present appearance of this feature?

(1) wind erosion
(2) volcanic eruption
(3) earthquake vibrations
(4) plate tectonics

Which group of organisms, some of which were preserved as fossils in early Paleozoic rocks, are still in existence today?

(1) brachiopods   (3) graptolites
(2) eurypterids   (4) trilobites

22 The diagram below shows the shadow cast by a telephone pole on March 21 at solar noon at a location in New York State.

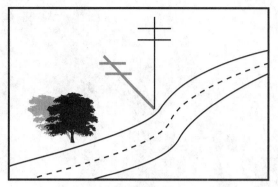

Shadow Cast on March 21

Which shadow was cast by the same telephone pole on June 21 at solar noon?

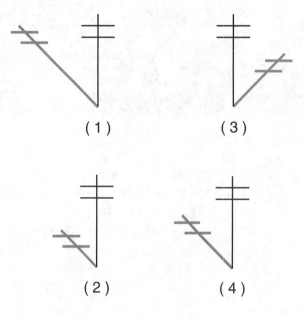

(1)   (3)

(2)   (4)

23 Which two New York State landscape regions are formed mostly of surface bedrock that is approximately the same geologic age?

(1) Manhattan Prong and Atlantic Coastal Plain
(2) Erie-Ontario Lowlands and Adirondack Mountains
(3) Adirondack Mountains and Allegheny Plateau
(4) Tug Hill Plateau and St. Lawrence Lowlands

24 The photograph below shows deformed rock structure found on Earth's surface.

Deformed rock structure like this is most often caused by

(1) crustal plate collisions   (3) extrusion of magma
(2) deposition of sediments   (4) glacial movement

---

25 The seismogram below shows the time that an earthquake *P*-wave arrived at a seismic station in Albany, New York.

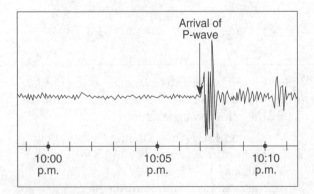

If the earthquake occurred at exactly 10:00 p.m., approximately how far from the earthquake epicenter was Albany, New York?

(1) 1,900 km   (3) 4,000 km
(2) 3,200 km   (4) 5,200 km

26 On each topographic map below, the straight-line distance from point *A* to point *B* is 5 kilometers. Which topographic map shows the steepest gradient between *A* and *B*?

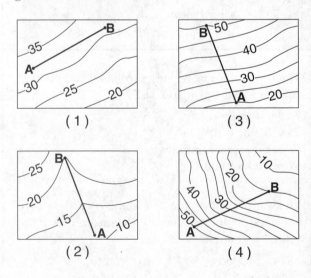

7 Which seismogram was recorded approximately 4,000 kilometers from an earthquake epicenter?

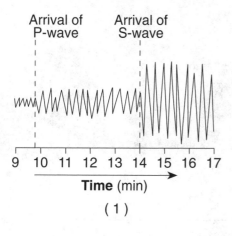

Arrival of P-wave   Arrival of S-wave

Time (min)

(1)

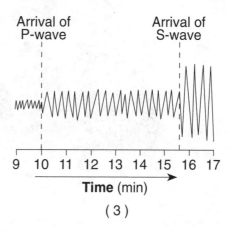

Arrival of P-wave   Arrival of S-wave

Time (min)

(3)

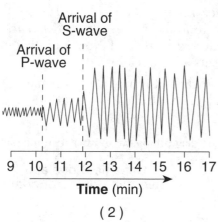

Arrival of S-wave

Arrival of P-wave

Time (min)

(2)

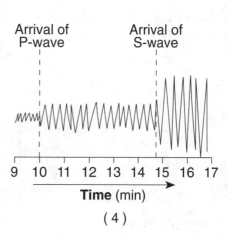

Arrival of P-wave   Arrival of S-wave

Time (min)

(4)

8 When the velocity of a stream suddenly *decreases,* the sediment being transported undergoes an increase in

(1) particle density
(2) erosion
(3) deposition
(4) mass movement

9 When granite melts and then solidifies, it becomes

(1) a sedimentary rock
(2) an igneous rock
(3) a metamorphic rock
(4) sediments

0 During the Permian Period, sedimentary bedrock in the Appalachian Region was subjected to high temperature and pressure. Calcite deposits that had existed in this environment would most likely have formed

(1) schist
(2) gabbro
(3) marble
(4) gneiss

31 The satellite photograph below shows a geologic feature composed of silt, sand, and clay.

The geologic feature shown in the photograph was primarily deposited by which agent of erosion?

(1) glaciers
(2) wind
(3) wave action
(4) running water

32 Which graph shows the relative duration of geologic time for the Precambrian, Paleozoic, Mesozoic, and Cenozoic time intervals?

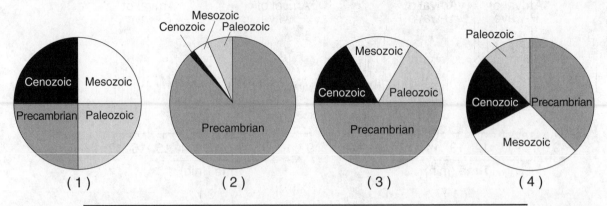

(1)   (2)   (3)   (4)

33 The graph below shows the relationship between the cooling time of magma and the size of the crystals produced.

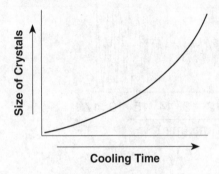

Which graph correctly shows the relative positions of the igneous rocks granite, rhyolite, and pumice?

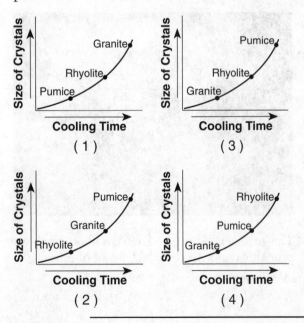

34 According to the Geologic History of New York State in the *Earth Science Reference Tables*, the inferred latitude of New York State 362 million years ago was closest to

(1) where it is now   (3) the Equator
(2) the North Pole   (4) 45° south

35 The diagram below shows a tectonic plate boundary.

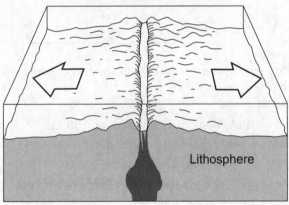

Which mantle hot spot is at a plate boundary like the one shown in this diagram?

(1) Hawaii Hot Spot
(2) Yellowstone Hot Spot
(3) Galapagos Hot Spot
(4) Canary Hot Spot

Answer all questions in this part.

Directions (36–50): For *each* statement or question, write on your separate answer sheet the *number* of the word or expression that, of those given, best completes the statement or answers the question. Some questions may require the use of the *Earth Science Reference Tables*.

Base your answers to questions 36 through 38 on the diagram below, which shows two possible sequences in the life cycle of stars, beginning with their formation from nebular gas clouds in space.

The Life Cycles of Stars

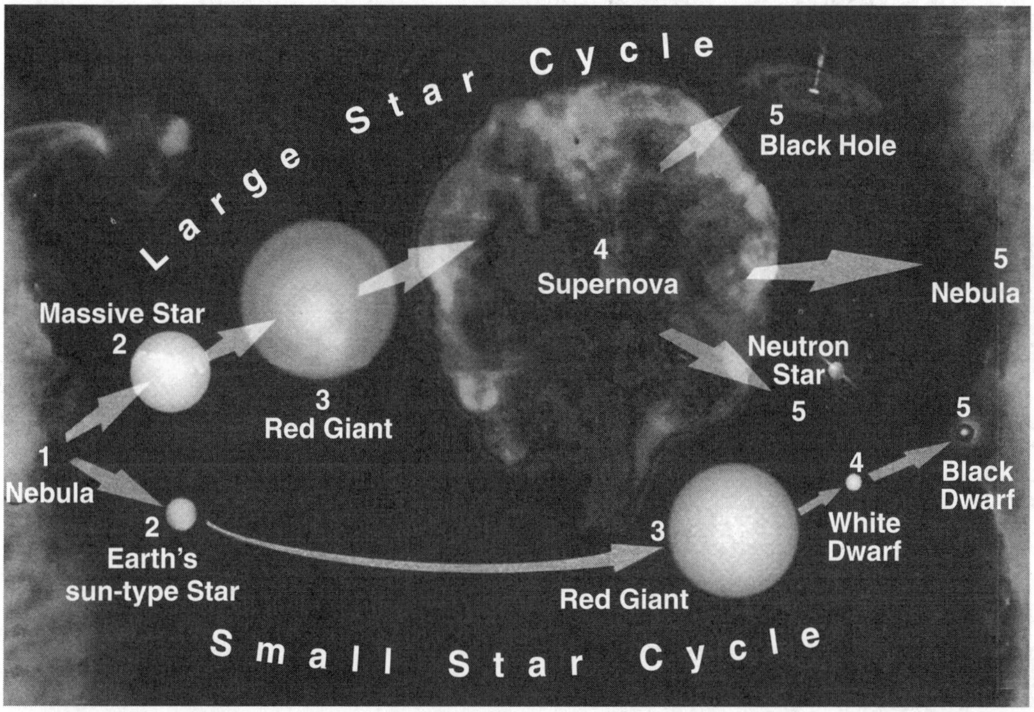

36 According to the diagram, the life-cycle path followed by a star is determined by the star's initial

(1) mass and size
(2) temperature and origin
(3) luminosity and color
(4) luminosity and structure

37 Stars like Earth's Sun most likely formed directly from a

(1) nebula   (3) red giant
(2) supernova   (4) black dwarf

38 According to the diagram, a star like Earth's Sun will eventually

(1) explode in a supernova
(2) become a black hole
(3) change into a white dwarf
(4) become a neutron star

Base your answers to questions 39 and 40 on the maps below, which show changes in the distribution of land and water in the Mediterranean Sea region that scientists believe took place over a period of 6 million years.

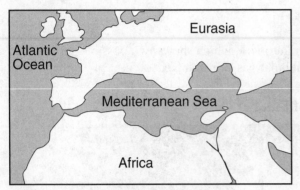

About 10 Million Years Ago

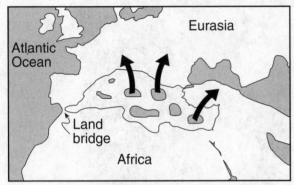

About 8 to 5.5 Million Years Ago
Evaporation from Mediterranean Sea

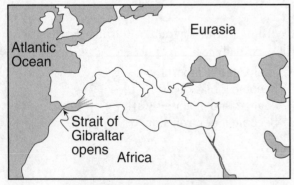

About 4 Million Years Ago
Mediterranean Sea Refills
with Atlantic Ocean Water

39 Which type of rock was precipitated from seawater as the Mediterranean Sea evaporated between 8 million years ago and 5.5 million years ago?

(1) rock salt   (3) sandstone
(2) basalt   (4) metaconglomerate

40 During which geologic time period did the changes shown in the maps take place?

(1) Cambrian   (3) Permian
(2) Cretaceous   (4) Neogene

Base your answers to questions 41 through 45 on the maps below. Points A, B, C, X, and Y are locations on the topographic map. The small map identifies the New York State region shown in the topographic map.

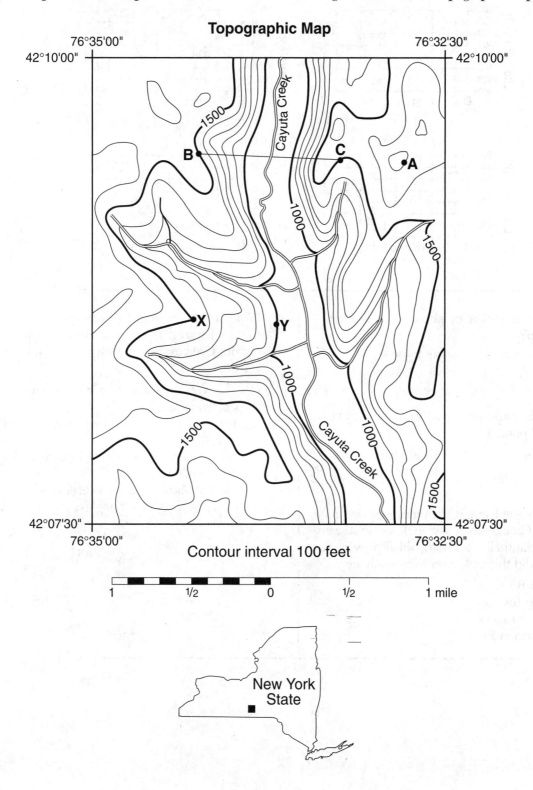

Topographic Map

Contour interval 100 feet

1   1/2   0   1/2   1 mile

New York State

41 Which graph best represents the profile from point *B* to point *C*?

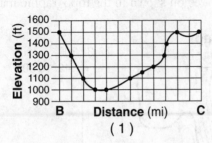
(1)

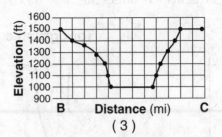
(3)

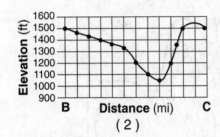
(2)

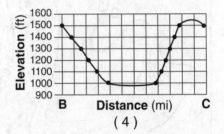
(4)

42 What is the elevation of point *A* on the topographic map?

(1) 1,700 ft (3) 1,600 ft
(2) 1,650 ft (4) 1,550 ft

43 What is the approximate gradient between point *X* and point *Y*?

(1) 100 ft/mi (3) 500 ft/mi
(2) 250 ft/mi (4) 1,000 ft/mi

44 At the end of the Ice Age, the valley now occupied by Cayuta Creek was a channel for southward flowing glacial meltwater. Into which present-day river valley did this meltwater most likely flow?

(1) Hudson River
(2) Genesee River
(3) Delaware River
(4) Susquehanna River

45 Which evidence best supports the inference that the meltwater river that once occupied the Cayuta Creek valley was larger than the modern Cayuta Creek?

(1) The modern Cayuta Creek occupies a V-shaped valley.
(2) The valley floor is wider than the modern Cayuta Creek.
(3) The modern Cayuta Creek lacks meanders and a flood plain.
(4) The tributary streams meet the modern Cayuta Creek at nearly right angles.

Base your answers to questions 46 through 50 on the two cross sections below, which represent the Pacific Ocean and the atmosphere near the Equator during normal weather (cross section A) and during El Niño conditions (cross section B). Sea surface temperatures (SST) are labeled and trade-wind directions are shown with arrows. Cloud buildup indicates regions of frequent thunderstorm activity. The change from normal sea level is shown at the side of each diagram.

Cross Section A: Normal Weather

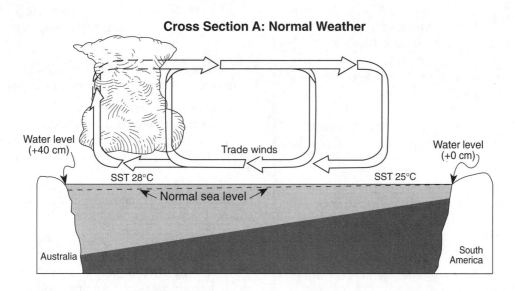

Water level (+40 cm)

Trade winds

Water level (+0 cm)

SST 28°C

SST 25°C

Normal sea level

Australia

South America

Cross Section B: El Niño Conditions

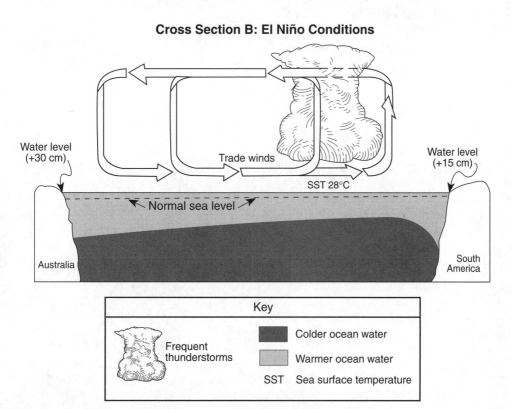

Water level (+30 cm)

Trade winds

Water level (+15 cm)

SST 28°C

Normal sea level

Australia

South America

Key		
Frequent thunderstorms		Colder ocean water
		Warmer ocean water
	SST	Sea surface temperature

46 Which statement correctly describes sea surface temperatures along the South American coast and Pacific trade winds during El Niño conditions?

(1) The sea surface temperatures are warmer than normal, and Pacific trade winds are from the west.
(2) The sea surface temperatures are warmer than normal, and Pacific trade winds are from the east.
(3) The sea surface temperatures are cooler than normal, and Pacific trade winds are from the west.
(4) The sea surface temperatures are cooler than normal, and Pacific trade winds are from the east.

47 Compared to normal weather conditions, the shift of the trade winds caused sea levels during El Niño conditions to

(1) decrease at both Australia and South America
(2) decrease at Australia and increase at South America
(3) increase at Australia and decrease at South America
(4) increase at both Australia and South America

48 During El Niño conditions, thunderstorms increase in the eastern Pacific Ocean region because the warm, moist air is

(1) less dense, sinking, compressing, and warming
(2) less dense, rising, expanding, and cooling
(3) more dense, sinking, compressing, and warming
(4) more dense, rising, expanding, and cooling

49 The development of El Niño conditions over this region of the Pacific Ocean has caused

(1) changes in worldwide precipitation patterns
(2) the reversal of Earth's seasons
(3) increased worldwide volcanic activity
(4) decreased ozone levels in the atmosphere

50 Earth's entire equatorial climate zone is generally a belt around Earth that has

(1) high air pressure and wet weather
(2) high air pressure and dry weather
(3) low air pressure and wet weather
(4) low air pressure and dry weather

Part B–2

Answer all questions in this part.

Directions (51–64): Record your answers in the spaces provided in your answer booklet. Some questions may require the use of the *Earth Science Reference Tables*.

51 The atmospheric conditions at a given location are represented by the weather station model below.

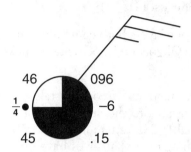

On the lines provided *in your answer booklet*, fill in the correct information for *each* variable listed, based on this weather station model.   [2]

Base your answers to questions 52 through 54 on the diagram provided *in your answer booklet*, which represents the Sun's rays striking Earth at a position in its orbit around the Sun.

52 On the diagram provided *in your answer booklet*, neatly and accurately shade the area of Earth that is in darkness.   [1]

53 On the diagram provided *in your answer booklet*, draw the line of latitude that is receiving the Sun's direct perpendicular rays on this date.   [1]

54 What month of the year is represented by the diagram?   [1]

_____

55 The diagram provided *in your answer booklet* shows the Sun, the Moon, and Earth in line with one another in space. On the diagram, draw *two* dots (•) on the surface of Earth to indicate the locations where the highest ocean tides are most likely occurring.   [1]

56 Using the "Luminosity and Temperature of Stars" graph in the *Earth Science Reference Tables*, list the five stars below in order of *decreasing* relative luminosity, with letter *a* being the brightest.   [1]

Aldebaran, Betelgeuse, Polaris, Sirius, the Sun

Base your answers to questions 57 through 61 on the geologic cross section provided *in your answer booklet*, which represents an outcrop of various types of bedrock and bedrock features in Colorado.

57 On the cross section provided *in your answer booklet*, indicate with arrows the direction of movement on *both* sides of the fault. [1]

58 According to this cross section, what is the amount of vertical movement of the shale along the fault? Express your answer to the *nearest tenth of a meter.* [1]

59 Place the geologic events listed *in your answer booklet* in order by numbering them from oldest (1) to youngest (4). [1]

60 The shale and sandstone layers both contain fossilized leaves from the *Fagopsis* tree, an index fossil for the Oligocene Epoch. State a possible age for these rock layers, in million years. [1]

61 The vesicular basalt includes zircon crystals containing the radioactive isotope U-235, which disintegrates to the stable isotope Pb-207. The zircon crystals have 98.44% of the original U-235 remaining, and 1.56% has decayed to Pb-207. Based on the table below, how many half-lives have elapsed since the formation of these crystals? [1]

Percent of U-235 Remaining	Percent Decayed to Pb-207	Half-Lives Elapsed
99.22	0.78	$\frac{1}{64}$
98.44	1.56	$\frac{1}{32}$
96.88	3.12	$\frac{1}{16}$
93.75	6.25	$\frac{1}{8}$
87.50	12.5	$\frac{1}{4}$
75.0	25.0	$\frac{1}{2}$
50.0	50.0	1
37.5	62.5	$1\frac{1}{2}$
25.0	75.0	2
12.5	87.5	3
6.25	93.75	4

Base your answers to questions 62 through 64 on diagram 1 below and on diagram 2 *in your answer booklet,* which show some constellations in the night sky viewed by a group of students. Diagram 1 below shows the positions of the constellations at 9:00 p.m. Diagram 2 *in your answer booklet* shows their positions two hours later.

Diagram 1 — 9:00 p.m.

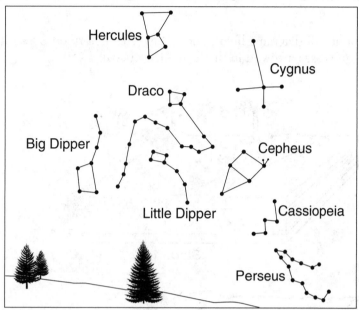

62 Circle *Polaris* on diagram 2 provided *in your answer booklet.* [1]

63 In which compass direction were the students facing? [1]

64 Describe the apparent direction of movement of the constellations Hercules and Perseus during the two hours between student observations. [1]

Part C

Answer all questions in this part.

Directions (65–81): Record your answers in the spaces provided in your answer booklet. Some questions may require the use of the *Earth Science Reference Tables*.

65 The sequence of diagrams below shows how coal is formed. Describe the material and *two* processes involved in the formation of coal.   [2]

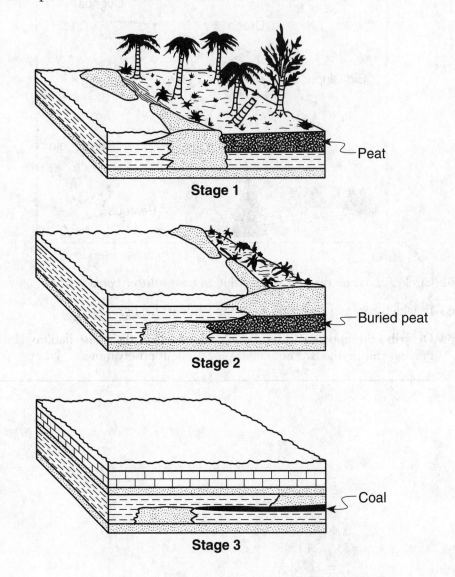

Base your answers to questions 66 and 67 on the table and graph below. The table labeled "Animal Key" shows symbols to represent various animal groups that exist on Earth. The graph shows inferred changes in Earth's average temperatures over the last 500 million years.

Animal Key

Letter	Picture	Animal Group
A		Birds
B		Fish
C		Amphibians
D		Mammals
E		Humans
F		Reptiles

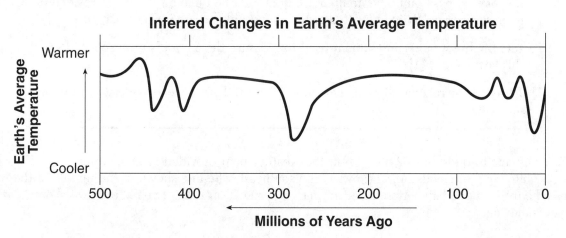

Inferred Changes in Earth's Average Temperature

66 On the graph provided *in your answer booklet*, indicate when each of the life-forms in the table is believed to have first appeared on Earth by placing the letter for *each* animal group in the correct box. The correct location for earliest fish, letter *B*, has already been plotted above the graph.   [2]

67 The two factors listed below could have caused the temperature variations shown on the graph. For *each* factor, state the effect that the increase described would have had on Earth's temperature, and explain why that temperature change would have taken place.   [2]

Factors

A Increase in carbon dioxide (CO_2) and water vapor (H_2O gas) content of Earth's atmosphere

B Increase in volcanic ash in Earth's atmosphere

Base your answers to questions 68 through 71 on the data table below, which shows recorded information for a major Atlantic hurricane. Use the map provided *in your answer booklet* to answer questions 68 and 69.

Hurricane Data

Date	Time	Latitude	Longitude	Maximum Winds (knots)	Air Pressure (mb)
Sept. 10	11:00 a.m.	19° N	59° W	70	989
Sept. 11	11:00 a.m.	22° N	62° W	95	962
Sept. 12	11:00 a.m.	23° N	67° W	105	955
Sept. 13	11:00 a.m.	24° N	72° W	135	921
Sept. 14	11:00 a.m.	26° N	77° W	125	932
Sept. 15	11:00 a.m.	30° N	79° W	110	943

68 Using the latitude and longitude data in the table, place an **X** on the map provided *in your answer booklet* for *each* location of the hurricane during these 6 days. Connect all the **X**s with a solid line.   [1]

69 Label the September 15 (9/15) position of the hurricane on the map. Starting from this plotted position on September 15, draw a dashed line on the map provided *in your answer booklet* to indicate the storm's most likely path for the next 5 days.   [1]

70 Identify the weather instrument used to measure the air pressure associated with this hurricane.   [1]

71 Describe the relationship between air pressure and wind speed associated with this hurricane.   [1]

Base your answers to questions 72 and 73 on the weather map provided *in your answer booklet*, which shows a large white band of clouds moving toward the southeast. The line shown in the middle of the white cloud band is the frontal boundary between a cP air mass and an mT air mass. Two large arrows show the direction the front is moving.

72 On the frontal boundary line on the weather map provided *in your answer booklet,* draw the weather front symbol to represent the front moving toward the southeast. [1]

73 On the same weather map, place an **X** centered on the geographic region that was most likely the source of the warm, moist (mT) air mass.   [1]

Base your answers to questions 74 through 79 on the reading passage and maps below and on your knowledge of Earth science. The enlarged map shows the location of volcanoes in Colombia, South America.

Fire and Ice — and Sluggish Magma

On the night of November 13, 1985, Nevado del Ruiz, a 16,200-foot (4,938 meter) snow-capped volcano in northwestern Colombia, erupted. Snow melted, sending a wall of mud and water raging through towns as far as 50 kilometers away, and killing 25,000 people.

Long before disaster struck, Nevado del Ruiz was marked as a trouble spot. Like Mexico City, where an earthquake killed at least 7,000 people in October 1985, Nevado del Ruiz is located along the Ring of Fire. This ring of islands and the coastal lands along the edge of the Pacific Ocean are prone to volcanic eruptions and crustal movements.

The ring gets its turbulent characteristics from the motion of the tectonic plates under it. The perimeter of the Pacific, unlike that of the Atlantic, is located above active tectonic plates. Nevado del Ruiz happens to be located near the junction of four plate boundaries. In this area an enormous amount of heat is created, which melts the rock 100 to 200 kilometers below Earth's surface and creates magma.

Nevado del Ruiz hadn't had a major eruption for 400 years before this tragedy. The reason: sluggish magma. Unlike the runny, mafic magma that makes up the lava flows of oceanic volcanoes such as those in Hawaii, the magma at this type of subduction plate boundary tends to be sticky and slow moving, forming the rock andesite when it cools. This andesitic magma tends to plug up the opening of the volcano. It sits in a magma chamber underground with pressure continually building up. Suddenly, tiny cracks develop in Earth's crust, causing the pressure to drop. This causes the steam and other gases dissolved in the magma to violently expand, blowing the magma plug free. Huge amounts of ash and debris are sent flying, creating what is called an explosive eruption.

Oddly enough, the actual eruption of Nevado del Ruiz didn't cause most of the destruction. It was caused not by lava but by the towering walls of sliding mud created when large chunks of hot ash and pumice mixed with melted snow.

Locator Plate Map

Enlarged Map Showing Volcanoes of Colombia

Key
▲ Volcanoes

74 What are the names of the *four* tectonic plates located near the Nevado del Ruiz volcano?   [1]

75 What caused most of the destruction associated with the eruption of Nevado del Ruiz?   [1]

76 What caused the magma to expand, blowing the magma plug free?   [1]

77 Vesicular texture is very common in igneous rocks formed during andesitic eruptions. Explain how this texture is formed.   [1]

78 Why are eruptions of Nevado del Ruiz generally more explosive than most Hawaiian volcanic eruptions?   [1]

79 Describe one emergency preparation that may reduce the loss of life from a future eruption of the Nevado del Ruiz volcano.   [1]

GO RIGHT ON TO THE NEXT PAGE ⇨

Base your answers to questions 80 and 81 on the cross section below. The cross section represents a part of Texas where weakly cemented sandstone is exposed at the surface. The mineral cement holding the sandstone grains together is calcite. Area *X* is a circular depression of loose sand that has been partially removed by prevailing winds. Sand dunes have developed downwind from depression *X*.

Present Day, Dry Climate

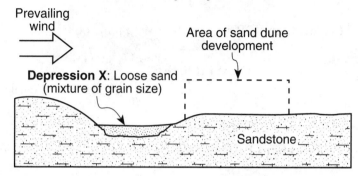

80 On the diagram of the area of sand dune development provided *in your answer booklet*, draw a sketch showing the general sideview of a sand dune formed by a wind blowing in the direction indicated. Your sketch should clearly show any variations in the slope of the sides of the dune.   [1]

81 The cross section below shows this same area of Texas near the end of the last ice age when this area had a much wetter climate. More infiltration of rainwater was occurring at area *X*. Scientists infer that depression *X* was an area where slightly acidic rainwater collected and infiltrated into the sandstone.

Late Pleistocene, Wetter Climate

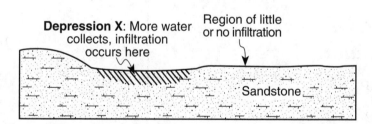

Describe the effect that the slightly acidic infiltrating water had on the calcite cement holding the sandstone together.   [1]

PHYSICAL SETTING
EARTH SCIENCE

Friday, June 18, 2004 — 1:15 to 4:15 p.m., only

ANSWER SHEET

Student .... Sex: ☐ Male ☐ Female Grade ....

Teacher .... School ....

Record your answers to Part A and Part B–1 on this answer sheet.

Part A			Part B–1	
1	13	25	36	44 ....
2	14	26	37	45 ....
3	15	27	38	46 ....
4	16	28	39	47 ....
5	17	29	40	48 ....
6	18	30	41	49 ....
7	19	31	42	50 ....
8	20	32	43	**Part B–1 Score**
9	21	33		
10	22	34		
11	23	35		
12	24	**Part A Score**		

Write your answers to Part B–2 and Part C in your answer booklet.

The declaration below should be signed when you have completed the examination.

I do hereby affirm, at the close of this examination, that I had no unlawful knowledge of the questions or answers prior to the examination and that I have neither given nor received assistance in answering any of the questions during the examination.

_____
Signature

PHYSICAL SETTING
EARTH SCIENCE

Friday, June 18, 2004 — 1:15 to 4:15 p.m., only

ANSWER BOOKLET

Student . . . . Sex: ☐ Male ☐ Female

Teacher . . . .

School . . . . Grade . . . .

Answer all questions in Part B–2 and Part C. Record your answers in this booklet.

	Performance Test Score (Maximum Score: 23)	
Part	Maximum Score	Student's Score
A	35	
B–1	15	
B–2	15	
C	20	

Total Written Test Score (Maximum Raw Score: 85) ☐

Final Score (from conversion chart) ☐

Raters' Initials:

Rater 1 . . . . Rater 2 . . . .

Part B–2

For Raters Only

51 Air pressure: _____ **mb**

Air temperature: _____ **°F**

Amount of precipitation during last six hours: _____ **inch(es)**

Cloud cover: _____ **%**

Present weather: _____

51 ☐

52 and 53

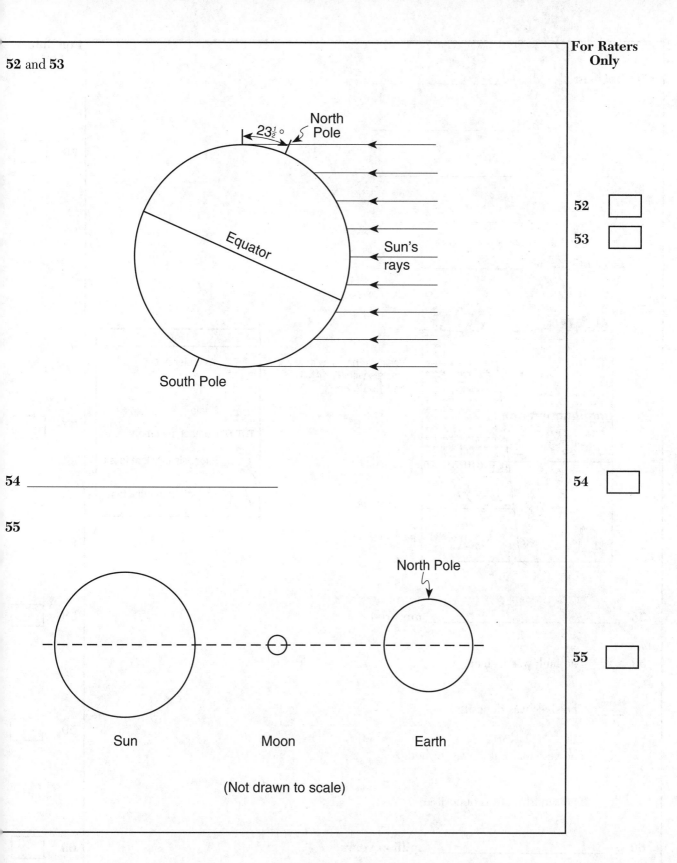

North
Pole

$23\frac{1}{2}°$

Equator

Sun's
rays

South Pole

52 ☐

53 ☐

54 _____

54 ☐

55

North Pole

Sun

Moon

Earth

(Not drawn to scale)

55 ☐

56 Brightest: (*a*) _____

(*b*) _____

(*c*) _____

(*d*) _____

Least bright: (*e*) _____

56 ☐

57

Vesicular basalt with zircon crystals with 98.44% U^{235} and 1.56% Pb^{207}

Key	
+ + + +	Vesicular basalt
░░░░	Sandstone
‒ ‒ ‒	Shale
⊓⊓⊓⊓⊓	Contact metamorphism
🍃	Fagopsis tree leaf fossil
🪵	Sequoia tree trunk fossil

— 2 meters

— 1

— 0

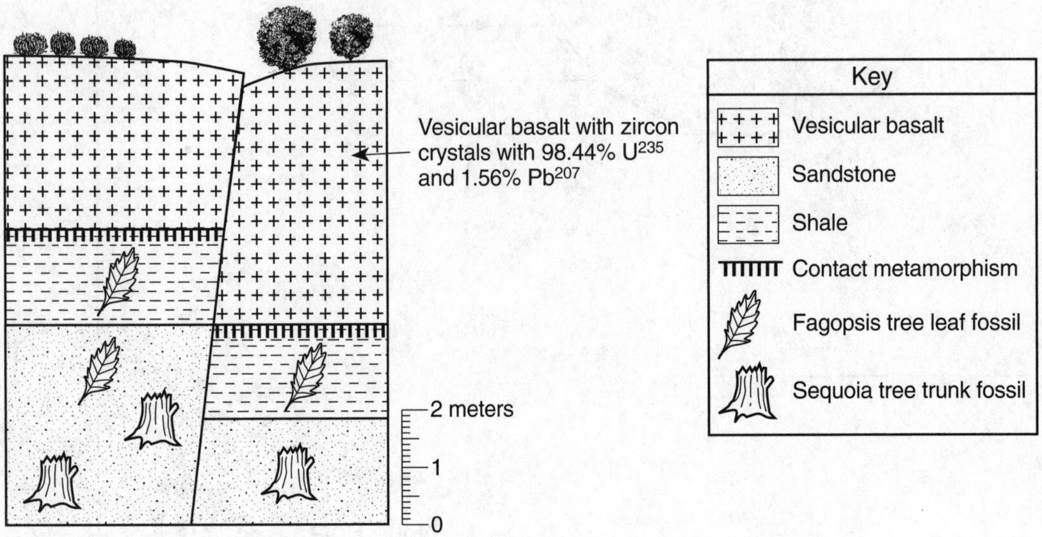

57 ☐

58 _____ **meter(s)**   58 ☐

59 _____ The fault was formed.

_____ The shale was deposited.

_____ The vesicular basalt was formed.   59 ☐

_____ The sandstone was deposited.

60 _____ **million years**   60 ☐

61 _____ **half-lives**   61 ☐

[3]

[OVER]

62

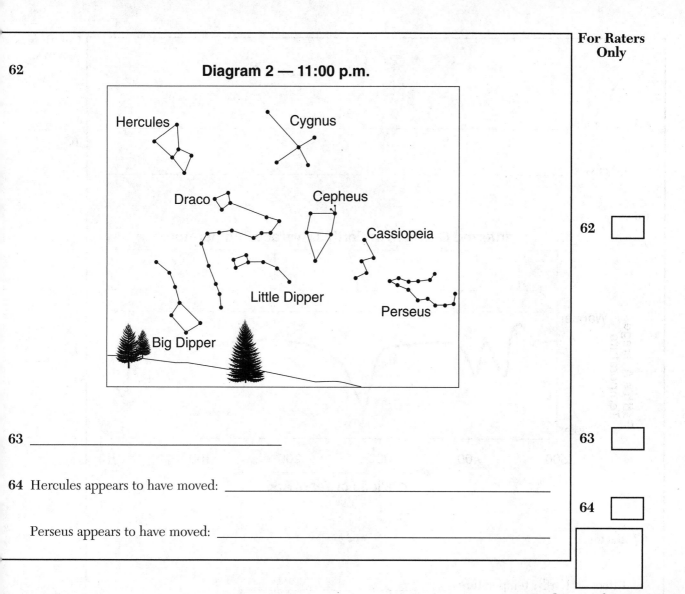

Diagram 2 — 11:00 p.m.

Hercules
Cygnus
Draco
Cepheus
Cassiopeia
Little Dipper
Perseus
Big Dipper

63 _____

64 Hercules appears to have moved: _____

Perseus appears to have moved: _____

[4]

Part C

65 Material: _____

Processes: _____ and _____

66

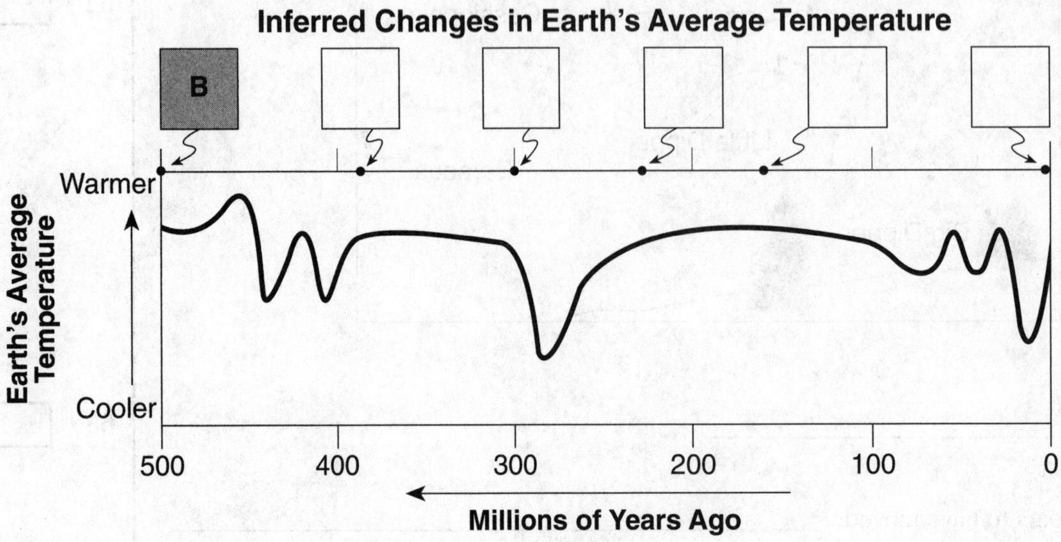

Inferred Changes in Earth's Average Temperature

67 Factor A: _____

Effect on Earth's temperature: _____

Why temperature changes: _____

_____

Factor B: _____

Effect on Earth's temperature: _____

Why temperature changes: _____

_____

[5]

[OVER]

68 and 69

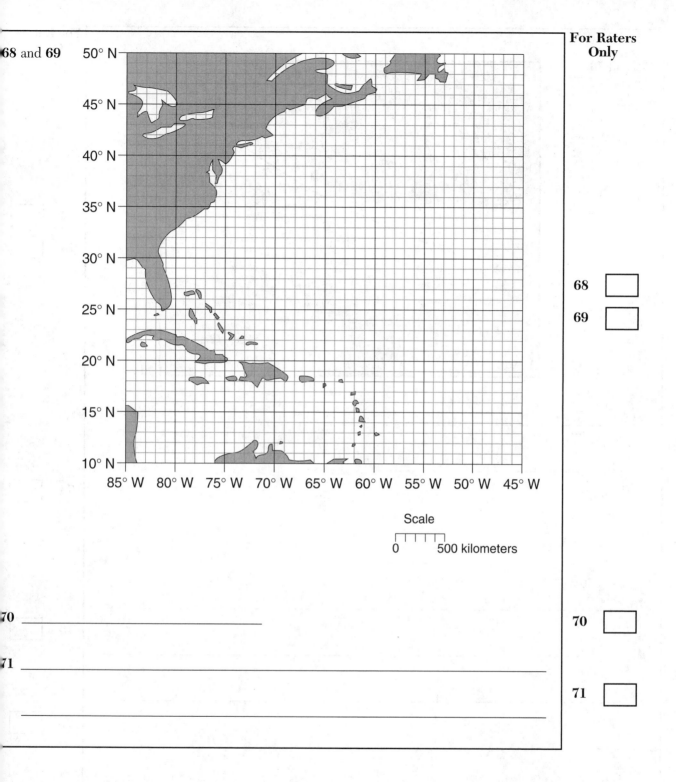

Scale

0   500 kilometers

70 _____

71 _____

_____

72 and **73**

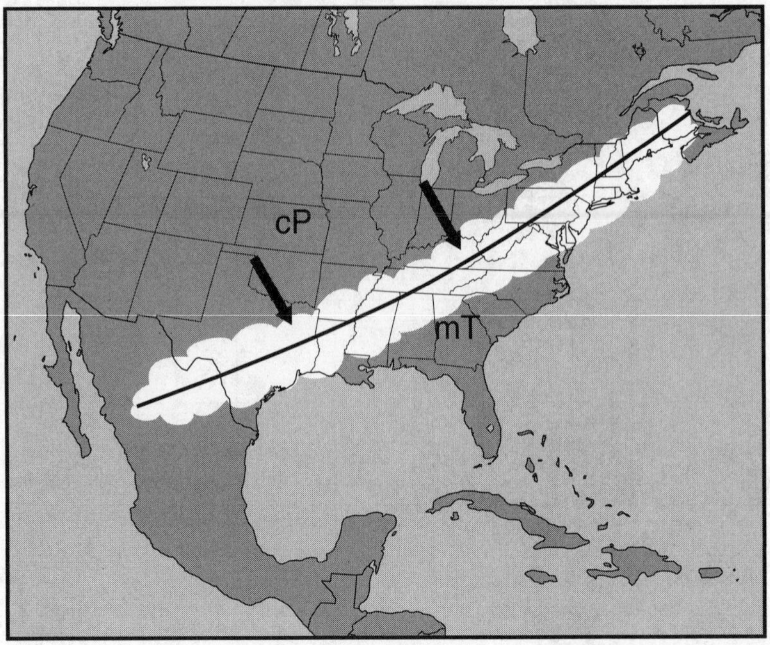

72 ☐

73 ☐

74 (1) _____

(2) _____

(3) _____   74 ☐

(4) _____

75 _____

_____   75 ☐

76 _____

_____   76 ☐

77 _____

_____   77 ☐

For Raters Only

78 ______________________________

______________________________ 78

79 ______________________________ 79

80

Prevailing wind
Ground surface

80

81 ______________________________

______________________________ 81

Total Score for Part C

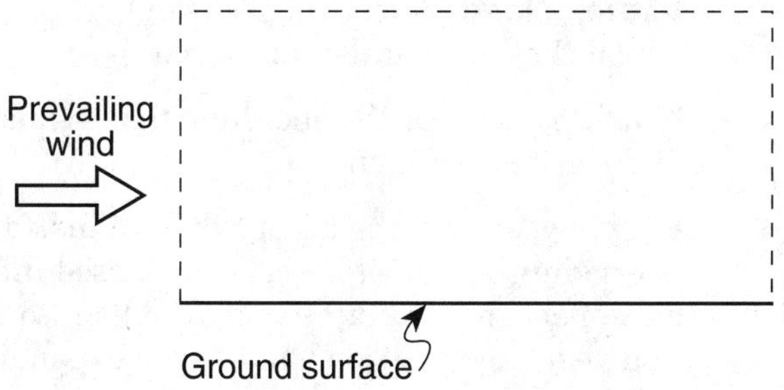

A

abrasion the grinding and wearing away of rock surfaces through the mechanical action of other rock or sand particles

absolute age the numeric age of an object or event, often stated in years before the present, as established by an absolute-dating process, such as radiometric dating

absolute brightness (absolute magnitude) the total amount of light emitted from a star

abyssal plain a large, flat, almost level area of the deep-ocean basin

air mass a large body of air throughout which temperature and moisture content are similar

anticyclone a weather system with a swirling center of high air pressure; in Northern Hemisphere winds circulate clockwise around an anticyclone

aphelion the point in the orbit of a planet at which the planet is farthest from the sun

apparent brightness (apparent magnitude) the brightness of a star as seen from Earth

aquifer a body of rock or sediment that stores groundwater and allows the flow of groundwater

arête a sharp, jagged ridge that forms between cirques

asteroid a small, rocky object that orbits the sun; most asteroids are located in a band between the orbits of Mars and Jupiter

asthenosphere the solid, plastic layer of the mantle beneath the lithosphere; made of mantle rock that flows very slowly, which allows tectonic plates to move on top of it

atmosphere a mixture of gases that surrounds a planet or moon

atmospheric pressure the force per unit area that is exerted on a surface by the weight of the atmosphere

atom the smallest unit of an element that maintains the chemical properties of that element

aurora colored light produced by charged particles from the solar wind and from the magnetosphere that react with and excite the oxygen and nitrogen of Earth's upper atmosphere; usually seen in the sky near Earth's magnetic poles

B

barometer an instrument that measures atmospheric pressure

barrier island a long ridge of sand or narrow island that lies parallel to the shore

beach an area of the shoreline that is made up of deposited sediment

big bang theory the theory that all matter and energy in the universe was compressed into an extremely small volume that 13 billion to 15 billion years ago exploded and began expanding in all directions

black hole an object so massive and dense that even light cannot escape its gravity

blue shift on a spectrograph, the shift of absorption lines toward the blue end of the spectrum, indicating that a star is moving toward Earth

body wave in geology, a seismic wave that travels through the body of a medium

C

carbon-14 dating absolute-dating method used to determine the age of wood, bone, shells, and other artifacts of biological origin up to about 50,000 years

cementation the process in which minerals precipitate into pore spaces between sediment grains and bind sediments together to form rock

Cenozoic Era the current geologic era, which began 65.5 million years ago; also called the Age of Mammals

chemical sedimentary rock sedimentary rock that forms when minerals precipitate from a solution or settle from a suspension

chemical weathering the process by which rocks break down as a result of chemical reactions

cirque a deep and steep bowl-like depression produced by glacial erosion

clastic sedimentary rock sedimentary rock that forms when fragments of preexisting rocks are compacted or cemented together

cleavage in geology, the tendency of a mineral to split along specific planes of weakness to form smooth, flat surfaces

climate the average weather conditions in an area over a long period of time

cloud a collection of small water droplets or ice crystals suspended in the air, which forms when the air is cooled and condensation occurs

cold front the front edge of a moving mass of cold air that pushes beneath a warmer air mass like a wedge

comet a small body of ice, rock, and cosmic dust that follows an elliptical orbit around the sun and that gives off gas and dust in the form of a tail as it passes close to the sun

compaction the process in which the volume and porosity of a sediment is decreased by the weight of overlying sediments as a result of burial beneath other sediments

condensation the change of state from a gas to a liquid

condensation nucleus a solid particle in the atmosphere that provides the surface on which water vapor condenses

conduction the transfer of energy as heat through a material

conservation the preservation and wise use of natural resources

constellation one of 88 regions into which the sky has been divided in order to describe the locations of celestial objects; a group of stars organized in a recognizable pattern

contact metamorphism a change in the texture, structure, or chemical composition of a rock due to contact with magma

continental drift the hypothesis that states that the continents once formed a single landmass, broke up, and drifted to their present locations

continental glacier a massive sheet of ice that may cover millions of square kilometers, that may be thousands of meters thick, and that is not confined by surrounding topography

continental margin the shallow sea floor that is located between the shoreline and the deep-ocean bottom

continental rise raised area near the bottom of a continental slope, formed by the accumulation of sediment

continental shelf land-border of varying width that slopes gently toward the deep-ocean bottom

continental slope the steep slope on the seaward side of the continental shelf

contour line a line that connects points of equal elevation on a map

convection the movement of matter due to differences in density that are caused by temperature variations; can result in the transfer of energy as heat

convection cells huge bands of wind caused by temperature variations across Earth's surface

convergent boundary the boundary between tectonic plates that are colliding

core the central part of Earth below the mantle; also the center of the sun

Coriolis effect the curving of the path of a moving object from an otherwise straight path due to Earth's rotation

cosmic background radiation radiation uniformly detected from every direction in space; considered a remnant of the big bang

creep the slow downhill movement of weathered rock material

crust the thin and solid outermost layer of the Earth above the mantle

crystal a solid whose atoms, ions, or molecules are arranged in a regular, repeating pattern

current in geology, a horizontal movement of water in a well-defined pattern, such as a river or a stream; the movement of air in a certain direction

cyclone a weather system with a center of low pressure; in Northern Hemisphere, winds circulate counterclockwise around a cyclone

D

deep-ocean basin the part of the ocean floor that is under deep water beyond the continental margin and that is composed of oceanic crust and a thin layer of sediment

delta a fan-shaped mass of rock material deposited at the mouth of a stream; for example, deltas form where streams flow into the ocean at the edge of a continent

density the ratio of the mass of a substance to the volume of the substance

deposition the release of sediments carried by an agent of erosion

dew point at constant pressure and water vapor content, the temperature to which air must cool to reach saturation (100% relative humidity)

divergent boundary the boundary between two tectonic plates that are moving away from each other

Doppler effect an observed change in the frequency of a wave when the source or observer is moving

drumlin long, low, tear-shaped mounds of glacial till; the long axes of drumlins are parallel to the direction of glacial movement

dune a mound of wind-deposited sand that moves as a result of the action of wind

E

earthquake a movement or trembling of the ground that is caused by a sudden release of energy when rocks along a fault move

eccentricity the degree of elongation of an elliptical orbit

eclipse an event in which the shadow of one celestial body falls on another

El Niño the warm-water phase of the El Niño Southern Oscillation; a periodic occurrence in the eastern Pacific Ocean in which the surface-water temperature becomes unusually warm

electron a subatomic particle that has a negative charge

element a substance that cannot be separated or broken down into simpler substances by chemical means; all atoms of an element have the same atomic number

elevation the height of an object above sea level

ellipse a closed curve whose shape is determined by two points, or foci, within the ellipse

epicenter the point on Earth's surface directly above an earthquake's starting point, or focus

equator imaginary line that circles Earth and divides it into Northern and Southern hemispheres

equinox the moment when the sun appears to cross the celestial equator

erosion a process in which the materials of Earth's surface are loosened, dissolved, or worn away and transported from one place to another by a natural agent, such as wind, water, ice, or gravity

esker a long, winding ridge of gravel and coarse sand deposited by glacial meltwater streams

extrusive igneous rock rock that forms from the cooling and solidification of lava at Earth's surface

F

fault a break in a body of rock along which one block slides relative to another; a form of brittle strain

fault-block mountain a mountain that forms where faulting breaks Earth's crust into large blocks, which causes some blocks to drop down relative to other blocks

fault zone a region of numerous, closely spaced faults

felsic describes magma or igneous rock that is rich in feldspars and silica and that is generally light in color

focus the location within Earth along a fault at which the first motion of an earthquake occurs

folded mountain a mountain that forms when rock layers are squeezed together and uplifted

foliation the metamorphic rock texture in which mineral grains are arranged in planes or bands

fossil the trace or remains of an organism that lived long ago, most commonly preserved in sedimentary rock

fossil fuel a nonrenewable energy resource formed from the remains of organisms that lived long ago; examples include oil, coal, and natural gas

G

galaxy a collection of stars, dust, and gas bound together by gravity

gas giant a planet that has a deep, massive atmosphere, such as Jupiter, Saturn, Uranus, or Neptune

geocentric model scientific model that suggests that Earth is the center of the solar system and that the sun, planets, and other celestial objects revolve around it

geologic time scale a record of Earth's history, beginning about 4.6 billion years ago, that shows geological and biological events, time units, and ages

geology the scientific study of the origin, history, and structure of Earth and the processes that shape Earth

giant a very large and bright star whose hot core has used most of its hydrogen

glacial drift the rock material carried and deposited by glaciers

glacier a large mass of moving ice

global ocean the body of salt water that covers nearly three-fourths of Earth's surface

global warming a gradual increase in the average global temperature that is due to a higher concentration of gases such as carbon dioxide in the atmosphere

gradient the change in a field value, such as elevation, over a given distance

greenhouse effect the warming of the surface and lower atmosphere of Earth that occurs when carbon dioxide, water vapor, and other gases in the air absorb and reradiate infrared radiation

groundwater the water that is beneath Earth's surface

Gulf Stream the swift, deep, and warm Atlantic current that flows along the eastern coast of the United States toward the northeast

gyre a huge circle of moving ocean water found above and below the equator

H

half-life the time required for half of a sample of a radioactive isotope to break down by radioactive decay to form a daughter isotope

hardness the resistance of a mineral to being scratched

heliocentric model scientific model that suggests that the sun is at the center of the solar system and that the planets and other celestial objects revolve around it

Hertzsprung-Russell diagram graph that plots the surface temperatures of stars against their luminosity

horizon the line where the sky and the Earth appear to meet; also a horizontal layer of soil that can be distinguished from the layers above and below it; also a boundary between two rock layers that have different physical properties

horizontal sorting process by which sediments are separated in order of decreasing size with increasing distance from the shore

hot spot a volcanically active area of Earth's surface, commonly far from a tectonic plate boundary

humidity a measure of the water vapor content of the air

humus dark, organic material formed in soil from the decayed remains of plants and animals

I

ice age a long period of climatic cooling during which the continents are glaciated repeatedly

ice wedging also called frost wedging; mechanical weathering process in which the freezing and thawing of water breaks apart rock

igneous rock rock that forms when magma cools and solidifies

index fossil a fossil that is used to establish the age of a rock layer because the fossil is distinct, abundant, and widespread and existed for only a short span of geologic time

inertia the tendency of an object to resist being moved or, if the object is moving, to resist a change in speed or direction until an outside force acts on the object

infiltration the process by which water seeps into the soil

insolation solar radiation that strikes Earth's surface

International Date Line the 180° meridian, on the other side of Earth from the prime meridian; an imaginary line in the Pacific Ocean where the calendar day changes

intrusive igneous rock rock formed from the cooling and solidification of magma beneath Earth's surface

ionosphere a layer of Earth's atmosphere where ions and free electrons absorb AM radio waves during the day and reflect them back toward Earth at night

island arc chain of volcanic islands; Japan is an example of an island arc

isobar a line on a weather map that connects locations that have the same atmospheric pressure

isotherm a line on a weather map that connects locations that have the same temperature

isotope an atom that has the same number of protons (or the same atomic number) as other atoms of the same element but that has a different number of neutrons (and thus a different atomic mass)

J

jet stream a narrow band of strong winds that blow in the upper troposphere

K

kettle a bowl-shaped depression in a glacial drift deposit

L

latent heat the heat energy that is absorbed or released by a substance during a phase change

latitude the distance north or south from the equator; expressed in degrees

lava magma that flows onto Earth's surface; the rock that forms when lava cools and solidifies

law of cross-cutting relationships the principle that a fault or body of rock is younger than any other body of rock that it cuts through

law of superposition the principle that a sedimentary rock layer is older than the layers above it and younger than the layers below it if the layers are not disturbed

light-year the distance that light travels in one year; about 9.46 trillion kilometers

lithosphere the solid, outer layer of Earth that consists of the crust and the rigid upper part of the mantle

longitude the angular distance east or west from the prime meridian; expressed in degrees

longshore current a water current that travels near and parallel to the shoreline

longshore transport the motion of sediment caused by a longshore current

luminosity the total amount of light emitted from a star; also called absolute brightness or absolute magnitude

lunar eclipse the passing of the moon through Earth's shadow at full moon

luster the way in which a mineral reflects light

M

mafic describes magma or igneous rock that is rich in magnesium and iron and that is generally dark in color

magma liquid rock produced under Earth's surface; igneous rocks are made of magma

main-sequence star a star that actively fuses hydrogen into helium at a stable rate

mantle in Earth science, the layer of rock between Earth's crust and core

mass movement the movement of a large mass of sediment or a section of land down a slope

matter anything that has mass and takes up space

meanders one of the bends, twists, or curves in a low-gradient stream or river

mechanical weathering the process by which rocks break down into smaller pieces by physical means

meridian any semicircle that runs north and south around Earth from the geographic North Pole to the geographic South Pole; a line of longitude

mesosphere literally, the "middle sphere"; the strong, lower part of the mantle between the asthenosphere and the outer core; also the coldest layer of the atmosphere, between the stratosphere and the thermosphere, in which temperature decreases as altitude increases

Mesozoic Era the geologic era that lasted from 251 million to 65.5 million years ago; also called the Age of Reptiles

metamorphic rock rock that is changed by heat, pressure, and/or chemical processes

meteor a bright streak of light that results when a meteoroid burns up in Earth's atmosphere

meteorite a meteoroid that strikes Earth's surface

meteoroid a relatively small, rocky body that travels through space

mid-ocean ridge a long, undersea mountain chain that has a steep, narrow valley at its center, that forms as magma rises from the asthenosphere, and that creates new oceanic lithosphere (sea floor) as tectonic plates move apart

Milky Way galaxy the spiral galaxy in which our solar system is located

mineral a natural, usually inorganic solid that has a characteristic chemical composition, an orderly internal structure, and a characteristic set of physical properties

modified Mercalli scale scale that classifies earthquake intensity, or the effects of an earthquake

Mohorovicic discontinuity (Moho) the boundary between Earth's crust and mantle; named in honor of the Croatian scientist who discovered it

Mohs hardness scale the standard scale against which the hardness of minerals is rated

moon a body that revolves around a planet and that has less mass than the planet does

moraine a landform that is made from unsorted sediments deposited by a glacier

N

neap tide a tide characterized by relatively low high tides and relatively high low tides; occurs when the sun and the moon are at right angles to each other in relation to Earth

nebula a large cloud of gas and dust in interstellar space; a region in space where stars are born

nebular theory scientific theory that states that the solar system formed from a rotating cloud of gas, ice, and dust, called a solar nebula

neutron a subatomic particle that has no charge and that is located in the nucleus of an atom

neutron star a star that has collapsed under gravity to the point that the electrons and protons have smashed together to form neutrons

nonfoliated the metamorphic rock texture in which mineral grains are not arranged in planes or bands

nonrenewable resource a resource that forms at a rate that is much slower than the rate at which it is consumed

nuclear fusion the process by which nuclei of small atoms combine to form new, more massive nuclei; the process releases energy

O

occluded front a front that forms when a cold air mass overtakes a warm air mass and lifts the warm air mass off the ground and over another air mass

orbital period the time required for a body to complete a single orbit

organic sedimentary rock sedimentary rock that forms from the remains of plants or animals

outwash plain a deposit of stratified glacial drift that lies in front of a terminal moraine and is crossed by many meltwater streams

oxidation a reaction that removes one or more electrons from a substance such that the substance's valence or oxidation state increases; in geology, the process by which a metallic element combines with oxygen

ozone layer area of relatively high ozone concentration in Earth's stratosphere

P

parallels any circle that runs east and west around Earth and that is parallel to the equator; a line of latitude

perihelion the point in the orbit of a planet at which the planet is closest to the sun

permeability the ability of a rock or sediment to let fluids pass through its open spaces, or pores

phases of the moon the changes in appearance of the moon as it orbits Earth, depending on the relative positions of the moon, Earth, and the sun

planet any of the primary bodies that orbit the sun; a similar body that orbits another star

planetary nebula a cloud of gas that forms around a dying star

planetisimal a small body from which a planet originated in the early stages of development of the solar system

plate tectonics the theory that explains how large pieces of the lithosphere, called plates, move and change shape

polar climate a climate that is characterized by average temperatures that are near or below freezing; typical of polar regions

polar easterlies prevailing winds that blow from east to west between 60° and 90° latitude in both hemispheres

Polaris the North Star; the star above Earth's North Pole that aligns almost exactly with Earth's rotation axis, and so does not appear to move day to day and season to season like other stars

porosity the percentage of the total volume of a rock or sediment that consists of open spaces

Precambrian Era the interval of time in the geologic time scale from Earth's formation to the beginning of the Paleozoic Era, from 4.6 billion to 542 million years ago

precipitation any form of water that falls to Earth's surface from the clouds; includes rain, snow, sleet, and hail

principle of original horizontality scientific principle that states that sedimentary rocks left undisturbed will remain in horizontal layers

proton a subatomic particle that has a positive charge and that is located in the nucleus of an atom; the number of protons of the nucleus is the atomic number, which determines the identity of an element

P-wave seismic wave that causes particles of rock to move in a back-and-forth direction parallel to the direction in which the wave is traveling; P-waves are the fastest seismic waves and can travel through solids, liquids, and gases

R

radiation the forms of energy that travel through space as waves; also, the transfer of energy by waves moving through space

radioisotope an isotope with an unstable nucleus

radiometric dating a method of determining the absolute age of an object by comparing the relative percentages of a radioactive (parent) isotope and a stable (daughter) isotope

rain shadow effect that occurs when a moving air mass encounters a mountain range; air mass rises, cools, and loses most of its moisture through precipitation

recycling the process of recovering valuable or useful materials from waste or scrap; the process of reusing some items

red shift on a spectrograph, the shift of absorption lines toward the red end of the spectrum, indicating that a star is moving away from Earth

regional metamorphism a change in the texture, structure, or chemical composition of a rock due to changes in temperature and pressure over a large area, generally as a result of tectonic forces

relative age the age of an object in relation to the ages of other objects

relative humidity the ratio of the amount of water vapor in the air to the amount of water vapor needed to reach saturation at a given temperature

relief the difference between the highest and lowest elevations in a given area; the variations in elevation of a land surface

revolution the motion of a body that travels around another body in space; one complete trip along an orbit

Richter scale scale that measures an earthquake's strength, or magnitude

rock Earth material made of a mixture of one or more minerals

rock cycle the series of processes in which rock forms, changes from one type to another, is destroyed, and forms again by geologic processes

rotation the spin of a body on its axis

S

sandbar long, underwater ridge of sand

satellite a natural or artificial body that revolves around a planet

sea-floor spreading the process by which new oceanic lithosphere (sea floor) forms as magma rises to Earth's surface and solidifies at a mid-ocean ridge

sedimentary rock rock formed when fragments of rocks, minerals, and/or organic matter are compacted or cemented together or precipitate out of solution

seismic wave a wave produced by an earthquake

seismogram a tracing of earthquake motion that is recorded by a seismograph

seismograph an instrument that records vibrations in the ground

shadow zone an area on Earth's surface where no direct seismic waves from a particular earthquake can be detected

soil a loose mixture of rock fragments and organic material that can support the growth of vegetation

soil profile a vertical section of soil that shows the layers of horizons

solar eclipse the passing of the moon between Earth and the sun; during a solar eclipse, the shadow of the moon falls on Earth

solar system the sun and all of the planets and other bodies that travel around it

solstice the point at which the sun is as far north or as far south of the equator as possible

specific heat the quantity of heat required to raise a unit mass of homogeneous material 1 K or 1°C in a specified way given constant pressure and volume

spectrograph instrument used to identify a star's chemical composition

spit a long, narrow deposit of sand connected at one end to the shore

spring tide a tide characterized by higher high tides and lower low tides; occurs when the moon, the sun, and Earth are aligned during full moon and new moon

star a large celestial body that is composed of gas and that emits light; the sun is a typical star

station model a pattern of meteorological symbols that represents the weather at a particular observing station and that is recorded on a weather map

stationary front a weather front at which air masses move either very slowly or not at all

stratosphere the layer of the atmosphere that lies between the troposphere and the mesosphere and in which temperature increases as altitude increases; contains the ozone layer

subduction zone the region along a tectonic plate boundary where one plate moves under another plate

supernova a late stage in the life cycle of some stars when the core collapses, causing the outer portion to explode

surface current a horizontal movement of ocean water that is caused by wind and that occurs at or near the ocean's surface

surface runoff water that neither soaks into the ground nor evaporates but instead flows across Earth's surface and eventually into streams, lakes, or oceans

surface wave in geology, a seismic wave that travels along the surface of a medium and that has a stronger effect near the surface of the medium than it has in the interior

S-wave a seismic wave that causes particles of rock to move in a side-to-side direction perpendicular to the direction in which the wave is traveling; S-waves are the second-fastest seismic waves and can travel only through solids

T

terrestrial planet one of the highly dense planets nearest to the sun; Mercury, Venus, Mars, and Earth

thermosphere the uppermost layer of the atmosphere, in which temperature increases as altitude increases; includes the ionosphere

tidal range the difference in levels of ocean water at high tide and low tide

tide the periodic rise and fall of the water level in the oceans and other large bodies of water

till unsorted rock material that is deposited directly by a melting glacier

topographic map a map that uses contour lines to show changes in elevation at Earth's surface; shows natural features such as lakes and constructed features such as roads

topography the size and shape of the land surface features of a region, including its relief

trace fossil a fossilized mark that formed in sedimentary rock by the movement of an animal on or within soft sediment

trade winds prevailing winds that blow from east to west from 30° latitude to the equator in both hemispheres

transform boundary the boundary between tectonic plates that are sliding past each other horizontally

trench a long, narrow, and steep depression that forms on the ocean floor as a result of subduction of a tectonic plate, that runs parallel to the trend of a chain of volcanic islands or the coastline of a continent, and that may be as deep as 11 km below sea level; also called an ocean trench or a deep-ocean trench

tropical climate a climate characterized by high temperatures and heavy precipitation during at least part of the year; typical of equatorial regions

troposphere the lowest layer of the atmosphere, in which temperature drops at a constant rate as altitude increases; the part of the atmosphere where weather conditions exist

U

unconformity a break in the geologic record created when rock layers are eroded or when sediment is not deposited for a long period of time

V

valley glacier a narrow, wedge-shaped mass of ice that forms in the mountains and that is confined to a small area

ventifact any rock that is pitted, grooved, or polished by wind abrasion

volcano a vent or fissure in Earth's surface through which magma and gases are expelled

W

warm front the front edge of an advancing warm air mass that replaces colder air with warmer air

watershed the area of land that is drained by a river system

water table the upper surface of underground water; the upper boundary of the zone of saturation

wavelength distance from the top of one wave to the top of the following wave

weather the conditions of the atmosphere—temperature, pressure, humidity, precipitation—at a particular time and place

weathering the natural process by which atmospheric and environmental agents, such as wind, rain, and temperature changes, disintegrate and decompose rocks

westerlies prevailing winds that blow from west to east between 30° and 60° latitude in both hemispheres

white dwarf a small, hot, dim star that is the leftover center of an old star

wind the movement of air from an area of high pressure to an area of low pressure

Note: Boldface page numbers refer to illustrative material, such as figures, tables, photographs, and illustrations. Pages cited in the Earth Science Reference Tables are indicated by *ESRT* following the citation.

A

abrasion, 53–54
absolute age
    carbon-14 dating, 103
    radiometric dating, 100–103, **102**
absolute error, 216
absolute magnitude, 197
absorption lines, 198
abyssal plains, 121, **121**
accepted value, percent deviation from, 220–**221**ESRT
accretion of planetisimals, 190
acids, chemical weathering and, 54–55
adiabatic cooling, 158
air masses
    fronts and storms, **146**, 146–147, **147**
    mountains and, 158
    types of, **145**, 145–146, **146**
    weather map symbols, 244–**245**ESRT
air movement. *See* global winds; wind
air pressure (atmospheric pressure), 130, 143, **143**, 246–**247**ESRT
    scales of, converting, 244–**245**ESRT
    weather map symbols, 149, 244–**245**ESRT
    winds and, 143–144
air temperature
    of atmospheric layers, 127–128, 246–**247**ESRT
    climatic change and, 159–161, **160**
    of climatic regions, 155–158, **156**
    humidity and, 141–142, 242–**243**ESRT
    measuring, 214, **214**
    ocean surface currents and, 116–117
    scales of, converting, **245**ESRT
    on weather maps, 149, 244–**245**ESRT
alpine glaciers, 74, 75, **75**
aneroid barometers, 144
anticyclones, 147, **147**
aphelion, 167, **167, 184,** 185
apparent magnitude, 197
aquifers, 59
arêtes, 75, **75**
asteroid belts, 188
asteroids, 188
asthenosphere, **2,** 3
atmosphere, 127
    pressure of. *See* air pressure
    properties of, 246–**247**ESRT
    solar energy and, 130–132
    structure of, **127,** 127–129
    water in. *See* water vapor
atomic numbers, 24
atoms, 23–24, **24**
auroras, 128–129
autumnal equinox, **172,** 173

B

balances, using, 213, **213**
barometers, 144, 244–**245**ESRT
barometric pressure, station models and, **245**ESRT
barrier islands, 72–73
basal slip, 74
basalt, 40, **41**
beaches, **72,** 72–73
bedrock of New York State, map, 224–**225**ESRT
big bang theory, 205, **205**
black holes, 203, **203**
blue shift, 204, **204**
body waves, 4–5, **5,** 91–93, **92**
breccia, 43, **43**

C

Cambrian Period, 107
carbon-14 dating, 103
carbonic acid, 54
celestial equator, 173
celestial navigation, **12,** 12–13

Celsius readings, converting, 244–**245**ESRT
Cenozoic Era, 108
change, equation for rate of, 220–**221**ESRT
chemical properties, 23
    of atmosphere, 127, **127**
    of crust, hydrosphere, and troposphere, 238–**239**ESRT
    of matter, 23
    of minerals, 250–**251**ESRT
chemical sedimentary rocks, 44
chemical symbols, **251**ESRT
chemical weathering, 54–55
cirques, 75, **75**
clastic sedimentary rocks, 43, **43**
cleavage, 27, 250–**251**ESRT
climate, 155
    changes in, 159–161, **160**
    factors influencing, 155–158, **156, 158**
    types of, 155
clouds, 142, 146, **146**
coastlines
    tides and, **118,** 118–120, **119**
    waves and, 71–73, **72**
    wind and, 70–71
cold fronts, 146, **146**
color
    of minerals, 26, 250–**251**ESRT
    of stars, 197, **197**
comets, 188
condensation, 220
conduction, atmospheric, 131
conglomerates, 43, **43**
conservation of natural resources, 30
constellations, Earth's rotation and, 168
contact metamorphism, 46
continental crust, 2
continental drift, 83–84
continental glaciers, 74, 76, **76,** 77
continental margins, 120–121, **121**
continental rise, 121, **121**
continental shelf, 121, **121**
continental slope, 121, **121**
contour intervals, 15